THE BIOLOGY
OF *EUGLENA*

Volume II
Biochemistry

CONTRIBUTORS TO THIS VOLUME

S. AARONSON

D. R. BARRAS

GEORGE BRAWERMAN

MARCIA BRODY

DENNIS E. BUETOW

WILLIAM F. DANFORTH

H. T. EPSTEIN

JOSEPH A. ERWIN

WILLIAM R. EVANS

AHARON GIBOR

HELEN A. HERRON

S. H. HUTNER

B. H. LEVEDAHL

JOHN L. MEGO

JEROME A. SCHIFF

ROBERT M. SMILLIE

B. A. STONE

A. C. ZAHALSKY

THE BIOLOGY
OF *EUGLENA*

Edited by DENNIS E. BUETOW

DEPARTMENT OF PHYSIOLOGY AND BIOPHYSICS
UNIVERSITY OF ILLINOIS
URBANA, ILLINOIS

Volume II

Biochemistry

1968

ACADEMIC PRESS New York and London

ACADEMIC PRESS, INC.
111 Fifth Avenue, New York, New York 10003

United Kingdom Edition published by
ACADEMIC PRESS, INC. (LONDON) LTD.
Berkeley Square House, London W.1

Library of Congress Catalog Card Number: 68-14645

PRINTED BY THE ST. CATHERINE PRESS, LTD., BRUGES, BELGIUM

LIST OF CONTRIBUTORS

Numbers in parentheses indicate the pages on which the authors' contributions begin.

S. AARONSON (193), Biology Department, Queens College City University of New York, Flushing, New York

D. R. BARRAS (149), Russell Grimwade School of Biochemistry, University of Melbourne, Parkville, Victoria, Australia

GEORGE BRAWERMAN (97), Department of Biochemistry, Yale University School of Medicine, New Haven, Connecticut

MARCIA BRODY (215), Department of Biological Sciences, Hunter College, The City University of New York, New York, New York[*]

DENNIS E. BUETOW (383), Department of Physiology and Biophysics, University of Illinois, Urbana, Illinois

WILLIAM F. DANFORTH (55), Department of Biology, Illinois Institute of Technology, Chicago, Illinois

H. T. EPSTEIN (285), Department of Biology, Brandeis University, Waltham, Massachusetts

JOSEPH A. ERWIN (133), Barnard College, Department of Biology, Columbia University, New York, New York[†]

WILLIAM R. EVANS (73), Charles F. Kettering Laboratory, Yellow Springs, Ohio

AHARON GIBOR (335), The Rockefeller University, New York, New York[‡]

HELEN A. HERRON (335), The Rockefeller University, New York, New York

S. H. HUTNER (193), Haskins Laboratories, New York, New York

B. H. LEVEDAHL (85), Department of Zoology, University of California, Los Angeles, California[§]

---

[*] *Present address:* Laboratoire de Photosynthesis, Centre Nationale de Recherches Scientifiques, Gif-sur-Yvette (Seine-et-Oise), France

[†] *Present address:* Department of Biology, Illinois Institute of Technology, Chicago Illinois

[‡] *Present address:* Biology Department, University of California, Santa Barbara, California

[§] *Present address:* Department of Chemistry, University of Alabama in Birmingham, Birmingham, Alabama

v

JOHN L. MEGO (351), Department of Biology, University of Alabama, University, Alabama

JEROME A. SCHIFF (285), Department of Biology, Brandeis University, Waltham, Massachusetts

ROBERT M. SMILLIE (1), Plant Physiology Unit, C.S.I.R.O. Division of Food Preservation and School of Biological Sciences, University of Sydney, Sydney, Australia

B. A. STONE (149), Russell Grimwade School of Biochemistry, University of Melbourne, Parkville, Victoria, Australia

A. C. ZAHALSKY (193), Biology Department, Queens College City University of New York, Flushing, New York

PREFACE

A comprehensive work on the biology of *Euglena* should cover the subject in all its aspects from taxonomy and ecology to biochemistry. It should also include a consideration of the role and use of *Euglena* in modern cell biology experimentation. This two-volume treatise was planned to be such a work. The literature on *Euglena* is so widely scattered that it was thought that it would be helpful, at the very least, to have available an inclusive set of references in one treatise.

A brief survey of the modern literature on *Euglena* will quickly indicate the wide variety of biological experimentation being done on these organisms. This is the result of course of the unique taxonomic position held by this genus. The obvious animal-like characteristics as well as the obvious plantlike characteristics of members of the genus *Euglena* make it the object of research in many laboratories.

Especial attention is given currently to the biology of the *Euglena* chloroplast. This attention is reflected by the amount of space that is given to the chloroplast in this treatise, particularly in Volume II. Inevitably, in so active a field, disagreements arise. It is hoped that all views are covered. Chapter 10 by Schiff and Epstein, which appears in Volume II, is an updated reprint of the article published in the 24th Symposium of the Society for Developmental Biology, "Reproduction: Molecular, Subcellular, and Cellular" (M. Locke, ed., Academic Press, 1966). This very good article on the *Euglena* chloroplast appeared during the early planning stages of this work. It was felt that it should be included here for complete coverage.

Each topic in "The Biology of *Euglena*" is reviewed in its historical context and development, but emphasis is placed on the current literature. The efforts of the authors as well as the efforts of that unsung group, the typists, are certainly appreciated. Especial thanks are due my wife, Mary Kathleen, who carefully checked all the manuscripts for typographical errors.

DENNIS E. BUETOW

Urbana, Illinois
July, 1968

vii

CONTENTS

Chapter 1. Enzymology of *Euglena*

ROBERT M. SMILLIE

Chapter 2. Respiration

WILLIAM F. DANFORTH

CONTENTS OF VOLUME I
General Biology and Ultrastructure

CHAPTER 1

ENZYMOLOGY OF *EUGLENA*

Robert M. Smillie

1

I. Introduction

The ease with which *Euglena* can be grown under a variety of growth conditions is well known (see Vol. I, Chapter 6); one or another of the commonly used strains can be readily grown in small amounts or in mass culture as a photoautotroph, or as a heterotroph on a variety of growth substrates including acetate, succinate, ethanol, and glucose. The development of chloroplasts is repressed in *Euglena* cells cultivated in continuous darkness, and a series of mutants containing defective chloroplasts, and others unable to form chloroplasts (bleached mutants), are available. For these reasons, *Euglena* has frequently been chosen as the experimental organism in investigations of photosynthetic and respiratory metabolism; indeed, the majority of studies on enzymes in *Euglena* have been confined to enzymes catalyzing reactions of photosynthesis or respiration. More recently, some properties of enzymic systems synthesizing proteins and fatty acids have been described, but with these exceptions, little is known about the properties of the enzymes in *Euglena* responsible for the synthesis and catabolism of nucleic acids, proteins, and lipids and their respective constitutents.

Although a large number of enzymes have now been found in *Euglena*, relatively few have been investigated in detail. Those that have been studied in some detail are described in Sections II–VIII of this chapter, and a complete list of enzymes detected in *Euglena* and the closely related nonphotosynthetic organism *Astasia* is given at the end of the chapter. In Sections IX and X some general comparisons are drawn, and changes in the activities of enzymes are correlated with changes in cell physiology. In Section XI, studies on the intracellular distribution of enzymes in *Euglena* are described.

II. Enzymes of Respiratory Metabolism

Included in this section are enzymes catalyzing the synthesis and breakdown of carbohydrates, the tricarboxylic acid and glyoxylate cycles, and respiratory electron-transfer reactions.

A. SYNTHESIS AND BREAKDOWN OF STORAGE POLYSACCHARIDE

The structure and enzymology of the main reserve carbohydrate of *Euglena*, paramylon, a β-1,3-glucan, has been the subject of several detailed studies (see Chapter 7) and several enzymes catalyzing the synthesis or breakdown of this polysaccharide have been characterized.

1. *Uridine Diphosphate Glucose-β-1,3-glucan β-3-Glucosyltransferase (Paramylon Synthetase, β-1,3-Glucan Synthetase)* *

An enzyme catalyzing the synthesis of β-1,3-glucan from

$$n \text{ UDP-Glucose} = (\beta\text{-}1,3\text{-glucosyl})_n + n \text{ UDP} \tag{1}$$

UDP-glucose [see Eq. (1)] has been isolated from *Euglena* by Maréchal and Goldemberg (1964). Higher plants contain a similar enzyme (Feingold *et al.*, 1958). Although the *Euglena* enzyme is insoluble, it has been obtained in a dispersed form by extracting with deoxycholate a washed insoluble residue obtained by centrifuging broken cells of *Euglena* between 2,000 and 10,000 g. This procedure yielded a 10- to 30-fold purified enzyme with the properties shown in Table I. Most enzymes catalyzing the synthesis

Table I

PROPERTIES OF PARAMYLON SYNTHETASE FROM *Euglena*[a]

Substrate specificity	UDP-α-glucose (no activity with UDP-β-glucose, ADP-glucose, or thymidinediphosphoglucose)
Primer requirement	None
K_m (UDP-glucose)	0.6 mM
pH optimum	7.5 (In glycylglycine buffer)
Temperature optimum	23°C
Activators	Laminaribiose stimulates 20–30%
Inhibitors	UDP, *p*-hydroxymercuribenzoate, high salt concentrations (e.g., 0.2 *M* NaCl inhibits 30–40%)
Possible control mechanisms	Product inhibition (K_i for UDP is 0.1 mM) pH Range for optimal activity is narrow Inhibitor present in green cells

[a] Data from Maréchal and Goldemberg (1964).

* The following abbreviations are used: AMP, ADP, and ATP for adenosine 5′-monophosphate, diphosphate, and triphosphate, respectively; CoA and CoASH for coenzyme A; FMN for flavin adenine mononucleotide; FMNH₂ for reduced FMN; EDTA for ethylenediaminetetraacetate; NAD⁺ for nicotinamide-adenine dinucleotide; NADH for reduced NAD⁺; NADP⁺ for nicotinamide-adenine dinucleotide phosphate; NADPH for reduced NADP⁺; RNA for ribonucleic acid; sRNA for soluble (transfer) RNA; tris for tris (hydroxymethyl) aminomethane and UDP for uridine 5′-diphosphate.

of reserve polysaccharides such as starch and glycogen are insoluble, and are bound to membranes closely associated with the polysaccharide itself. But the glucan-synthesizing enzyme from *Euglena* did not appear to be closely associated with the granules of paramylon. Another unusual property of the enzyme from *Euglena* was its apparent lack of any requirement for a primer. The enzyme from higher plants, for instance, required either D-glucose or certain D-glucosides for activity (Feingold *et al.*, 1958). Attempts to destroy possible endogenous primers by treating preparations of the *Euglena* enzyme with a β-1,3-glucanase failed to decrease enzyme activity.

Cells accumulating the largest amounts of paramylon also yielded the most active preparations of enzyme. Cells grown in light contained less paramylon than dark-grown cells and showed a lower synthetase activity, although the difference may have been partly due to the existence of an inhibitor of the enzyme in green cells.

2. *β-1,3-Glucan Hydrolase (Laminarinase)*

Cell-free extracts of *Euglena* or *Astasia longa* liberate glucose from the soluble β-1,3-glucan, laminarin (Fellig, 1960; Tocher, 1962; Meeuse, 1964). The active enzymic component has not been purified and detailed studies of its properties are not available. Nor is it known whether the activity arises from one or from several enzymes. The optimal pH for activity is 5.0–5.2 which is similar to values obtained for the majority of β-1,3-glucan hydrolases so far isolated from other algae, higher plants, and invertebrates. Mn^{2+} ions activated the *Euglena* hydrolase in the range 0.1–1.0 mM (Fellig, 1960). Hg^{2+} ions inhibited activity, but Fe^{3+}, Ba^{2+}, and Mg^{2+} had little or no effect.

The physiological function of the *Euglena* hydrolase is unknown; presumably it is involved in the utilization of paramylon, although Meeuse (1964) pointed out that the extracted enzyme failed to degrade native paramylon.

Fellig (1960) was unable to detect enzymes in *Euglena* capable of hydrolyzing α-1,4-linked glucosyl units.

3. *β-1,3-Oligoglucan: Orthophosphate Glucosyltransferase (Laminaribiose Phosphorylase)*

Enzymes catalyzing the reaction of Eq. (2) have been isolated from *Euglena* and *Astasia ocellata*. A 240-fold purification

3-*O*-β-D-Glucopyranosyl-D-glucose (laminaribiose) + orthophosphate
$$= \text{glucose 1-phosphate} + \text{D-glucose} \qquad (2)$$

of the enzyme from *Euglena* was obtained from cell-free extracts by precipitating impurities with protamine sulfate and fractionating the extract

with ammonium sulfate, followed by absorption to and elution from calcium phosphate gel and chromatography on a column of DEAE-cellulose (Goldemberg *et al.*, 1966). The final yield was 8.4%.
The properties of the purified enzyme are shown in Table II. When the enzyme was incubated with glucose and glucose 1-phosphate for short

Table II

PROPERTIES OF β-1,3-OLIGOGLUCAN: ORTHOPHOSPHATE GLUCOSYLTRANSFERASE
(PARAMYLON PHOSPHORYLASE)[a]

Specificity	Specific for α-D-glucose 1-phosphate
	Glucose can be replaced by several β-glucosyl derivatives
	Laminaribiose can be replaced by the corresponding tri-, tetra- and pentasaccharides
K_m values	
Laminaribiose	5 mM
Phosphate	2.5 mM
Glucose	19 mM
Glucose 1-phosphate	2.1 mM
Equilibrium	
(glucose) (glucose 1-P)/(laminaribiose) (orthophosphate)	0.3
pH optimum	6.3–6.9 (In phosphate buffer)
Inhibitors	p-Hydroxymercuribenzoate (80% at 2 mM), glucose (above 0.1 M)

[a] Data from Goldemberg *et al.* (1966).

periods, laminaribiose was the only product; but by increasing the time of incubation, laminaritriose, laminaritetrose, and traces of laminaripentose were also formed. The *Euglena* enzyme did not liberate phosphate in the presence of glucose 1-phosphate and solubilized paramylon or laminarin, but Manners and Taylor (1965) found that with laminaribiose phosphorylase from *A. ocellata*, laminarin was a moderately good acceptor of β-D-glucosyl residues, as compared with laminaribiose.

Goldemberg *et al.* (1966) have concluded that the mechanism of action of laminarin phosphorylase is similar to that of maltose and cellobiose phosphorylases in that an intermediate glucosyl–enzyme complex is not formed, the reaction occurring by a single displacement mechanism.

4. Other Enzymes

Two other enzymes likely to be involved in the interconversion of β-1, 3-glucan and glucose 6-phosphate, UDP-glucose pyrophosphorylase and phosphoglucomutase, have been detected in *Euglena* (Table XVI). Their properties have not been studied.

B. Glycolysis

All enzymes of the glycolytic or Embden–Meyerhof–Parnas pathway have been demonstrated in extracts of *Euglena* (Table XVI). Only a few have been studied in any detail.

1. Hexokinase

Hexokinase, which promotes the reaction shown in Eq. (3), has been demonstrated in centrifuged extracts of *Euglena*

$$\text{Glucose} + \text{ATP} = \text{glucose 6-phosphate} + \text{ADP} \qquad (3)$$

(Belsky and Schultz, 1962; Hurlbert and Rittenberg, 1962) and *A. longa* (Barry, 1962), but the enzyme has not been purified. However, it is apparent from the studies of Belsky and Schultz (1962) that, in many respects, the *Euglena* enzyme resembles yeast hexokinase. Table III summarizes some

Table III

PROPERTIES OF *Euglena* HEXOKINASE[a]

Substrate specificity	Glucose, fructose, mannose ATP (inosine 5′-triphosphate inactive)
K_m (glucose)	0.5 mM
pH optimum	8.5 (In glycylglycine buffer)
Activators	Mg^{2+}, Mn^{2+}, Co^{2+}
Inhibitor	ADP; no inhibition by *p*-chloromercuribenzoate

[a] Data from Belsky and Schultz (1962).

properties of *Euglena* hexokinase. The comparative rates of phosphorylation of glucose, fructose, and mannose and the apparent Michaelis constant (K_m) for glucose were similar to the corresponding values obtained for yeast hexokinase (Berger *et al.*, 1946). Unlike hexokinases from higher plants (Saltman, 1953) and brain (Crane and Sols, 1953), *Euglena* hexokinase was not associated with mitochondrial fractions.

The probable function of hexokinase in *Euglena* is the phosphorylation of glucose supplied exogenously or of glucose arising from the hydrolysis of reserve glucan.

2. *Fructose-1,6-diphosphate Aldolase*

Rutter (1964) has distinguished between two distinct types of fructose-1,6-diphosphate aldolases (designated as class I and class II aldolases) exhibiting different molecular features and apparently different catalytic mechanisms. Class II aldolases contain a bound divalent metal that is essential for activity. They are inhibited by chelating compounds, require the presence of sulfhydryl reagents for maximum activity, and are stimulated by K^+ ions. Class I aldolases do not contain bound metal that is essential for activity, are not inhibited by chelating agents, and are not stimulated by sulfhydryl reagents or K^+ ions. Class I aldolases also show appreciable activity with fructose 1-phosphate, whereas Class II aldolases show a much greater specificity toward fructose 1,6-diphosphate. Differences also exist in molecular weights and sedimentation constants between the two classes.

The phylogenetic distribution of the two classes of aldolases is most interesting. Aldolases of class I are largely confined to animals, plants, and protozoa. Fungi, including yeast, bacteria, and blue-green algae, possess only class II aldolases. *Euglena gracilis* and *Chlamydomonas reinhardi*, however, each contain both classes of aldolase. The two aldolases from *Euglena* were separated by centrifugation in a sucrose gradient. One of these enzymes, identified as a class I aldolase, had a sedimentation constant of 7.8 S and its activity was inhibited only slightly by high concentrations of EDTA and was unaffected by K^+ ions. The other enzyme showed a sedimentation constant of 5.4 S. Its activity was almost completed inhibited by 5 mM EDTA and was stimulated by K^+ ions.

It is not possible to establish on the basis of the available evidence whether both aldolases or only one of them is active in glycolysis. However, changes in the levels of the two aldolases in *Euglena* and *Chlamydomonas* as a response to growth under different environmental conditions suggest that the class I enzyme may be primarily involved in photosynthesis and the class II enzyme in glycolysis and gluconeogenesis (see Section III,A).

3. *Lactate Dehydrogenase*

a. Soluble Lactate Dehydrogenase. The experiments of Price (1962b) have shown the presence of a soluble NAD^+-dependent lactate dehydrogenase [Eq. (4)] in extracts of *Euglena.*

$$\text{Lactate} + NAD^+ = \text{pyruvate} + NADH + H^+ \tag{4}$$

The D-enantiomorph of lactate was oxidized about three times faster than the L-form. Lactate dehydrogenase from rabbit muscle, on the other hand, is L-specific.

b. Insoluble Lactate Dehydrogenase. Price (1962b) also obtained evidence for a particulate lactate dehydrogenase in *Euglena*. The activity of this enzyme, which was assayed manometrically employing phenazine methosulfate as a coupling agent between the enzyme and oxygen, was significantly decreased in cells deficient in zinc, a condition which also strikingly reduced the capacity of the cells to oxidize lactate. In contrast, the activity of the soluble NAD$^+$-dependent enzyme did not decrease as a result of zinc deficiency.

C. Oxidative Pentose Phosphate Pathway

As indicated in Table XVI, all enzymes of the oxidative pentose phosphate pathway are present in *Euglena*, but detailed studies of their properties have not been made.

D. Gluconeogenesis

Acetate supplied exogenously to *Euglena* is rapidly converted to glucose (Marzullo and Danforth, 1964). In liver and kidney, gluconeogenesis is accomplished by a reversal of the glycolytic pathway. The equilibrium constants of two of the glycolytic enzymes, phosphofructokinase and pyruvate kinase, are unfavorable for carbohydrate synthesis, and in gluconeogenesis the steps catalyzed by these enzymes are by-passed by two additional enzymes, alkaline fructose-1,6-diphosphatase and phosphopyruvate carboxykinase. The last-mentioned two enzymes also have important regulatory functions in gluconeogenesis (Krebs, 1964). Both green and bleached mutant cells of *Euglena* contain a fructose-1,6-diphosphatase, which while active at alkaline pH, exhibits maximum activity near neutrality. This enzyme, designated as neutral fructose-1,6-diphosphatase, may fulfil a role in *Euglena* analogous to that of alkaline fructose-1,6-diphosphatase in liver (Smillie, 1960b). The properties of the neutral fructose-1,6-diphos-phatase are described in the section on phosphatases (Section VII,A). The occurrence of phosphopyruvate carboxykinase in *Euglena* has not been reported.

E. Tricarboxylic Acid Cycle

The individual enzymes of the tricarboxylic acid cycle have been assayed in *Euglena* and *Astasia* (Table XVI) and Buetow and Buchanan (1965) have shown that mitochondrial fractions from *Euglena* can carry out the phosphorylation of ADP coupled to the oxidation of tricarboxylic acid cycle intermediates. The properties of the enzymes have not been investigated.

F. Acetate Assimilation and the Glyoxylate Cycle

In many microorganisms capable of growing on acetate, the glyoxylate cycle (Kornberg and Krebs, 1957) provides a pathway for net assimilation of the acetate carbon. *Euglena* can utilize acetate as a sole carbon source and when fed acetate-^{14}C shows a labeling pattern in assimilated carbon compounds consistent with operation of the glyoxylate cycle (Danforth, 1961). Two important enzymes of this cycle, isocitrate lyase (isocitritase) and malate synthase, have been found in *Euglena* (Table XVI). Growth on acetate is not an essential requirement for isocitrate lyase production, as the enzyme was also synthesized in cells grown on ethanol (Haigh and Beevers, 1964). The ratio of the specific activities of isocitrate lyase and malate synthase in acetate-grown *Euglena* was less than 1 : 10 and was of the same order as values reported for *Tetrahymena pyriformis* and *Escherichia coli* (Reeves et al., 1962). Isocitrate lyase was not detected in cells grown autotrophically (Haigh and Beevers, 1964).

The remaining enzymes of the glyoxylate cycle form part of the tricarboxylic acid cycle and evidence for their existence in *Euglena* has already been cited (Section II,E and Table XVI).

Acetate enters the glyoxylate cycle as the CoA derivative. Acetate thiokinase, the enzyme converting acetate to acetyl-CoA, has been partially purified from *Euglena* and has been demonstrated in extracts of *A. longa* (Hunter and Lee, 1962). Its properties are discussed below.

1. *Acetate Thiokinase (Acetocoenzyme-A Kinase, Acetate-Activating Enzyme)*

This enzyme, catalyzing the reaction of Eq. (5), was

$$\text{Acetate} + \text{ATP} + \text{CoA} = \text{acetyl-CoA} + \text{AMP} + \text{pyrophosphate} \qquad (5)$$

purified 20-fold from *E. gracilis* strain 1224-5/25, by Ohmann (1964) with a 44% yield; a 10-fold purification (yield 51%) was obtained by Abraham and Bachhawat (1962) from *E. gracilis* strain Z.

Acetate thiokinase occurs in a wide range of organisms, including animals, plants, fungi, algae, and photosynthetic bacteria. Berg (1956) has studied the mechanism of action of acetate thiokinase from yeast and on the basis of ^{32}P-exhange reactions and the use of synthetic acetyl adenylate as a substrate for the enzyme he has proposed a two-step mechanism [Eqs. (6) and (7)] involving the intermediate formation of acetyl adenylate.

$$\text{Acetate} + \text{ATP} = \text{acetyl adenylate} + \text{pyrophosphate} \qquad (6)$$

$$\text{Acetyl adenylate} + \text{CoA} = \text{acetyl-CoA} + \text{AMP} \qquad (7)$$

Experimental evidence obtained by Abraham and Bachhawat (1962) and

Ohmann (1964) suggests the *Euglena* enzyme catalyzes a similar two-step reaction.

Table IV shows properties of the acetate thiokinase isolated from *Euglena*.

Table IV

PROPERTIES OF ACETATE THIOKINASE FROM *Euglena*[a]

Substrate specificity	Acetate (higher homologs not tested) Acetyl adenylate, acetyl deoxyadenylate, propionyl adenylate [see Eq. (6) in text]
K_m values	
[Eq. (6)]: Acetate	1.2 mM
Acetyl adenylate	0.37 mM
Pyrophosphate	1.2 mM
Complete reaction: CoA	82 μM
pH optima	
Complete reaction	7.2–7.4 (In tris buffer)
Eq. (6)	5.0
Eq. (7)	8.2
Activators	Mg^{2+}, Co^{2+}, (Mn^{2+}, Ni^{2+}, Zn^{2+}, Cu^{2+} inactive)
Inhibitor	Pyrophosphate (>3.3 mM)

[a] Data from Abraham and Bachhawat (1962) and Ohmann (1964).

Acetyl and propionyl adenylates and acetyl deoxyadenylate served as substrates for the reaction of Eq. (6), but palmitoyl adenylate, acetyl uridylate, and acetyl cytidylate, were inactive. The pH optimum for Eq. (6), measured in the reverse direction, was 5.0 (Abraham and Bachhawat, 1962). This value was much lower than the optimal pH value of 7.0 found for the same reaction catalyzed by an enzyme from ox brain (Rao *et al.*, 1961). The pH optimum of 7.0–7.2 found for the complete reaction was comparable with values between pH 7 and 8 obtained for acetate thiokinases from several different sources, including yeast (Lipmann *et al.*, 1952), plants (Millerd and Bonner, 1954), and *Rhodospirillum rubrum* (Eisenberg, 1955).

Mg^{2+} ions were essential for the activity of acetate thiokinase from *Euglena*, but the effect of K^+ ions was not tested even though this ion is required, in addition to Mg^{2+}, for the activity of acetate thiokinases from animal and plant sources.

The specific activity of acetate thiokinase increased throughout the logarithmic growth of cultures grown on acetate (Abraham and Bachhawat, 1962). Ohmann (1964) observed that cells grown heterotrophically yielded extracts containing 6 to 10 times the specific activity found in extracts from cells grown autotrophically.

G. ELECTRON-TRANSFER PATHWAY IN MITOCHONDRIA

Particulate fractions containing mitochondria from *Euglena* carry out oxidative phosphorylation (Buetow and Buchanan, 1965) and contain NAD^+-linked diaphorase, succinate dehydrogenase, and c- and a-type cytochromes (Perini *et al.*, 1964a,b). In certain features, however, the electron-transfer pathway of *Euglena* appears to differ from well-characterized systems such as those found in yeast or heart muscle mitochondria. Cyanide at 1 mM inhibited the respiration of *Euglena* but carbon monoxide at concentrations as high as 95% had only a marginal effect (Perini *et al.*, 1964b), and Webster and Hackett (1965) were unable to demonstrate cytochrome oxidase activity in mitochondria purified from *A. longa*. The c-type cytochrome of *Euglena* mitochondria in some respects resembled an autoxidizable b-type cytochrome rather than cytochrome c, and a typical b-type respiratory cytochrome has not been detected (although low-temperature difference spectra of *A. longa* (Webster and Hackett, 1965) revealed a minor peak at 563 mμ). Because of the apparent absence of a b-type cytochrome and the low P : O ratios obtained with *Euglena* mitochondria, Buetow and Buchanan (1965) raised the possibility that these mitochondria lack one of the three phosphorylation sites normally found in mitochondria.

These observations suggest the mitochondrial electron-transfer pathway of the Euglenophyta may prove to be a particularly interesting biochemical system and one that warrants further study.

The properties of the two respiratory cytochromes found in *Euglena* are described below.

1. *Cytochrome 556*

A cytochrome showing an α-band maximum at 556 mμ was first detected by Gross and Wolken (1960) in digitonin extracts of dark-grown *Euglena*. Perini *et al.* (1964a) purified the cytochrome by column chromatography, first on DEAE-cellulose and then on CM-cellulose, and obtained a preparation with an absorption ratio at 558 mμ to 280 mμ of 0.7–0.75. Properties of this preparation are shown in Table V. In earlier studies Wolken and Gross (1963) obtained a value for E_0' of $+0.32$ and a molecular weight of 12,800 based on sedimentation and diffusion rates. The values shown in Table V compare well with these, although the estimated molecular weight is somewhat higher.

Although the α-band centers at 556 mμ, Perini *et al.* (1964a) have pointed out that the peak is actually asymmetrical, with a maximum at 558 mμ and a shoulder at 554.5 mμ.

Table V

PROPERTIES OF *Euglena* CYTOCHROME 556[a]

Absorption maxima, reduced	558, 554.5 (shoulder), 525, 421, 317 mμ
Absorption maxima, oxidized	530, 560, 412, 365, 275 mμ
Absorption maxima, reduced hemochromes	
Pyridine	552.5, 523, 417 mμ (ϵ_{mM} = 24.1 cm^2 at 552.5 mμ)
Cyanide	558, 532, 427 mμ
CO Binding	None
E_0' (pH 7, 25°)	+307 mV
Molecular weight (from sedimentation and diffusion rates)	18000 ± 2000
Molecular weight (heme and Fe content)	27000 ± 1000
Reduced by	Ascorbate, dithionite, borohydride
Oxidized by	Oxygen, potassium ferricyanide

[a] Data from Perini *et al.* (1964a).

The identification of cytochrome 556 as a c-type cytochrome is still tentative. The absorption spectra of the reduced hemochromes were intermediate between the expected spectra for b- and c-type cytochromes and the fission product with Ag_2SO_4 could not be identified with heme c.

Cytochrome 556 does not function in photosynthesis and is clearly associated with the respiratory mechanism. It was found in *A. longa* (Webster and Hackett, 1965) and in dark-grown and bleached mutant cells of *Euglena* as well as in the green cells, and its cellular concentration did not change appreciably during chloroplast development (Wolken and Gross 1963; Perini *et al.*, 1964b). The addition of succinate or acetate to a suspension of cells caused a spectroscopically measurable reduction of cytochrome 556 which could be reversed by aerating the suspension.

2. Cytochrome a Type (605, Euglena)

Euglena contains a second autoxidizable respiratory cytochrome, whose prosthetic group is heme a (Perini *et al.*, 1964a). Its cellular concentration is approximately the same as cytochrome 556 and it shows absorption maxima in the reduced form at 605 mμ (α-band) and at 442–444 mμ (γ-band). It is reduced *in vivo* by succinate and the effect is abolished by 0.5 mM cyanide. A similar a-type cytochrome is present in *A. longa* (Webster and Hackett, 1965).

III. Enzymes of Photosynthesis

A. CARBON REDUCTIVE CYCLE

The pathway of photosynthetic CO_2 fixation in *Euglena* appears to be typical of that found in *Chlorella* and many higher plants. This was first indicated by the pattern of labeled compounds formed during short-term feedings of $^{14}CO_2$ to photosynthesizing *Euglena* cells (Lynch and Calvin, 1953; Norris *et al.*, 1955) and subsequently all of the enzymes of the photosynthetic carbon reductive cycle (Calvin cycle) were demonstrated in green cells of *Euglena* (Table XVI). Several of these enzymes such as aldolase are common to both photosynthetic reductive pathways and respiratory oxidative pathways, but it should be pointed out that such enzymes, although common to both pathways, are not necessarily identical. Although the aldolase content of autotrophic and heterotrophic cells is comparable, intracellular distribution studies have disclosed that the transformation from heterotrophy to autotrophy is accompanied by a marked increase in the aldolase content of chloroplasts and a decrease in nonplastid aldolase (Smillie, 1963). Either nonplastid aldolase is transferred to the chloroplasts or, alternatively, it is inactivated or degraded and a new chloroplast aldolase is synthesized.

The latter alternative appears to be most likely the correct one since Rutter (1964) has found two distinct aldolases in *Euglena*, one requiring a divalent metal for activity, the other being metal-independent (see Section II,B,2). Cells grown in the presence of chloramphenicol (1 mg/ml), which preferentially inhibits the formation of chloroplast proteins, contained lower amounts of the nonmetal aldolase (N.F. Tobin and R. M. Smillie, unpublished results). In line with these findings, Russell and Gibbs (1966) found that in *Chlamydomonas mundana*, which like *Euglena* contains both metal-dependent and metal-independent aldolases, the addition of acetate to the medium not only resulted in repression of the Calvin-cycle enzymes ribulose-1,5-diphosphate carboxylase and ribulose-5-phosphate kinase, but also the nonmetal aldolase. The metal-dependent aldolase was not repressed.

It would not be surprising if other enzymes that are functional in both photosynthesis and respiration, including the triosephosphate and ribosephosphate isomerases, 3-phosphoglycerate kinase and transketolase, existed in more than one form in autotrophic cells, each form differing slightly in structural and catalytic properties.

Several enzymes of the carbon reductive pathway appear to be functionally restricted to chloroplasts in eucaryotic organisms and are described below.

1. D-Ribulose-5-phosphate Kinase

An enzyme catalyzing the phosphorylation of D-ribulose 5-phosphate, as shown in Eq. (8), has been detected in extracts of

$$\text{D-Ribulose 5-phosphate} + \text{ATP} = \text{D-ribulose 1,5-diphosphate} + \text{ADP} \qquad (8)$$

Euglena autotrophs (see Table XVI), but it has not been purified nor have its properties been studied. In extracts of *Euglena* the enzyme has been assayed by measuring the ADP produced in the reaction by means of a coupled enzymic system containing excess pyruvate kinase, lactate dehydrogenase, phosphoenolpyruvate, and NADH. The oxidation of NADH was measured spectrophotometrically. In crude dialyzed extracts of *Euglena*, the addition of compounds containing thiol groups (e.g., glutathione) and Mg^{2+} ions were required for maximal activity; in this aspect the enzyme resembled spinach D-ribulose-5-phosphate kinase which contains an essential sulfhydryl group and requires a divalent cation for activity.

2. D-Ribulose-1,5-diphosphate Carboxylase (Carboxydismutase)

An enzyme carboxylating D-ribulose 1,5-diphosphate [see Eq. (9)] has been detected in extracts of autotrophically grown

$$\text{D-Ribulose 1,5-diphosphate} + CO_2 = 2 \ \text{3-phosphoglycerate} \qquad (9)$$

Euglena (Fuller and Gibbs, 1959; Peterkofsky and Racker, 1961; Smillie, 1963) and may be conveniently assayed in a mixture containing ribulose 1,5-diphosphate and $NaH^{14}CO_3$ by the fixation of label into compounds (mainly 3-phosphoglycerate, see Fuller and Gibbs, 1959) soluble in 50% alcohol. Details of an assay procedure based on the methods of Fuller and Gibbs (1959) and Weissbach et al. (1956) that has proved satisfactory for assaying the enzyme in extracts of *Euglena* was described by Smillie (1962). As in the case of the same enzyme from spinach, the activity of the *Euglena* enzyme was extremely low unless both Mg^{2+} ions and reduced glutathione were included in the reaction mixture. An additional stimulation resulted from the inclusion of EDTA. Dark-grown heterotrophic cells contained trace amounts of the enzyme (Fuller and Gibbs, 1959).

Ribulose-1,5-diphosphate carboxylase has frequently been identified with the major soluble protein fraction of chloroplasts known as fraction I protein (e.g., see Trown, 1965) and the same protein fraction has been identified in extracts of both green heterotrophic and autotrophic cells of *Euglena* by ultracentrifugation (Anderson, 1967) and by electrophoresis on polyacrylamide gels (A. M. Grieve and R. M. Smillie, unpublished experiments).

3. *NADP+-Glyceraldehyde-3-phosphate Dehydrogenase*

Although NAD+-linked glyceraldehyde-3-phosphate dehydrogenase is widely distributed, a second enzyme specifically linked to NADP+ [see Eq. (10)] appears to function in the carbon reductive

D-Glyceraldehyde 3-phosphate + orthophosphate + NADP+ =

1,3-diphosphoglycerate + NADPH + H+   (10)

cycle of photosynthesis (Gibbs, 1952; Arnon, 1952). The NADP+-linked enzyme is either absent, or present in only trace amounts, in dark-adapted *Euglena*, streptomycin-bleached mutants, and *Astasia* (Fuller and Gibbs, 1959); but its synthesis is rapidly induced when dark-adapted *Euglena* cells are exposed to light (Brawerman and Konigsberg, 1960; Smillie et al., 1963; Hudock and Fuller, 1965). The enzyme is assayed in the same way as the NAD+-linked enzyme (see Fuller and Gibbs, 1959), a preincubation period with glutathione being required to attain maximal activity. The purification of the *Euglena* enzyme has not been reported.

Although there is general agreement that the NADP+-linked enzyme is active in photosynthesis, it cannot yet be assumed that the NAD+-linked enzyme is not functional in photosynthetic CO_2 fixation. In extracts prepared from rapidly growing *Euglena* autotrophs, the NAD+ enzyme is in fact the more active of the two enzymes. The NAD+ enzyme is the only glyceraldehyde-3-phosphate dehydrogenase present in the photosynthetic sulfur bacteria (Smillie et al., 1962), and there is some evidence to suggest a role for the enzyme in the photosynthesis of higher organisms (Smillie and Fuller, 1960). Hudock and Fuller (1965) have considered the possible interconversion of the two enzymes *in vivo*, but their results indicated that this was most unlikely in *Euglena*.

4. *Alkaline Fructose-1,6-diphosphatase and Sedoheptulose-1,7-diphosphatase*

These enzymes are treated in a later section on phosphatases (Section VII,A).

B. PHOTOSYNTHETIC ELECTRON-TRANSFER PATHWAY

Two proteins of the photosynthetic electron-transfer system of *Euglena*, chloroplast ferredoxin and cytochrome 552, are released from the lamellae when cells are broken, and both have been extensively purified. A third protein, transhydrogenase, is partially released, and some properties of the soluble enzyme have been studied. A second cytochrome corresponding to the cytochrome b_6 of higher plant chloroplasts is tightly bound to the lamellae, but our knowledge of its properties and function is fragmentary.

Electron-transfer reactions taking place in illuminated intact cells and isolated lamellae are described in Chapter 3.

1. Chloroplast Ferredoxin (Photosynthetic Pyridine Nucleotide Reductase)

This iron-containing protein participates in the photoreduction of NADP+ by isolated lamellae from chloroplasts (San Pietro and Lang, 1958). Its presence in *Euglena* has been reported by Shapiro (1961), Smillie (1963), Perini *et al.* (1964a), and Nagai and Bloch (1966). Since details of the purification of chloroplast ferredoxin from *Euglena* have not been published, a procedure which gives a highly purified preparation in good yield is described here.

Green cells of *E. gracilis* strain Z, are grown, preferably autotrophically, and harvested while still in the logarithmic phase of growth. The cells (100 gm fresh weight) are washed twice by centrifuging at 1000 g for 10 minutes in 0.05 M tris buffer, pH 7.8. Washed cells are suspended in the same buffer and broken by passage through a French pressure cell at 10,000 psi. The enzyme can also be extracted by freezing and thawing the cells, or by grinding them with small glass beads (diam. 1–2 mm). After centrifuging the cell extract at 10,000 g for 10 minutes, ammonium sulfate is added to the supernatant fluid to 60% of saturation and the mixture recentrifuged. After saturating the supernatant fluid with ammonium sulfate, it is allowed to stand at 0°C for 60 minutes before being centrifuged at 10,000 g for 10 minutes and the supernatant fluid is then decanted off; the residue is dissolved in 0.05 M tris buffer, pH 7.8, and the ammonium sulfate removed from it by filtration through Sephadex, or by dialysis against the pure buffer (prolonged dialysis should be avoided since it results in losses of protein through aggregation). A column of DEAE-cellulose (15.0 × 0.9 cm) is prepared and equilibrated with 0.05 M tris buffer, pH 7.8. The protein is absorbed onto this column, and elution is begun immediately from a mixing vessel initially containing 300 ml of 0.05 M tris buffer, pH 7.8. The same buffer containing 0.6 M NaCl is fed into the mixing vessel. The brown-colored fractions containing chloroplast ferredoxin are combined and concentrated if required by precipitation with saturated ammonium sulfate.

The purified *Euglena* protein is very similar to other chloroplast ferredoxins isolated from algae and higher plants. It mediates between the reduction of NADP+ and photoreductive reactions in chloroplasts from *Euglena*, and from several other sources including *Chlamydomonas reinhardi* and spinach, pea, and wheat leaves, at rates comparable to spinach ferredoxin (R. M. Smillie, unpublished experiments). It is also a component of an enzymic system from *Euglena* catalyzing the desaturation of stearic acid and it is interesting that in this system the chloroplast ferredoxin from *Euglena* is much more active that either the ferredoxin from spinach chloroplasts or that from *Clostridium pasteurianum* (Nagai and Bloch, 1966). The *Euglena* protein is autoxidizable and, like other plant and algal chloroplast ferredoxins, contains acid-labile iron and sulfur. It is reduced under anaerobic conditions by dithionite or by a mixture of chloroplast transhydrogenase and reduced $NADP^+$. Reduction results in the disappearance of the absorption peaks at 420 and 460 mμ. Perini *et al.* (1964a) have estimated a value of 400 for the molar ratio of chlorophyll to chloroplast ferredoxin in *Euglena* cells.

2. *Cytochrome c (552, Euglena)*, *(Euglena Cytochrome f, Cytochrome 552)*

Two cytochromes are prominent in the chloroplasts of higher plants: cytochrome f, which is closely related to c-type cytochromes (Davenport and Hill, 1952); and a b-type cytochrome designated by Hill (1954) as cytochrome b_6. Cytochrome f functions in photosystem 1 of photosynthesis, probably at a point very close to the primary photoact (Bonner and Chance, 1963). A cytochrome showing an α-band maximum at 552 mμ in the reduced state fulfills a similar role in photosynthesizing *Euglena* (Olson and Smillie, 1963). This cytochrome was first noted by Davenport and Hill (1952) and was later studied by Nishimura (1959), Wolken and Gross (1963), and Perini *et al.* (1964a). As revealed by intracellular distribution studies (Smillie, 1963; Perini *et al.*, 1964b), cytochrome 552 is associated entirely with the chloroplasts.

Cytochrome 552 is rendered soluble by extracting acetone powders of *Euglena* with buffer, or more simply by thawing frozen cells in 0.9% NaCl (Colmano and Wolken, 1963). Perini *et al.* (1964a) have purified the extracted cytochrome by precipitation of impurities with ammonium sulfate (40% saturated) followed by DEAE-cellulose column chromatography. The ratio of the α-band absorption at 552 mμ to the absorption at 280 mμ was 0.92 in the purified preparation (reduced form). The properties of cytochrome 552 are summarized in Table VI. The values shown are taken from the paper by Perini *et al.* (1964a) and are substantially in agreement with earlier results obtained by Nishimura (1959) and Wolken and Gross (1963).

Cytochrome 552 may be classified as a c-type cytochrome. The absorption properties of the pyridine and cyanide hemochromes were similar to the corresponding hemochromes prepared from mammalian cytochrome c, and treatment with Ag_2SO_4 yielded heme c (Perini *et al.*, 1964a). Ascorbic acid, sodium borohydride, and sodium dithionite reduced cytochrome 552. The cytochrome was not autoxidizable but was oxidized slowly by

Table VI

PROPERTIES OF Euglena CYTOCHROME 552[a]

Absorption maxima, reduced	552, 522, 416, 317 mμ
Absorption maxima, oxidized	525, 410, 355–358, 275 mμ
ϵ_{mM} (reduced)	27.0 cm^2 (at 552 mμ), 151.5 cm^2 (at 416 mμ)
ϵ_{mM} (oxidized)	7.4 cm^2 (at 552 mμ)
Absorption maxima, reduced hemochromes	
Pyridine	549, 524, 415 mμ
Cyanide	553, 419 mμ
CO binding	None
E_0' (pH 7, 25°)	+370 mV
Molecular weight (from sedimentation and diffusion rates)	17400 ± 1600
Molecular weight (Fe and heme content, amino acid composition)	13500 ± 500
Isoelectric point	pH 5.5

[a] Data from Perini et al. (1964a).

ferricyanide. It was partially oxidized by illuminated lamellae from *Euglena* and was completely oxidized by illuminated lamellae in the presence of 3-(3,4-dichlorophenyl)-1,1-dimethylurea (D. C. Wildon and R. M. Smillie, unpublished experiments).

The properties of cytochrome 552 shown in Table VI are similar to the known properties of other c-type algal cytochromes and the cytochrome f of higher plants. There are, however, certain minor differences. In contrast to cytochrome f, cytochrome 552 is readily extractable from cells; furthermore, its molecular weight is about one-tenth that of cytochrome f and it contains one heme prosthetic group per molecule rather than two. Several c-type cytochromes from other algae exhibit similar variances in properties from cytochrome f (Katoh, 1959). However, cytochrome 552 differs from other low molecular weight cytochromes of the c-type in having an asymmetrical α-band absorption and a higher trytophan content (Perini et al., 1964a).

3. *Cytochrome b (561, Euglena), (Euglena Cytochrome b_6)*

Green *Euglena* cells contain a b-type cytochrome which appears to correspond to the cytochrome b_6 of higher plant chloroplasts (Hill, 1954). Little is known about the properties of these cytochromes and it is only quite recently that cytochrome b_6 has been solubilized from chloroplasts (Criddle and Park, 1964). The b-type cytochrome of *Euglena* was recognized by spectroscopic examination of acetone-extracted chloroplasts (Smillie, 1963; Perini *et al.*, 1964a) and by its prominent photooxidation in *Euglena* autotrophs poisoned with the *m*-chlorophenylhydrazone of carbonyl cyanide (Olson and Smillie, 1963). Reduced absorption maxima occur at 561, 530, and 432 mμ. The prosthetic group is probably protoheme (Perini *et al.*, 1964a). Like cytochrome b_6 from higher plants, but unlike other b-type cytochromes, cytochrome 561 is not denatured by cold acetone.

4. *Pyridine Nucleotide Transhydrogenase (NADPH-Diaphorase, NADPH-Oxidase, Ferredoxin NADP+-Reductase, NADP+-Photoreductase)*

Either NADH or NADPH act as substrate for this chloroplast flavo-protein, but the physiological significance of NADH as a substrate is doubtful because of its low affinity for the enzyme. In the presence of NADPH the enzyme reduces a variety of acceptors including NADP+, certain structural analogues of NADP+, 2,6-dichlorophenolindophenol, chloroplast ferredoxin, cytochrome f (but not mammalian cytochrome c), plastocyanin, phytoflavin, and flavin adenine nucleotides. The reaction is reversible and the enzyme is thought to function *in vivo* as the terminal enzyme of the photosynthetic electron-transfer pathway by transfering electrons from reduced chloroplast ferredoxin to NADP+.

Transhydrogenase has been extracted from acetone powders of green *Euglena* by Lazzarini and San Pietro (1963) and in its general properties it resembled the transhydrogenase purified from spinach leaves (Keister *et al.*, 1960). It showed transhydrogenase activity between NADP+ and its structural analogs and like the spinach enzyme, it functioned as a NADPH-linked cytochrome c reductase in the presence of chloroplast ferredoxin from either spinach or *Euglena*. The K_m for the deamino analog of NADP+ was estimated to be 50 μM, which compared with the value of 30 μM found for the spinach enzyme. However, the two enzymes differed in certain other kinetic constants and cross-reactivity with antiserum prepared against the spinach enzyme.

Dark-adapted and permanently bleached cells contained appreciable amounts of transhydrogenase activity, from one-eighth to one-quarter the amount present in green heterotrophic cells, and in all respects the enzymes from the three types of cells appeared to be identical. While the transhydrogenase of dark-adapted and permanently bleached cells is possibly localized in small plastids, the relatively high activities found in these cells, coupled with the results of intracellular distribution studies reported by Smillie (1963) suggest that, contrary to the generally accepted

3

opinion, the enzyme may not be confined to chloroplasts in green cells but may also occur in the cytoplasm.

The illumination of dark-adapted cells resulted in a rapid increase in transhydrogenase activity after an initial lag of 10–14 hours (Lazzarini and San Pietro, 1963). It is of interest that this lag was eliminated by brief irradiation with red light 12 hours prior to the continuous exposure to white light (Lazzarini and Woodruff, 1964).

5. *Other Proteins*

Wolken (1961) has obtained a chlorophyll–protein complex, which he termed chloroplastin, by treating *Euglena* cells with digitonin. Since the enzymic properties of chloroplastin have not been studied, it will not be dealt with in this chapter. Lewis *et al.* (1961) have isolated a *Euglena* protein, possibly a flavoprotein, that catalyzed the photooxidation of cytochrome 552. Two other soluble proteins found in photosynthetic algal cells, plastocyanin and phytoflavin, have not been found in *Euglena*, although both will function in photosynthetic electron-transfer reactions with *Euglena* chloroplasts (Katoh and Takamiya, 1965; Smillie, 1965). Nitrate and nitrite reductases are also frequently linked with electron-transfer pathways in green cells, but neither enzyme has been reported in *Euglena*. The ability of *E. gracilis* var. *bacillaris* to reduce nitrite (Huzisige and Satoh, 1960) suggests that this organism contains nitrite reductase.

IV. Enzymes of Nucleotide and Nucleic Acid Metabolism

Ribonuclease and enzymes catalyzing the synthesis of nucleoside monophosphates and the metabolism of 3'-phosphoadenylylsulfate and ADP-ribose are discussed in this section. In addition to these enzymes, adenylate kinase (Table XVI) and hydrolytic enzymes acting on ATP and UDP (Section VII,B and Table XVI) have been demonstrated in extracts of *Euglena*.

A. RIBONUCLEASE

The properties of *Euglena* ribonuclease have been investigated by Fellig and Wiley (1960) who obtained a 15-fold purification of the enzyme (yield 20%) by a series of fractionations with ammonium sulfate and removal of inactive protein with calcium phosphate gel. The enzyme was less specific than pancreatic ribonuclease, and degraded both polyuridylic and poly-adenylic acids as well as ribonucleic acid that had already been exhaustively digested with pancreatic ribonuclease. The pancreatic enzyme acts on the 3'-phosphate of pyrimidine nucleotides only, and consequently does not degrade polyadenylic acid. The enzyme from *Euglena* was heat labile and showed a narrow pH range of activity, with an optimum at 4.5. Like pancreatic ribonuclease, its activity was increased at high ionic strengths; with NaCl optimal activity occurred at 0.5 M. *Euglena* ribonuclease was less sensitive than pancreatic ribonuclease toward inhibition by divalent metal ions.

B. SYNTHESIS OF NUCLEOTIDES

The inhibition of growth of *A. longa* by concentrations of 8-azaguanine that failed to inhibit growth of the SM-L1 (streptomycin-bleached) strain of *E. gracilis* var. *bacillaris* prompted Kahn and Blum (1965) to compare the activities of nucleotide pyrophosphorylase in the two organisms. The differences in growth inhibition could not be explained in terms of this enzyme since both organisms contained enzymes catalyzing the conversion of adenine, hypoxanthine, guanine, and 8-azaguanine to the corresponding nucleotides in the presence of 5-phospho-α-D-ribosylpyrophosphate, as in Eq. (10).

$$\text{Purine} + \text{5-phospho-}\alpha\text{-D-ribosylpyrophosphate} =$$
$$\text{nucleoside 5'-phosphate} + \text{pyrophosphate} \qquad (10)$$

At least two enzymes, one reacting with adenine and hypoxanthine, the other with guanine and 8-azaguanine, are probably involved. The K_m values of the *Astasia* enzyme on guanine and 8-azaguanine substrates were 1.4 μM and 120 μM, respectively. The activities in extracts of the *Euglena* strain were nearly double the values obtained with *Astasia*.

C. SYNTHESIS AND DEGRADATION OF 3'-PHOSPHOADENYLYLSULFATE

1. Synthesis

Extracts of *Euglena* contain a soluble enzymic system catalyzing the synthesis of 3'-phosphoadenylylsulfate, an intermediate in the synthesis of other sulfonated compounds. The enzymes are present in extracts of green, dark-grown, and streptomycin-bleached cells (Abraham and Bachhawat, 1964) as well as in extracts of chloroplasts isolated from *Euglena* (Davies *et al.*, 1966). Although the individual enzymes of this system have not been separated, two enzymes are likely involved, namely sulfate adenylyl transferase [Eq. (11)] and adenylylsulfate kinase [Eq. (12)].

$$\text{ATP} + \text{sulfate} = \text{adenylylsulfate} + \text{pyrophosphate} \qquad (11)$$

$$\text{ATP} + \text{adenylylsulfate} = \text{ADP} + \text{3'-phosphoadenylylsulfate} \qquad (12)$$

Enzymes catalyzing these reactions have been found in a wide range of organisms, and the *Euglena* system, as indicated by its properties shown in Table VII, is quite similar. One point of difference is the activity obtained

Table VII

PROPERTIES OF AN ENZYMIC SYSTEM FROM *Euglena*
SYNTHESIZING 3'-PHOSPHOADENYLYLSULFATE[a]

Substrate specificity	ATP, and deoxy-ATP (guanosine and cytidine 5'-triphosphates inactive)
pH Optimum	6.5 (In tris-phosphate)
Activators	Mg^{2+}, Co^{2+} (Mn^{2+}, Ni^{2+}, Zn^{2+} inactive), sulfhydryl reagents

[a] Data from Abraham and Bachhawat (1964).

with deoxyadenosine 5'-triphosphate. Deoxyribonucleotides are inactive with preparations from other organisms, but with preparations from *Euglena*, deoxyadenosine 5'-triphosphate showed 50% of the activity given by ATP.

2. Hydrolysis

An enzyme hydrolyzing 3'-phosphoadenylylsulfate [Eq. (13)] has been demonstrated in extracts of etiolated and green *Euglena* (Abraham and Bachhawat, 1964). Some properties of the enzyme are listed in Table VIII.

Table VIII

PROPERTIES OF 3'-PHOSPHOADENYLYLSULFATASE FROM *Euglena*[a]

K_m	22.5 μM
pH optimum	5.5 (In tris–acetate)
Activators	Mg^{2+}, Co^{2+}, sulfhydryl agents
Inhibitors	3'-Phosphoadenylylsulfate ($>50 \mu M$), ADP (other nucleotides also inhibit to a lesser extent)

[a] Data from Abraham and Bachhawat (1964).

A similar enzyme has been found in sheep brain (Balasubramanian and Bachhawat, 1962).

$$3'\text{-Phosphoadenylylsulfate} = 3',5'\text{-diphosphoadenosine} + \text{sulfate} \qquad (13)$$

D. PHOSPHOROLYSIS OF ADENOSINE-5'-DIPHOSPHATE RIBOSE

Evans and San Pietro (1966) and Stern and Avron (1966) have studied an enzyme from *Euglena* catalyzing irreversibly the reaction shown in Eq. (14). The enzyme, adenosine-5'-diphosphate ribose: orthophosphate adenylyl transferase, also catalyzed a reversible exchange between orthophosphate and ADP.

$$\text{ADP-Ribose} + \text{orthophosphate} = \text{ADP} + \text{ribose 5'-phosphate} \qquad (14)$$

A 50-fold purification of the enzyme was obtained by Evans and San Pietro (1966) with a yield of 4.5%. The enzyme was specific for ADP-ribose and ADP (exchange reaction), except for a slight activity toward inosine 5'-diphosphate in the exchange reaction. Values for the K_m of 40 μM for ADP-ribose, 0.4 mM for orthophosphate, and 0.6 mM for ADP obtained by Evans and San Pietro (1966) agreed closely with values reported by Stern and Avron (1966). The pH optimum was 7.4–7.8 and metal activators were not required. Several inhibitors of the enzyme were studied and K_i values published for most of them. Arsenate and ribose 5'-phosphate were competitive inhibitors of orthophosphate but not of ADP-ribose, while in the exchange reaction, AMP and ATP were competitive with ADP but not with orthophosphate. The inhibition by ribose 5'-phosphate was complex, it also acted both competitively and noncompetitively with orthophosphate and ADP (exchange reaction), depending on substrate levels, and noncompetitively with ADP-ribose. *p*-Chloromercuribenzoate and selenate also inhibited the activity of the enzyme.

The physiological function of the enzyme is unknown. It was found in green and dark-adapted cells and did not appear to be associated with chloroplast metabolism.

V. Enzymes of Amino Acid and Protein Metabolism

The integrated enzymic systems synthesizing proteins in *Euglena* have been well characterized in a series of important studies and are treated in a separate chapter (Chapter 5). In contrast, little attention has been paid to the individual enzymes catalyzing the synthesis and catabolism of amino acids and proteins.

"Amino acid–activating" enzymes have been found in several algae, including *Euglena* (Table XVI), by measuring the formation of amino acid hydroxymates in the presence of a cell-free extract, a mixture of amino acids, ATP, MgCl$_2$, and hydroxylamine. This assay indicates the activity of enzymes whose individual catalytic function in the cell is the addition of an amino acid to its specific soluble RNA (aminoacyl-sRNA synthetases).

Extracts of *Euglena* showed activities comparable with activities measured in extracts of pea seedlings and spinach leaves (Raacke and Allen, 1960). The specific enzyme for leucine in *Euglena* has been studied by Eisenstadt and Brawerman (1966). Among the other enzymes metabolizing amino acids, glutamic dehydrogenase and transaminases have been detected in *Euglena* (Table XVI).

Cathepsin, a peptide hydrolase, has been demonstrated in extracts of *Euglena* by Bertini *et al.* (1965). Its activity was particularly high in cells starved of carbon.

VI. Enzymes of Lipid Metabolism

The composition and biosynthesis of *Euglena* lipids are covered in a separate chapter (Chapter 6) and only some enzymic systems involved in the synthesis of long-chain fatty acids and pigments are described in this section.

In addition to these enzymes, an enzyme hydrolyzing phenolic esters (arylesterase) has been detected in extracts of streptomycin-bleached *Euglena* by Bertini *et al.* (1965).

A. Synthesis of Long-Chain Fatty Acids

1. *Synthesis of Saturated Long-Chain Fatty Acids*

Cheniae (1962, 1963, 1964) and Cheniae and Kerr (1965) have described a soluble enzymic system from *Euglena* catalyzing the synthesis of saturated long-chain fatty acids from acetyl-CoA. From 60 to 70% of the substrate was incorporated into fatty acids containing from 16 to 20 carbon atoms, and at least one of these acids, stearic acid, was synthesized *de novo*. The overall reaction is represented by Eq. (15), although it should be noted that the release of free CoA and the identity of the products of ATP utilization have not been definitely established.

$$CH_3COOH + 8\ CH_3CO\text{-}SCoA + 8\ ATP + 16\ (NADH + NADPH) + 16\ H^+$$
$$= CH_3(CH_2)_{16}COOH + 8\ CoASH + 8\ ADP + 8\ \text{orthophosphate}$$
$$+ 16\ (NAD^+ + NADP^+) + 8\ H_2O \qquad (15)$$

The requirements and properties of the soluble enzymic system are shown in Table IX. Protein precipitated from a centrifuged extract of *Euglena* by between 35% and 60% of saturation with ammonium sulfate was used as the source of enzymes. ATP, Mg^{2+} ions, and a mixture of NADH and NADPH were required for maximum activity. Protein sulfhydryl groups were essential for activity, as shown by the inhibition induced by *p*-chloromercuriphenylsulfonate and iodoacetamide, and by the preventive action of cysteine and reduced glutathione. Arsenite and Cd^{2+} ions were not inhibitory.

Table IX

PROPERTIES OF ENZYMIC SYSTEM CATALYZING
THE SYNTHESIS OF LONG-CHAIN FATTY ACIDS FROM ACETYL-CoA[a]

Substrate specificity	Acetyl-CoA (malonyl-CoA inactive)
Cofactor requirements	ATP (partially replaced by other nucleotide triphosphates but not by ADP or AMP), NADH + NADPH
K_m values	
Acetyl-CoA	24 μM
ATP	0.4 mM
Activators	Mg^{2+}, Mn^{2+}
Inhibitors	*p*-Mercuriphenylsulfonate, iodoacetamide (avidin is noninhibitory)

[a] Data from Cheniae (1962, 1963, 1964) and Cheniae and Kerr (1965).

The mechanism of fatty acid synthesis by the *Euglena* system appears to differ from the known pathways of fatty acid synthesis, namely, the reversal of the β-oxidation pathway and pathways involving the intermediate formation of malonyl-CoA. Cheniae and Kerr (1965) listed several properties of the *Euglena* system which are at variance with synthesis via the malonate-CoA pathway. Malonyl-CoA was neither incorporated into fatty acids by the *Euglena* enzymes nor caused significant isotopic dilution of the label incorporated from acetyl-1-^{14}C-CoA. Avidin, an inhibitor of the malonyl-CoA pathway and other reactions in which biotin is an essential cofactor, was noninhibitory in the *Euglena* system, and HCO_3^-, which is required in the malonyl-CoA pathway, also had no effect. Finally, decarboxylation of acetyl-CoA was not observed.

On the other hand, the *Euglena* system exhibited a definite requirement for ATP. While ATP is necessary for the synthesis of fatty acids via the malonyl-CoA route, it is not necessary for reversal of the β-oxidation pathway. Cheniae (1964) has suggested that the ATP may function in the synthesis of an intermediate phosphorylated derivative of acetyl-CoA.

Cheniae (1964) and Cheniae and Kerr (1965) were unable to obtain evidence for the participation of acyl-CoA compounds of intermediate chain length such as octanoyl-CoA and decanoyl-CoA in the synthesis of the longer chain acids from acetyl-CoA. However, recent experiments of Nagai and Bloch (1965) have indicated that, at least in green cells, the most likely active intermediates are acyl–protein derivatives rather than the acyl-CoA thioesters, since extracts from autotrophic cells elongated the octanoate and decanoate derivatives of acyl carrier protein, a heat-stable protein from *E. coli.* Unsaturated fatty acids were similarly elongated.

2. *Conversion of Saturated Fatty Acids to Monounsaturated Acids*

Two distinct enzymic systems for the formation of monounsaturated fatty acids are present in *Euglena;* one predominates in heterotrophic cells, the other in autotrophic cells (Nagai and Bloch, 1965). Properties of the two systems are contrasted in Table X. The direct desaturation of long-chain acyl-CoA thioesters which occurred in dark-grown heterotrophic cells has been found in many other nonphotosynthetic organisms. Autotrophic cells, on the other hand, formed long-chain monounsaturated fatty acids, either by elongation of unsaturated short-chain acids, as mentioned above or, in the case of oleic acid, by a desaturase specific for the acyl carrier protein derivative of stearic acid. At least three proteins are necessary to accomplish the desaturation of the stearoyl–acyl carrier protein in the presence of NADPH and O_2, a NADPH oxidase, chloroplast ferredoxin, and a desaturase (Nagai and Bloch, 1966).

Table X

COMPARISON OF ENZYMIC SYSTEMS FORMING
MONOUNSATURATED FATTY ACIDS IN HETEROTROPHIC AND AUTOTROPIC *Euglena*[a]

	Dark-grown heterotrophs	Autotrophs
Solubility of proteins in cell-free homogenates	Soluble and particulate fractions required	Soluble, three components have been separated: a NADPH-oxidase, a chloroplast ferredoxin, and a desaturase
Active substrates	Stearoyl-CoA Palmitoyl-CoA	Stearoyl-ACP[b]
Inactive substrates	Stearoyl-ACP Palmitoyl-ACP	Acyl-CoA derivatives Palmitoyl-ACP Myristoyl-ACP
Other requirements	NADPH	NADPH, O_2

[a] Data from Nagai and Bloch (1965, 1966).
[b] ACP, acyl carrier protein.

B. PIGMENT INTERCONVERSION AND SYNTHESIS

1. *De-epoxidation of Carotenoid*

About 75% of the carotenoids of green cells of *Euglena* occur as epoxides. Bamji and Krinsky (1965) have investigated the decrease in epoxides that occurs when rapidly growing green cells are transferred to the dark under anaerobic conditions. Cell-free homogenates from the green cells were shown to carry out a reductive de-epoxidation of endogenous 5,6-epoxyzeaxanthin (antheraxanthin), the major epoxide pigment in the green cells [Eq. (16)]. Incubations were carried out anaerobically in the

$$5,6\text{-Expoxyzeaxanthin} + FMNH_2 = zeaxanthin + FMN + H_2O \tag{16}$$

dark and in the presence of $FMNH_2$ (or a mixture of malate, $NADP^+$, and FMN), which served as the source of reducing power. De-epoxidation also occurred upon illumination in the presence of FMN, provided the preparations contained active chloroplasts. This was of interest because a photochemical de-epoxidation of 5,6-epoxyzeaxanthin had previously been demonstrated in intact cells (Krinsky, 1964). However, the possible role of the enzymic system in this photochemical de-epoxidation which occurred in both growing and stationary-phase cells after transfer to anaerobic conditions is not clear, since only the growing cells yielded an active enzymic preparation.

2. *Porphyrin Synthesis*

Enzymes synthesizing porphyrins from 5-aminolevulinate have been detected in *Euglena*. Cell-free homogenates prepared from green cells contained the enzyme 5-aminolevulinate dehydrase, which converts two molecules of 5-aminolevulinate to porphobilinogen (Carell and Kahn, 1964), and a significant fraction of the activity was tightly bound to chloroplasts. Both 5-aminolevulinate acid and porphobilinogen were converted to porphyrins by *Euglena* enzymes (Gibor and Granick, 1962; Karali and Price 1963; Carell and Kahn, 1964); with preparations derived from purified chloroplasts several porphyrins, including protoporphyrin, uroporphyrin, and coproporphyrin, were formed (Carell and Kahn, 1964).

VII. Phosphatases

Enzymes hydrolyzing phosphate esters have been grouped together partly for convenience and partly because their properties and function in *Euglena* have received a good deal of attention. Most investigations have been concerned with one of three groups of phosphatases, namely, nonspecific acid phosphatases, phosphatases specific for fructose 1,6-diphosphate, and pyrophosphatases.

A. PHOSPHOMONOESTERASES

1. *Acid Phosphatases*

Euglena and *Astasia* contain phosphatases showing maximum activities at an acid pH but, in general, the activities are low when compared with the levels of acid phosphatase usually encountered in higher plant tissues or with the activities of the other, more specific, phosphatases in *Euglena* acting on fructose 1,6-diphosphate and pyrophosphate, respectively. Acid phosphatase from *Euglena* is nonspecific, and hydrolyzes such compounds as β-glycerophosphate, *p*-nitrophenylphosphate and *o*-carboxyphenyl-phosphate [Eq. (17)].

$$\text{Orthophosphoric monoester} + H_2O = \text{alcohol} + H_3PO_4 \qquad (17)$$

The acid phosphatase content of the different strains of *E. gracilis* is variable. Acid phosphatase in normal cells of the Z strain was barely detectable (Price, 1962a; Smillie, 1964), while a streptomycin-bleached mutant of var. *bacillaris* showed fairly good activity [*p*-nitrophenylphosphate was hydrolyzed at the rate of 4.0 μmoles per minute per 10^6 cells (Blum *et al.*, 1965)]. The acid phosphatase activity of *A. longa* was one-fifth as great. The activity of the *Euglena* mutant was due to several enzymes and Bennun and Blum (1966) have distinguished between two major phosphatases both of which were particle bound.

The acid phosphatase activities of the strain Z and a streptomycin-bleached mutant (SM-L1) of var. *bacillaris* are increased by phosphate deficiency (Price, 1962a; Blum, 1965). This inducible phosphatase, which Blum (1965) regards as a separate enzyme, is not ubiquitous among the Euglenophyta. Only a trace of inducible phosphatase could be found by Blum (1965) in a strain similar to the one used by Price (1962a) and *A. longa* failed to show inducible activity (Blum *et al.*, 1965).

The properties of the constitutive acid phosphatase of the SM-L1 mutant as exemplified by its lack of specificity, pH optimum at 5.0, and inhibition by NaF (90% at 2 m*M*), are typical of the properties of acid phosphatases from higher plants. The inducible phosphatase appears to be of the same general type, but Blum (1965) and Bennun and Blum (1966) cited experimental evidence to support the contention that the constitutive and inducible activities are due to different enzymes. The acid phosphatase of cells grown in a phosphate-deficient medium was less readily extractable, was more heat labile, showed a broader pH range of activity, and was less sensitive to NaF than the phosphatase from cells grown in a medium containing ample phosphate. *p*-Fluorophenylalanine inhibited the synthesis of the inducible enzyme without affecting the level of the constitutive enzyme. Centrifugation of cell-free extracts of induced cells in a sucrose gradient separated peaks of phosphatase activity not present in extracts from non-induced cells. Studies on the cytochemical localization of acid phosphatase in *Euglena* were consistent with these observations (Sommer and Blum, 1965).

Increased acid phosphatase has also been noted in cells deprived of a source of carbon (Bertini *et al.*, 1965), but this enzyme appeared to be distinct from the acid phosphatase induced during phosphate deficiency, since each was localized in different regions of the cell. Brandes *et al.* (1964) considered that most of the increased acid phosphatase activity found in cells starved of carbon originated in the Golgi bodies, and if this was the case, the inducible activity may have been largely the result of an increased synthesis of the constitutive phosphatase of the Golgi bodies.

The function of acid phosphatases in *Euglena* is obscure. Blum (1965) observed that the induction of acid phosphatase was accompanied by an increased ability of the cells to extract phosphate from the medium. Since increased acid phosphatase, at least in *Euglena*, is symptomatic of phosphate deficiency, it might be argued that the inducible phosphatase functions as a scavenger of phosphate from nonessential phosphate esters. This increase in phosphatase, coupled with the increased ability of phosphate-deficient cells to extract phosphate from the medium (Blum, 1965), may be important factors in their survival under certain adverse conditions.

2. *Neutral Fructose-1,6-diphosphatase*

Euglena possesses at least two hydrolases which are specific for the phosphate attached to carbon-1 of fructose 1,6-diphosphate, [see Eq. (18)]; one enzyme shows maximum activity near neutrality, the other at alkaline pH.

$$\text{Fructose 1,6-diphosphate} + H_2O = \text{fructose 6-phosphate} + H_3PO_4 \qquad (18)$$

In certain mammalian tissues such as liver, kidney, and skeletal muscle and in *Candida utilis*, alkaline fructose-1,6-diphosphatase functions in gluconeogenesis in by-passing the irreversible step in glycolysis catalyzed by phosphofructokinase (Krebs, 1964; Salas *et al.*, 1964; Rosen *et al.*, 1965). The enzyme also plays a key role in the regulation of the process. Krebs (1964) has described it as one of the "pacemakers" of gluconeogenesis, and it is subject to feedback control by AMP and high concentrations of its substrate.

In *Euglena*, and also in higher plants, it would appear to be the neutral fructose-1,6-diphosphatase and not the enzyme acting at an alkaline pH that functions in gluconeogenesis linked to respiratory mechanisms (Smillie, 1960a, b, 1964). Neutral fructose-1,6-diphosphatase is found in both green and permanently bleached mutants of *Euglena*, and in higher plants it occurs in tissues, such as germinating castor beans, which actively convert fat to carbohydrate (Smillie, 1964). The alkaline fructose-1,6-diphosphatase has not been detected in plant tissues or algal cells lacking chloroplasts (Smillie, 1964).

Neutral fructose-1,6-diphosphatase has been purified 60-fold from a streptomycin-bleached mutant of *E. gracilis* strain Z, by precipitation of inert protein with $MnCl_2$ and fractionation by precipitation with first acetone and then ammonium sulfate (R. M. Smillie, unpublished experiments). Some properties of the partially purified enzyme are shown in Table XI. The enzyme was highly specific for fructose 1,6-diphosphate, the

Table XI

PROPERTIES OF NEUTRAL FRUCTOSE-1,6-DIPHOSPHATASE
FROM *E. gracilis* (STREPTOMYCIN-BLEACHED MUTANT OF Z STRAIN)[a]

Specificity	Specific for fructose 1,6-diphosphate
K_m	13 μM
pH optimum	7.3 (In tris–HCl buffer)
Activators	Mg^{2+}, Mn^{2+}, stimulated by EDTA
Inhibitors	*p*-Chloromercuribenzoate, NaF, $BeCl_2$

[a] Data from Smillie (1964) and unpublished results.

products of the reaction having been identified as fructose 6-phosphate and orthophosphate. Glucose 1,6-diphosphate, ribulose 1,6-diphosphate, and a wide range of monophosphate esters, including fructose 1-phosphate and fructose 6-phosphate, were tested as substrates, but all were completely inactive. The enzyme showed more than a 10-fold higher affinity for fructose 1,6-diphosphate when compared with the alkaline fructose-1,6-diphosphatases from spinach and *Euglena*. The pH optimum was 7.3 but the enzyme was fairly active in the alkaline range; at pH 8.5 the activity was about 50% of the maximum value. Below pH 7 activity decreased sharply, the enzyme being almost inactive at pH 6.0. The requirement of a divalent metal for activity, the stimulation by EDTA, and the inhibition by NaF, $BeCl_2$, and *p*-chloromercuribenzoate are properties shown by other specific fructose-1,6-diphosphatases.

The activity of fructose-1,6-diphosphatase may be regulated to some extent by its substrate since most fructose-1,6-diphosphatases are inhibited by concentrations of fructose 1,6-diphosphate above 0.1 m*M*. A potentially more important regulatory mechanism involves the allosteric inhibition of fructose-1,6-diphosphatase by AMP. Several fructose-1,6-diphosphatases, including those from rabbit liver (Taketa and Pogell, 1963), frog muscle (Salas *et al.*, 1964), *C. utilis* (Rosen *et al.*, 1965), and *E. coli* (Fraenkel *et al.*, 1966) are inhibited by AMP. The inhibition occurs at relatively low concentrations of AMP (5–500 μM), is specific for AMP, and is reversible. The neutral fructose 1,6-diphosphate of *Euglena* was inhibited by high concentrations of fructose 1,6-diphosphate (5 mM and higher), but AMP at concentrations up to 10 mM showed no inhibition. Taketa and Pogell (1965) have previously noted the failure of AMP to inhibit the neutral fructose-1,6-diphosphatase of *Euglena* as well as the inhibitory effect of excess substrate. Thus in the case of the *Euglena* enzyme, a sensitive regulatory mechanism has not yet been found. A fructose-1,6-diphosphatase from the slime mold *Polysphendylium pallidum* (Rosen, 1966) is similarly not inhibited by AMP.

3. Alkaline Fructose-1,6-diphosphatase

This plant enzyme may be an integral enzyme of the carbon reductive cycle of photosynthesis catalyzing a step in the conversion of 3-phosphoglycerate to hexose monophosphate (Smillie, 1960a, 1964). The enzyme is either absent, or is present in only trace amounts, in streptomycin-bleached mutants. Its activity in normal cells parallels changes in chlorophyll occurring during the greening of etiolated cells (App and Jagendorf, 1963) or during the adaptation of light-grown heterotrophs to autotrophic growth (Smillie, 1963). In the autotrophic cells the enzyme is localized in the chloroplasts (see Section XI).

The alkaline fructose-1,6-diphosphatase of chloroplasts has been purified from two sources: first from spinach leaves by Racker and Schroeder (1958), and subsequently from *Euglena* by App and Jagendorf (1964). An approximately 400-fold purification of the *Euglena* enzyme with a 30% yield was achieved by chromatography on a column of DEAE-cellulose after prior removal of inert protein by (1) heat treatment, (2) acidification to pH 4.35 and (3) precipitation with protamine sulfate.

Some properties of *Euglena* alkaline fructose-1,6-diphosphatase are shown in Table XII. Except for the more alkaline pH optimum and the apparently higher Michaelis constant, the properties were strikingly similar to those of neutral fructose-1,6-diphosphatase. The enzyme was quite specific for fructose 1,6-diphosphate; fructose 1-phosphate, and fructose 6-phosphate, ribulose 1,5-diphosphate being completely inactive (App and Jagendorf, 1964; Smillie, 1964). The activity of the purified enzyme decreased sharply as the pH was lowered; by pH 7.5, where the neutral

Table XII

PROPERTIES OF ALKALINE FRUCTOSE-1,6-DIPHOSPHATASE FROM GREEN *Euglena*[a]

Specificity	Fructose 1,6-diphosphate
K_m	0.3 mM
pH optimum	8.25
Activators	Mg^{2+} (optimal ratio of Mg: substrate = 25), EDTA
Inhibitors	*p*-Chloromercuribenzoate, NaF

[a] Data from App and Jagendorf (1964).

fructose-1,6-diphosphatase exhibited maximum activity, it had fallen to less than 10%. The apparent K_m value for the *Euglena* enzyme was the same as found for spinach alkaline fructose-1,6-diphosphatase, and in other respects the two enzymes were very similar. Both required Mg^{2+} ions for activity, were stimulated by EDTA, and were inhibited by NaF and *p*-chloromercuribenzoate.

The behavior of the enzyme toward excess substrate and AMP was similar to that of the neutral fructose-1,6-diphosphatase. Significant inhibition by fructose 1,6-diphosphate did not occur until concentrations in excess of 5 mM were used. AMP at 10 mM was not inhibitory.

4. *Sedoheptulose-1,7-diphosphatase*

This specific phosphatase converts sedoheptulose 1,7-diphosphate to sedoheptulose 7-phosphate and is also thought to function in the photosynthetic fixation of CO_2 (Bassham and Calvin, 1957). Extracts of green *Euglena* contained this enzyme, but the activity was quite low (Peterkofsky and Racker, 1961).

B. PYROPHOSPHATASES

Ohmann (1964) has shown that extracts of *Euglena* contained a very active inorganic pyrophosphatase. The optimal pH for activity in extracts of either autotrophic cells or streptomycin-bleached cells of *E. gracilis* strain Z was found to be about 8.0 (R. M. Smillie, unpublished experiments) and although the levels of activity in both types of cells were very similar, part of the activity in autotrophic cells was localized in chloroplasts (Smillie *et al.*, 1963). Metaphosphate was split at the same rate as pyrophosphate (Table XIII). Mg^{2+} ions and EDTA were required for maximum activity and NaF was inhibitory.

Table XIII

PYROPHOSPHATASE ACTIVITY OF EXTRACTS
OF STREPTOMYCIN-BLEACHED *E. gracilis* STRAIN Z[a]

Reaction mixture[a]	Orthophosphate (μmoles/minute/gm protein)
P–P	140
Meta-P	138
P–P ($-Mg^{2+}$)	2
P–P ($-EDTA$)	26
P–P ($+NaF$, 20 mM)	5

[a] R. M. Smillie, unpublished data. Complete reaction mixture contained *Euglena* extract, inorganic pyrophosphate (P–P) or metaphosphate (meta-P) (5 mM), tris–HCl buffer, pH 8.0 (100 mM), $MgCl_2$ (5 mM), and EDTA (1.6 mM).

Crude extracts of *Euglena* also contain magnesium-dependent enzymes which split phosphate from ATP (R. M. Smillie, unpublished experiments) and convert UDP to uridine 5′-phosphate (Maréchal and Goldemberg, 1964).

VIII. Miscellaneous Enzymes

Several enzymes not included in the foregoing sections have been found in cell-free extracts of *Euglena*. These include glyceraldehyde-3-phosphate $NADP^+$-reductase, malic enzyme, $NAD^+(P)$-glyoxylate reductases, glutathione reductase, and acetyl-CoA deacylase (see also Table XVI). Their properties have not been investigated.

IX. Comparison of Cellular Levels of Enzymes in Autotrophic and Heterotrophic *Euglena* with Those in Other Organisms

Peterkofsky and Racker (1961) have compared the activities of the enzymes of the carbon reductive cycle of photosynthesis in extracts of autotrophically grown *Euglena*, spinach leaves, and two strains of *Chlorella*. The activities of some of the *Euglena* enzymes, namely, ribulose-1,5-diphosphate carboxylase, fructose-1,6-diphosphatase, sedoheptulose-1,7-diphosphatase, and transaldolase appeared to be too low to support the rate of CO_2 fixation shown by intact cells. However, with the exception of ribulose-1,5-diphosphate carboxylase from spinach, this was also true of these same enzymes in the other organisms. There was in fact a close correspondence between activities of the same enzyme in different organisms, even though the activities of different enzymes in the one organism were widely divergent. The chief exceptions were: aldolase, transketolase, ribulose 1,5-diphosphate carboxylase, and the diphosphatases, all of which were up to four times higher on a chlorophyll basis in spinach as compared with the algal cells; and ribulose-5-phosphate 3-epimerase, which was very low in one of the strains of *Chlorella*.

The cellular levels of many of the enzymes involved in the respiration of carbohydrates in *Euglena* autotrophs are likewise comparable with those in other photosynthetic cells. Table XIV summarizes data from experiments in which the activities of enzymes in extracts of *Euglena* and pea leaves were compared. Some values obtained when using the photosynthetic bacterium *Chromatium* are included.

The same assay procedures were used for each organism, and all assays were carried out at 23°C. Four types of cells of *E. gracilis* strain Z, each harvested near the midpoint of the logarithmic phase of growth, were compared: (1) cells grown autotrophically in an inorganic medium plus 5% CO_2 in air and under 700 ft-c of white light, (2) cells grown heterotrophically under 700 ft-c of light in an inorganic medium supplemented with glucose, amino acids, and organic acids (Hutner *et al.*, 1956), (3) cells grown heterotrophically but in the dark, and (4) streptomycin-bleached cells, also grown heterotrophically under 700 ft-c of white light. For comparison, some values taken from Peterkofsky and Racker (1961) are included; these are only approximate estimates of the published values, since the latter were expressed per milligram of chlorophyll.

$NADP^+$-glyceraldehyde-3-phosphate dehydrogenase was restricted to cells containing chloroplasts and was higher in autotrophic cells than in green heterotrophic cells, its amount thus being related to the extent of chloroplast development. Of the glycolytic enzymes assayed, those that also function in photosynthesis, namely, aldolase, triosephosphate isomerase, and 3-phosphoglycerate kinase, were slightly more active in green *Euglena* cells than in dark-grown heterotrophs, and the reverse was true of enolase and lactate dehydrogenase. In general, however, the activities of the glycolytic enzymes as well as those of the oxidative pentose phosphate pathway and tricarboxylic acid cycle were remarkably similar in the different organisms. Except for the high values obtained for *Euglena* triosephosphate isomerase, the specific activities of the same enzyme in different organisms were comparable. Although a change in the absolute activities of enzymes with increasing age of the cultures was noted, the ratio of the activities of the various enzymes in each organism remained relatively constant. Drobnica and Ebringer (1963) have also assayed several of the enzymes listed in Table XIV, as well as pyruvate kinase and glutamate oxalacetate

Table XIV

ACTIVITIES OF SOME ENZYMES IN EXTRACTS OF *Euglena* AND OTHER ORGANISMS[a]

Enzyme	Auto-trophs[b]	Auto-trophs	Green hetero-trophs	Dark hetero-trophs	Streptomycin-bleached hetero-trophs	Pea leaves	*Chromatium*[c]
Aldolase	91	165	99	114	119	92	180
Triosephosphate isomerase	3,380	28,000	21,000	26,000	32,000	4,800	4,320
NAD+-Ga-3-P dehydrogenase	450	1,780	2,300	2,260	3,840	550	1,830
NADP+-Ga-3-P dehydrogenase	370	230	130	0[d]	0[d]	780	0
3-Phosphoglycerate kinase	7,600	16,300	15,800	13,400	23,500	3,500	6,020
Enolase	—	99	92	134	130	24	—
Lactate dehydrogenase	—	2.1	2.8	4.0	1.6	2.5	—
Glucose-6-phosphate dehydrogenase	—	53	50	38	68	48	—
6-Phosphogluconate dehydrogenase	—	22	23	23	37	21	—
Aconitate hydratase	—	11	11	8	6	25	—
NADP+-isocitrate dehydrogenase	—	41	43	48	75	64	—
Malate dehydrogenase	—	1,800	2,070	3,290	3,290	2,030	—

[a] Activities are micromoles of substrate per minute per gm soluble protein. Values for *Euglena* and leaves of pea (*Pisum sativum* L.) are from unpublished data of the author. Assay temperature was 23°C.

[b] Data calculated from Peterkofsky and Racker (1961). Assay temperature was 20°C.

[c] Data from Fuller *et al.* (1961).

[d] Traces of this enzyme may be present but were undetectable in the assay used.

transaminase, and found comparable activities in green and in two bleached strains of *E. gracilis* var. *bacillaris* grown heterotrophically on acetate. When considered together, these studies suggest that the main photosynthetic and respiratory pathways of *Euglena*, whether grown autotrophically or heterotrophically, are basically similar to those found in higher plants. As noted previously, this generalization probably does not apply to the mitochondrial electron-transfer system of *Euglena* (see Section II,G).

X. Changes in Enzymic Activities in Response to Environmental and Physiological Changes

Changes in cellular activities of several enzymes during the growth and division of *Euglena* have been recorded in the literature and some of these have already been cited in the preceding sections of this chapter, but systematic studies of the significance of altered patterns of enzymic activity to growth and division have not been attempted. Similarly, several isolated observations on the changes in cellular levels of enzymes as a response to nutritional variations have been made, and among those already discussed are the effects of acetate on the cellular levels of isocitrate lyase and acetate thiokinase, the decreased activity of particulate lactate dehydrogenase as a result of zinc deficiency and the induction of nonspecific acid phosphatase in cells deficient in phosphate.

Changes in the activities of *Euglena* enzymes in response to two other physiological conditions have received attention, namely, in cells starved of a carbon growth source and in nondividing cells forming chloroplasts. These are discussed below.

A. CARBON STARVATION

The morphological changes occurring in a streptomycin-bleached strain (SM-L1) of *Euglena* deprived of a carbon growth source have been described by Malkoff and Buetow (1964) and by Brandes *et al.* (1964). Upon removal of exogenous carbon sources, a rapid disappearance of paramylon granules ensued, extensive vacuolization of the endoplasmic reticulum occurred, and membrane-bound bodies (cytolysomes) which enclosed and digested sections of the cytoplasm appeared. These changes were accompanied by large decreases in RNA, protein, and oxidative capacity (Blum and Buetow, 1963).

The loss of oxidative capacity is partly due to degradation of mitochondria within the cytolysomes, but this in itself is insufficient to explain the 30-fold decrease in the oxidative capacity of starved cells observed by Blum and

Buetow (1963) and a second more subtle mechanism must operate on the mitochondria that escape encapsulation in order to reduce further the overall oxidative capacity of the cells. The latter mitochondria showed little in the way of structural alterations during starvation and rapidly regained their oxidative capacity when a suitable carbon source was supplied to the cells.

Concomitant with the appearance of cytolysomes, the activities of enzymes hydrolyzing peptides and phosphate esters increased. Cathepsin and acid phosphatase activities increased more than 5-fold during the first 2–3 days of carbon starvation and thereafter slowly declined (Bertini *et al.*, 1965). Both of these enzymes are associated with lysosomes in animal tissues.

In green cells chloroplasts appear to be remarkably stable during carbon starvation, even in cells kept in darkness. Ben-Shaul *et al.* (1965) observed a slow decrease in chlorophyll and in cells maintained in darkness for 6 days in the absence of a utilizable carbon source, but the internal structure of the chloroplasts remained virtually unchanged.

B. Chloroplast Formation in Nondividing Cells

1. *Plastid Enzymes*

Some of the changes in enzymic activities in cells adapting to autotrophic conditions have already been described (Sections III,A and IX). There are striking increases in the activities of chloroplast enzymes such as NADP$^+$-glyceraldehyde-3-phosphate dehydrogenase and cytochrome 552, but smaller changes in the cellular levels of chloroplast enzymes which also function in respiratory metabolism (e.g., aldolase). Chloroplast development in *Euglena* involves not only the synthesis of the functional proteins of photosynthesis, but also the formation of a completely new protein-synthesizing system within the chloroplasts (Brawerman, 1962; Eisenstadt and Brawerman, 1963, 1964a,b) and, in addition, the production of enzymes that catalyze the synthesis of the diverse electron-transfer carriers and structural components of the chloroplast. Thus, the appearance of new enzymic systems for the synthesis of unsaturated fatty acids in autotrophic *Euglena* (Nagai and Bloch, 1965, 1966), and the presence of enzymes synthesizing 3′-phosphoadenylylsulfate in chloroplasts (Davies *et al.*, 1966), can be correlated with the high content of unsaturated fatty acids and sulfolipids in chloroplasts.

The sequence in which these proteins and the other components of chloroplasts are synthesized, and the regulatory mechanisms involved, still remain to be elucidated, although some progress has been made. The synthesis of chlorophyll and chloroplast protein does not begin immediately after dark-adapted cells are exposed to light, and during the lag period of synthesis (usually 8–12 hours) there is an increase in plastid ribosomal RNA (Brawerman *et al.*, 1962). The appearance of this ribosomal RNA not only precedes the synthesis of chloroplast proteins such as cytochrome 552, but is essential for their synthesis. Thus, if the light-induced formation of functional ribosomal RNA is prevented by the addition of 5-fluorouracil, the synthesis of cytochrome 552 is also suppressed, as is the synthesis of chlorophyll and the incorporation of manganese, an essential component of chloroplast lamellae (Eyster *et al.*, 1958). Since the effective period of inhibition by 5-fluorouracil is restricted to the lag period of chlorophyll synthesis (Smillie *et al.*, 1963), there appears to be a period of critical RNA synthesis, associated with the formation of a new protein-synthesizing system, which precedes the main period of chloroplast protein synthesis.

Some differences in the rate of increase of chloroplast activities have been noted, especially during the early stages of chloroplast development. The increase in Hill reaction activity is more rapid than that of chlorophyll and cytochrome 552, and Lazzarini and San Pietro (1963) showed that in rapidly growing cells, the synthesis of transhydrogenase, once induced, proceeds at a constant rate with respect to total protein biosynthesis, whereas the rate of chlorophyll synthesis continues to increase. Using a quite different experimental approach, Lewis *et al.* (1965) have demonstrated the sequential appearance of chloroplast antigens during chloroplast development in nondividing cells.

2. Cytoplasmic Enzymes

Since chloroplasts contain DNA and a mechanism for protein synthesis, they are often considered autonomous and consequently, there is a tendency to think of chloroplast development as primarily a process of organelle biosynthesis rather than as a cellular process in which synthetic and other processes located in the cytoplasm are directly involved in the synthesis of chloroplast constituents. This view of chloroplast development is not yet fully justified. Demonstrable changes in cytoplasmic protein metabolism do occur in cells forming chloroplasts, and the relation of these to chloroplast development will be considered under several headings.

a. Repression of the Synthesis of Enzymes Involved in the Utilization of Organic Growth Substrates. The formation of autotrophic cells from dark-adapted heterotrophic cells is accompanied by the disappearance of certain inducible cytoplasmic enzymes. For instance, autotrophic cells lack isocitrate lyase (Haigh and Beevers, 1964) and presumably conditions favoring chloroplast development also result in degradation of the existing enzyme and repression of the synthesis of isocitrate lyase. It is interesting that inducers of isocitrate lyase such as acetate and ethanol also act as repressors of chloroplast development (App and Jagendorf, 1963), so that a balance between heterotrophy and autotrophy is maintained depending on the availability of growth substrates other than CO_2.

b. Partial Repression of the Synthesis of Cytoplasmic Enzymes, and the Utilization of Cytoplasmic Protein for the Synthesis of Chloroplast Protein. The synthesis of other cytoplasmic enzymes may only be partially repressed under conditions favoring autotrophy. The specific activity of acetate thiokinase in autotrophic cells is less than one-fifth the value found in cells grown in the presence of acetate (Ohmann, 1964) and the level of paramylon synthetase in cells containing chloroplasts is much lower than in dark-grown cells fed on glucose (Maréchal and Goldemberg, 1964). The activity of aconitate hydratase, but not of $NADP^+$-isocitrate dehydrogenase, is also significantly decreased in autotrophic cells (Cook and Carver, 1966). Indeed a reduction in the levels of key respiratory enzymes may conceivably take place as respiration is superseded by photosynthesis as the major source of cellular energy. There is evidence, at least in nondividing cells, for the synthesis of chloroplast protein occurring at the expense of cytoplasmic protein, since the activities of many cytoplasmic enzymes decrease during chloroplast development (Smillie *et al.*, 1963). This decrease coincides with the onset of the most active period of synthesis of chloroplast protein, and appears to be linked to it since the decline in the activities of cytoplasmic enzymes is delayed by compounds that specifically inhibit the synthesis of the chloroplast protein.

c. Utilization of Reserve Carbohydrate for Chloroplast Development. When dark-adapted cells are exposed to light the requisite energy and carbon for the synthesis of chloroplast protein and lipid, at least during the early stages of chloroplast development, must be provided by existing cellular reserves. Changes in the activities of enzymes catabolizing β-1,3-glucan and its breakdown products have been measured during chloroplast development in nondividing cells and some representative results are shown in Fig. 1. Illuminated cells showed increased activities of the enzymes of glycolysis, the oxidative pentose phosphate pathway, and the tricarboxylic acid cycle (Smillie *et al.*, 1963), and similar changes have since been found for laminaribiose phosphorylase and β-1,3-glucan hydrolase (M. R. Dwyer and R. M. Smillie, unpublished results). The increases in activity, as well as the decrease in glucan, occurred during the lag period of chlorophyll synthesis, and thereafter the activities decreased. Although the magnitude of these light-induced changes in the activities of respiratory enzymes proved to be quite variable with different populations of dark-adapted cells, it was nevertheless apparent that exposure to light induced changes in the activities of respiratory enzymes that could be correlated with the utilization of reserve carbohydrate for synthetic reactions associated with chloroplast development. Experiments in which the β-1,3-glucan of dark-adapted cells was labeled with ^{14}C disclosed that after illumination of the cells, approximately half of the label was lost as $^{14}CO_2$ during the first 24 hours and the remainder was incorporated almost equally into protein and lipid.

  d. Cytoplasmic Synthesis of Chloroplast Protein. Since isolated chloroplasts carry out protein synthesis, the chloroplast is usually assumed to be the *in vivo* site for the synthesis of chloroplast protein. Direct evidence for this is lacking and while the chloroplast is almost certainly a site of protein synthesis, the possibility remains that certain chloroplast proteins

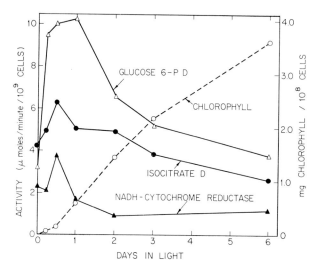

Fig. 1. Light-induced changes in glucose-6-phosphate dehydrogenase, NADP$^+$-isocitrate dehydrogenase, and NADH-cytochrome c reductase during chloroplast development. Reproduced from Smillie *et al.* (1963).

are synthesized in the cytoplasm, as is the case with the synthesis of certain mitochondrial proteins (Beattie *et al.*, 1966). An important problem for future studies will be to establish the intracellular sites for the synthesis of chloroplast proteins and the relative roles of nuclear DNA and plastid DNA in this synthesis.

  e. Synthesis of Cytoplasmic Enzymes Involved in the Metabolism of Photosynthetic Products. Another group of cytoplasmic enzymes whose synthesis may be linked to the formation of chloroplasts are certain enzymes involved in the metabolism of photosynthetic products excreted by chloroplasts. Enzymes metabolizing glycolate such as glyoxylate reductase and serine glyoxylate transaminase may fit into this category. The transaminase has not been assayed in *Euglena*, but in wheat leaves its synthesis is induced by light (King and Waygood, 1963). Another cytoplasmic enzyme of interest is malate dehydrogenase, since autotrophic cells of *Euglena* contain an isoenzyme of this enzyme which is absent in heterotrophic cells (Chancellor-Maddison and Noll, 1963). In most photosynthesizing cells, malate is one of the most rapidly labeled compounds formed during short-term feeding experiments with $^{14}CO_2$ and it is interesting to speculate if the additional isoenzyme found in autotrophic cells functions specifically toward the malate arising from photosynthesis.

XI. Intracellular Distribution of Enzymes

A. FRACTIONATION IN AQUEOUS AND NONAQUEOUS MEDIA

Techniques involving the isolation of cellular fractions in either aqueous or nonaqueous media have been employed to study the intracellular distribution of enzymes in *Euglena*. Fractionation in an aqueous medium has been largely restricted to the localization of insoluble enzymes such as paramylon synthetase (Maréchal and Goldemberg, 1964), acid phosphatase (Bertini *et al.*, 1965), and mitochondrial dehydrogenases (Danforth, 1953; Buetow and Buchanan, 1965), and more use has been made of fractionation in a nonaqueous medium. The latter technique has the advantage of being applicable to proteins that may be solubilized and leached from their original sites during fractionation in an aqueous medium. In this technique, lyophilized cells are broken in a nonaqueous suspending medium and cellular fractions separated by successive flotations in media of increasing density.

Although fractionation in nonaqueous medium was originally developed by Behrens (1932) to isolate nuclei from animal tissues, the main application to *Euglena* has been in the localization of enzymes in chloroplasts. Details of a fractionation procedure that yields preparations enriched for chloroplast proteins are given by Smillie (1963). Table XV shows the results of a study of the intracellular distribution of enzymes in autotrophic *Euglena*, using this procedure. In this study, three groups of enzymes were distinguished, namely, enzymes found only in the chloroplasts, cytoplasmic enzymes, and enzymes found both in chloroplasts and the surrounding cytoplasm. Several respiratory enzymes such as aldolase and transketolase were present in chloroplasts, where they presumably functioned in the photosynthetic fixation of CO_2. The implications of these results and others shown in Table XV to the mechanism of photosynthesis in *Euglena* have been discussed by Smillie (1963).

Table XV

<small>INTRACELLULAR DISTRIBUTION OF ENZYMES IN *Euglena* AUTOTROPHS[a]</small>

	Localization		
Enzyme	Chloro-plasts	Cyto-plasm	Chloroplasts + cytoplasm
Respiratory enzymes			
UDP-glucose pyrophosphorylase		+	
Phosphoglucomutase		+	
Phosphohexoisomerase		+	
Phosphofructokinase		+	
Neutral fructose-1,6-diphosphatase		+	
Aldolase			+
Triosephosphate isomerase			+
3-Phosphoglycerate kinase			+
Phosphoglycerate mutase		+	
Enolase		+	
Pyruvate kinase		+	
Glucose-6-phosphate dehydrogenase		+	
6-Phosphogluconate dehydrogenase		+	
Transaldolase		+	
Transketolase			+
Ribosephosphate isomerase			+
Isocitrate dehydrogenase		+	
Malate dehydrogenase		+	
NADH-cytochrome c reductase		+	
Malic enzyme		+	
NADH-glyoxylate reductase		+	
NADPH-glyoxylate reductase		+	
Photosynthetic enzymes			
Ribulose-1,5-diphosphate carboxylase	+		
Ribulokinase	+		
NADP$^+$-glyceraldehyde-3-phosphate dehydrogenase	+		
Alkaline fructose-1,6-diphosphatase	+		
Chloroplast ferredoxin	+		
Cytochrome 552	+		
Cytochrome 561	+		
Transhydrogenase			+
Other enzymes			
Ribonuclease		+	
Adenylate kinase			+
Inorganic pyrophosphatase			+
Glutathione reductase		+	

[a] Data from Smillie (1963) and Smillie *et al.* (1963).

B. CYTOCHEMICAL LOCALIZATION

The localization of acid phosphatases in the streptomycin-bleached strain, SM-L1 of *E. gracilis,* var. *bacillaris* and in *A. longa* have been studied with the aid of cytochemical techniques (Brandes *et al.,* 1964; Sommer and Blum, 1965). In growing cells of *Euglena* the acid phosphatase was localized in the Golgi bodies and, in addition, Sommer and Blum (1965) observed regions of activity surrounding the paramylon granules by light microscopy. Some of this latter activity may have been actually localized in mitochondria, since the electron microscopic observations of Brandes *et al.* (1964) disclosed sites of acid phosphatase activity in these organelles. Not all mitochondria contained acid phosphatase and the distribution of activity within individual mitochondria was variable; activity was generally localized in the cristae, but in some instances clusters of activity were located in the matrix. Some acid phosphatase activity also appeared to be associated with small reservoirs surrounding the main reservoir of the cell (Sommer and Blum, 1965). The distribution of activity in growing cells of the *Euglena* strain and of *A. longa* was very similar (Sommer and Blum, 1965; Blum *et al.,* 1965).

Two new regions of acid phosphatase activity were found in starved cells. Digestive bodies or cytolysomes, which were prominent in cells starved of an exogenous source of carbon (Malkoff and Buetow, 1964), contained localized regions of acid phosphatase which probably originated from the Golgi bodies (Brandes *et al.,* 1964). In contrast, the acid phosphatase induced by phosphate starvation (see Section VII,A,1) was localized in discrete regions of the pellicle (Sommer and Blum, 1965).

XII. List of Enzymes Found in *Euglena* and *Astasia*

Table XVI contains a list of enzymes found in *Euglena* and *Astasia* together with the relevant references.

Table XVI

LIST OF ENZYMES FOUND IN *Euglena* AND *Astasia*

Protein	Organism[a]	Reference
Polysaccharide metabolism		
Paramylon synthetase	Strain Z	Goldemberg and Maréchal (1963), Maréchal and Goldemberg (1964)

[a] Refers to *E. gracilis* unless otherwise specified.

Table XVI (Continued)

Protein	Organism[a]	Reference
Laminaribiose phosphorylase	Strain Z	Maréchal and Goldemberg (1963), Goldemberg *et al.* (1966)
β-1,3-Glucan hydrolase	*A. ocellata* Z and other strains	Manners and Taylor (1965) Fellig (1960), Tocher (1962), Meeuse (1964)
Phosphoglucomutase	*A. longa* var. *bacillaris* (dark-grown, ultraviolet-bleached) Strain Z	Tocher (1962) Belsky (1957), Hurlbert and Rittenberg (1962) Smillie (1963)
UDP-glucose-pyrophosphorylase	*A. longa* strain J *bacillaris* (ultraviolet-bleached) Strain Z	Barry (1962) Hurlbert and Rittenberg (1962) Smillie (1963)
Glycolysis		
Hexokinase	var. *bacillaris* (dark-grown and ultraviolet-bleached)	Belsky (1957), Belsky and Schultz (1962), Hurlbert and Rittenberg (1962)
Phosphohexoisomerase	*A. longa* strain J var. *bacillaris* (dark-grown and ultraviolet-bleached)	Barry (1962) Belsky (1957), Belsky and Schultz (1962), Hurlbert and Rittenberg (1961, 1962)
Phosphofructokinase	Strain Z var. *bacillaris* (ultraviolet-bleached)	Smillie (1963) Hurlbert and Rittenberg (1962)
Fructose-1,6-diphosphate aldolase	Strain Z var. *bacillaris* (green, ultraviolet-, streptomycin-, and erythromycin-bleached) Strain Z	Smillie (1963) Hurlbert and Rittenberg (1961, 1962), Drobnica and Ebringer (1963), Rutter (1964) Smillie (1963), Smillie *et al.* (1963)
Triosephosphate isomerase	Strain Z	Smillie (1963)
NAD⁺-glyceraldehyde-3-phosphate dehydrogenase	var. *bacillaris* (green, ultraviolet-streptomycin-, and erythromycin-bleached) Strain Z	Hurlbert and Rittenberg (1961, 1962), Drobnica and Ebringer (1963) Fuller and Gibbs (1959), Brawerman and Konigsberg (1960), Smillie and Fuller (1960), Peterkofsky and Racker

Table XVI (Continued)

Protein	Organism[a]	Reference
3-Phosphoglycerate kinase	*Astasia* var. *bacillaris* (green, ultraviolet-, streptomycin-, and erythromycin-bleached)	(1961), Smillie (1963), Hudock and Fuller (1965) Fuller and Gibbs (1959) Hurlbert and Rittenberg (1962), Drobnica and Ebringer (1963)
	Strain Z	Smillie (1963)
Phosphoglycerate mutase	Strain Z	Smillie (1963)
Enolase	Strain Z	Smillie (1963)
Pyruvate kinase	var. *bacillaris* (green, streptomycin- and erythromycin-bleached)	Drobnica and Ebringer (1963)
	Strain Z	Smillie (1963)
Pyruvate decarboxylase	var. *bacillaris* (ultraviolet-bleached)	Hurlbert and Rittenberg (1962)
NAD⁺-alcohol dehydrogenase	var. *bacillaris* (ultraviolet-bleached)	Hurlbert and Rittenberg (1962)
NADP⁺-alcohol dehydrogenase	var. *bacillaris*	Danforth and Hunter (1966)
Lactate dehydrogenase	Strain Z	Price (1962b, 1966), Rutner and Price (1964)
	A. longa strain J	Barry (1962)

Oxidative pentose phosphate pathway

Glucose-6-phosphate dehydrogenase	var. *bacillaris* (dark-grown and ultraviolet-bleached)	Belsky (1957), Belsky and Schultz (1962), Hurlbert and Rittenberg (1961, 1962)
	Strain Z	Smillie (1963), Smillie et al. (1963)
6-Phosphogluconate dehydrogenase	var. *bacillaris* (dark-grown and ultraviolet-bleached)	Belsky (1957), Hurlbert and Rittenberg (1961, 1962)
	Strain Z	Smillie (1963)
Ribosephosphate isomerase	var. *bacillaris* (ultraviolet-bleached)	Hurlbert and Rittenberg (1962)
	Strain Z	Peterkofsky and Racker (1961), Smillie (1963)
Ribulose-5-phosphate 3-epimerase	Strain Z	Peterkofsky and Racker (1961)
Transketolase	Strain Z	Peterkofsky and Racker (1961), Smillie (1963)
Transaldolase	Strain Z	Peterkofsky and Racker (1961), Smillie (1963)

Table XVI (Continued)

Protein	Organism[a]	Reference
Gluconeogenesis		
Neutral fructose-1,6-diphosphatase	Strain Z (green and streptomycin-bleached)	Smillie (1960a,b, 1964), Smillie *et al.* (1963)
Tricarboxylic acid cycle		
Pyruvate oxidase	var. *bacillaris* (streptomycin-bleached) *A. longa* strain J	Danforth (1953) Hunter and Lee (1962)
Citrate synthase	var. *bacillaris* (streptomycin-bleached) *A. longa* strain J	Danforth (1953) Hunter and Lee (1962)
Aconitate hydratase	var. *bacillaris* (streptomycin-bleached)	Danforth (1953), Cook and Carver (1966)
α-Ketoglutarate dehydrogenase	var. *bacillaris* (streptomycin-bleached)	Danforth (1953)
NAD^1-isocitrate dehydrogenase	var. *bacillaris*	Danforth and Hunter (1966)
NADP$^+$-isocitrate dehydrogenase	Strain Z	Smillie (1963), Smillie *et al.* (1963), Cook and Carver (1966)
Succinate dehydrogenase	*A. longa* strain J var. *bacillaris* (bleached mutants)	Hunter and Lee (1962) Danforth (1953), Perini (1964b), Levedahl (1965)
Fumarate hydratase	*A. longa* strain J	Hunter and Lee (1962)
Malate dehydrogenase	var. *bacillaris* (green, streptomycin- and erythromycin- bleached) Strain Z *A. longa* strain J	Danforth (1953), Chancellor-Maddison and Noll (1963), Drobnica and Ebringer (1963) Smillie (1963) Hunter and Lee (1962)
Glyoxylate by-pass		
Acetate thiokinase	Strain Z	Abraham and Bachhawat (1962)
Isocitrate lyase	Strain 1224–5/25 *A. longa* Various strains including Z (not found in autotrophs)	Ohmann (1963, 1964) Hunter and Lee (1962) Haigh and Beevers (1962, 1964), Reeves *et al.* (1962), Wiessner and Kuhl (1962); Cook and Carver (1966)
Malate synthase	Strain Z	Reeves *et al.* (1962), Cook and Carver (1966)

Table XVI (Continued)

Protein	Organism[a]	Reference
Mitochondrial electron transfer system		
NADH-diaphorase	var. *bacillaris*	Perini (1964b)
NADH-cytochrome c reductase	Strain Z	Smillie (1963), Smillie *et al.* (1963)
Cytochrome 556 (c-type cytochrome)	var. *bacillaris* (including several mutants) Strain Z (normal and a heat-bleached mutant) *A. longa*	Butler and Baker (1963), Perini *et al.* (1964a,b) Gross and Wolken (1960), Wolken and Gross (1963) Webster and Hackett (1965)
Cytochrome 605 (a-type cytochrome)	var. *bacillaris* and several mutants *A. longa*	Perini *et al.* (1964a,b) Webster and Hackett (1965)
Oxidative phosphorylation	var. *bacillaris*, SM-L1[b]	Buetow and Buchanan (1965)
Other enzymes of respiratory metabolism		
Glyceraldehyde-3-phosphate NADP⁺-reductase	Strain Z (streptomycin-bleached)	Smillie and Fuller (1960)
Malic enzyme	Strain Z	Smillie (1963)
NAD⁺(P)H-glyoxylate reductases	Strain Z	Smillie (1963)
Carbon reductive cycle of photosynthesis		
Fraction I protein	Strain Z	Anderson (1967), Grieve and Smillie (unpublished data)
Ribulose-1,5-diphosphate carboxylase	Strain Z	Fuller and Gibbs (1959), Peterkofsky and Racker (1961), Smillie (1963), Hudock and Fuller (1965)
Ribulose-5-phosphate kinase	Strain Z	Peterkofsky and Racker (1961), Smillie (1963)
NADP⁺-glyceraldehyde-3-phosphate dehydrogenase	Strain Z	Fuller and Gibbs (1959), Brawerman and Konigsberg (1960), Smillie and Fuller (1960), Peterkofsky and Racker (1961), Smillie (1963), Smillie *et al.* (1963), Hudock and Fuller (1965)
Alkaline fructose-1,6-diphosphatase	Strain Z	Smillie (1960a,b, 1963, 1964), Peterkofsky and Racker (1961), App and Jagendorf (1963, 1964)

[b] A streptomycin-bleached mutant of var. *bacillaris*.

Table XVI (Continued)

Protein	Organism[a]	Reference
Sedoheptulose-1,7-diphosphatase	Strain Z	Peterkofsky and Racker (1961)
Photosynthetic electron transfer system		
Hill reaction	var. *bacillaris* Strain Z	Stern (1962) Smillie *et al.* (1963), Hutner *et al.* (1966)
Photoreduction of of NADP+	Strain Z	Katoh and Takamiya (1965), Smillie (1965), Hutner *et al.* (1966)
Chloroplast ferredoxin (photosynthetic pyridine nucleotide reductase)	Strain Z	Shapiro (1961), Smillie (1963, 1965), Nagai and Bloch (1966)
Cytochrome 552	var. *bacillaris* var. *bacillaris*	Perini *et al.* (1964a) Nishimura (1959), Gross and Wolken (1960), Butler and Baker (1963), Colmano and Wolken (1963), Olson and Smillie (1963), Smillie (1963), Smillie *et al.* (1963), Wolken and Gross (1963), Perini *et al.* (1964a,b)
Cytochrome 561 (b-type cytochrome)	*A. longa*[c] var. *bacillaris* Strain Z	Webster and Hackett (1965) Perini *et al.* (1964a,b) Olson and Smillie (1963), Smillie (1963)
Transhydrogenase (ferredoxin NADP+-reductase)	var. *bacillaris* (green, dark-adapted and bleached) Strain Z	Lazzarini and San Pietro (1963), Lazzarini and Woodruff (1964) Smillie (1963), Smillie *et al.* (1963), Nagai and Bloch (1966)
Euglena flavoprotein	var. *bacillaris*	Lewis *et al.* (1961)
Nucleic acid and nucleotide metabolism		
RNA synthesis (in isolated chloroplasts)	Strain Z	Shah and Lyman (1966)
Ribonuclease	Strain not stated Strain Z	Fellig and Wiley (1960), Smillie *et al.* (1963)

[c] Trace amounts of a cytochrome with an α-band at 522 mμ are present in this organism.

Table XVI (Continued)

Protein	Organism[a]	Reference
Nucleotide pyrophosphorylases	var. *bacillaris*, SM-L1[b] and *A. longa*	Kahn and Blum (1965)
Adenylate kinase	Strain Z	Smillie (1963)
Deoxyadenylate kinase	Strain Z	Cook (1966)
Synthesis of 3′-phosphoadenylylsulfate from ATP and sulfate	Strain Z (green, dark-adapted and streptomycin-bleached)	Abraham and Bachhawat (1963, 1964), Davies *et al.* (1966)
3′-phosphoadenylyl-sulfatase	Z (green, dark-adapted and streptomycin-bleached)	Abraham and Bachhawat (1964)
Adenosine-5′-diphosphate ribose: orthophosphate adenylyltransferase	var. *bacillaris* Strain Z	Stern and Avron (1966) Evans and San Pietro (1966)

Amino acid metabolism and protein synthesis

NADP⁺-glutamate dehydrogenase	Strain Z	Kempner and Miller (1965)
Glutamate oxalacetate transaminase	var. *bacillaris* (green, streptomycin- and erythromycin-bleached)	Drobnica and Ebringer (1963)
	Strain Z	Kempner and Miller (1965)
Glutamate-pyruvate transaminase	Strain Z	Kempner and Miller (1965)
"Amino acid–activating" enzymes	Strain E-1.1.2	Raacke and Allen (1960)
Leucyl-sRNA synthetase	Strain Z	Eisenstadt and Brawerman (1966)
Incorporation of amino acids into proteins		Eisenstadt and Brawerman (1963, 1964a,b)
Cathepsin (peptide hydrolase)	var. *bacillaris*, SM-L1[b]	Bertini *et al.* (1965)

Lipid metabolism

Synthesis of long chain fatty acids	Strain Z	Cheniae (1962, 1963, 1964), Cheniae and Kerr (1965), Nagai and Bloch (1965)
Acyl-CoA desaturase	Strain Z (dark-grown heterotrophs)	Nagai and Bloch (1965)
Stearoyl-ACP desaturase	Strain Z (autotrophs)	Nagai and Bloch (1965, 1966)

Table XVI (Continued)

Protein	Organism[a]	Reference
Hydroxy fatty acid dehydrogenase	Strain Z	Gurr and Bloch (1966)
Reductive de-epoxidation of 5,6-epoxyzeaxanthin	Strain Z	Bamji and Krinsky (1963, 1965)
5-Aminolevulinate dehydratase	Strain Z	Granick and Mauzerall (1958), Gibor and Granick (1962), Carell and Kahn (1964)
Conversion of porphobilinogen to porphyrin	Strain Z	Granick and Mauzerall (1958), Gibor and Granick (1962), Karali and Price (1963), Carell and Kahn (1964)
Arylesterase	var. *bacillaris*, SM-L1[b]	Bertini *et al.* (1965)
Phosphatases		
Acid phosphatase Constitutive	Strain Z var. *bacillaris*. SM-L1[b]	Price (1962a), Smillie (1964) Brandes *et al.* (1964), Bertini *et al.* (1965), Blum (1965), Blum *et al.* (1965), Sommer and Blum (1965), Bennun and Blum (1966)
Inducible	*A. longa* Strain Z var. *bacillaris*, SM-L1[b]	Blum *et al.* (1965) Price (1962a) Bertini *et al.* (1965), Blum (1965), Blum *et al.* (1965), Sommer and Blum (1965), Bennun and Blum (1966)
Inorganic pyrophosphatase ATPase UDPase	Strain 1224-5/25 Strain Z Strain Z Strain Z	Ohmann (1964) Smillie *et al.* (1963) (Smillie, unpublished data) Maréchal and Goldemberg (1964)
Miscellaneous enzymes		
Glutathione reductase Acetyl-CoA deacylase	Strain Z Strain Z	Smillie (1963) Abraham and Bachhawat (1962)

Note Added in Proof: Recent experiments in the author's laboratory have shown that a streptomycin-bleached mutant of *E. gracilis* strain Z contains at least one b-type mitochondrial cytochrome, that there are two b-type cytochromes in *Euglena* chloroplasts, and that chloroplasts isolated from *Euglena* contain chloroplast-DNA polymerase.

ACKNOWLEDGMENTS

I should like to thank several of the other authors of chapters in this book for their cooperation and help in the preparation of Table XVI.

References

Abraham, A., and Bachhawat, B. K. (1962). *Biochim. Biophys. Acta* **62**, 376.
Abraham, A., and Bachhawat, B. K. (1963). *Biochim. Biophys. Acta* **70**, 104.
Abraham, A., and, Bachhawat, B. K. (1964). *Indian J. Biochem.* **1**, 192.
Anderson, L. (1967). *Abstr. N.E. Regional Plant Physiol. Soc. Meetings, Boston.*
App, A. A., and Jagendorf, A. T. (1963). *J. Protozool.* **10**, 340.
App, A. A., and Jagendorf, A. T. (1964). *Biochim. Biophys. Acta* **85**, 427.
Arnon, D. I. (1952). *Science* **116**, 635.
Balasubramanian, A. S., and Bachhawat, B. K. (1962). *Biochim. Biophys. Acta* **59**, 389.
Bamji, M. S., and Krinsky, N. I. (1963). *Abstr. Am. Chem. Soc. 145th Meeting New York, N.Y.* p. 6C.
Bamji, M. S., and Krinsky, N. I. (1965). *J. Biol. Chem.* **240**, 467.
Barry, S. C. (1962). *J. Protozool.* **9**, 395.
Bassham, J. A., and Calvin, M. (1957). "The Path of Carbon in Photosynthesis." Prentice-Hall, Englewood Cliffs, New Jersey.
Beattie, D. S., Basford, R. E., and Koritz, S. B. (1966). *Biochemistry* **5**, 926.
Behrens, M. (1932). *Z. Physiol. Chem.* **209**, 59.
Belsky, M. M. (1957). *Bacteriol. Proc.* **57**, 123.
Belsky, M. M., and Schultz, J. (1962). *J. Protozool.* **9**, 195.
Bennun, A., and Blum, J. J. (1966). *Biochim. Biophys. Acta* **128**, 106.
Ben-Shaul, Y., Epstein, H. T., and Schiff, J. A. (1965). *Can. J. Botany* **43**, 129.
Berg, P. (1956). *J. Biol. Chem.* **222**, 991.
Berger, L., Slein, M. W., Colowick, S. P., and Cori, C. F. (1946). *J. Gen. Physiol.* **29**, 379.
Bertini, F., Brandes, D., and Buetow, D. E. (1965). *Biochim. Biophys. Acta* **107**, 171.
Blum, J. J. (1965). *J. Cell Biol.* **24**, 223.
Blum, J. J., and Buetow, D. E. (1963). *Exptl. Cell Res.* **29**, 407.
Blum, J. J., Sommer, J. R., and Kahn, V. (1965). *J. Protozool.* **12**, 202.
Bonner, W. D. Jr., and Chance, B. (1963). *In* "Photosynthetic Mechanisms of Green Plants," Publ. 1145, p. 66. Natl. Acad. Sci.—Natl. Res. Council., Washington, D. C.
Brandes, D., Buetow, D. E., Bertini, F., and Malkoff, D. B. (1964). *Exptl. Mol. Pathol.* **3**, 583.
Brawerman, G. (1962). *Biochim. Biophys. Acta* **61**, 313.
Brawerman, G., and Konigsberg, N. (1960). *Biochim. Biophys. Acta* **43**, 374.
Brawerman, G., Pogo, A.O., and Chargaff, E. (1962). *Biochim. Biophys. Acta* **55**, 326.
Buetow, D. E., and Buchanan, P. J. (1965). *Biochim. Biophys. Acta* **96**, 9.
Butler, W. L., and Baker, J. E. (1963). *Biochim. Biophys. Acta* **66**, 206.
Carell, E. F., and Kahn, J. S. (1964). *Arch. Biochem. Biophys.* **108**, 1.
Chancellor-Maddison, J., and Noll, C. R., Jr. (1963). *Science* **142**, 60.
Cheniae, G. M. (1962). *Plant Physiol.* **37** (Suppl.), lx.
Cheniae, G. M. (1963). *Biochim. Biophys. Acta* **70**, 504.
Cheniae, G. M. (1964). *Arch. Biochem. Biophys.* **105**, 163.
Cheniae, G. M., and Kerr, P. C. (1965). *Plant. Physiol.* **40**, 452.
Colmano, G., and Wolken, J. J. (1963). *Nature* **198**, 783.

Cook, J. R. (1966). *J. Cell Biol.* **29**, 369.

Cook, J. R., and Carver, M. (1966). *Plant Cell Physiol.* (*Tokyo*) **7**, 377.

Crane, R. K., and Sols, A. (1953). *J. Biol. Chem.* **203**, 273.

Criddle, R. S., and Park, L. (1964). *Biochem. Biophys. Res. Commun.* **17**, 74.

Danforth, W. F. (1953). *Arch. Biochem. Biophys.* **46**, 164.

Danforth, W. F. (1961). *J. Protozool.* **8**, 152.

Danforth, W., and Hunter, F. R. (1966). *J. Protozool.* **13**, 654.

Davenport, H. E., and Hill, R. (1952). *Proc. Roy. Soc.* B**139**, 327.

Davies, W. H., Mercer, E. I., and Goodwin, T. W. (1966). *Biochem. J.* **98**, 369.

Drobnica, L., and Ebringer, L. (1963). *Folia Microbiol.* (*Prague*) **8**, 56.

Eisenberg, M. A. (1955). *Biochim. Biophys. Acta* **16**, 58.

Eisenstadt, J., and Brawerman, G. (1963). *Biochim. Biophys. Acta* **76**, 319.

Eisenstadt, J., and Brawerman, G. (1964a). *Biochim. Biophys. Acta* **80**, 463.

Eisenstadt, J., and Brawerman, G. (1964b). *J. Mol. Biol.* **10**, 392.

Eisenstadt, J., and Brawerman, G. (1966). *Biochemistry* (in press).

Evans, W. R., and San Pietro, A. (1966). *Arch. Biochem. Biophys.* **113**, 236.

Eyster, C., Brown, T. E., Tanner, H. A., and Hood, S. L. (1958). *Plant Physiol.* **33**, 235.

Feingold, D. S., Neufeld, E. F., and Hassid, W. Z. (1958). *J. Biol. Chem.* **233**, 783.

Fellig, J. (1960). *Science* **131**, 832.

Fellig, J., and Wiley, C. E. (1960). *Science* **132**, 1835.

Fraenkel, D. G., Pontromoli, S., and Horecker, B. L. (1966). *Arch. Biochem. Biophys.* **114**, 4.

Fuller, R. C., and Gibbs, M. (1959). *Plant Physiol.* **34**, 324.

Fuller, R. C., Smillie, R. M., Sisler, E. C, and Kornberg, H. L. (1961). *J. Biol. Chem.* **236**, 2140.

Gibbs, M., (1952). *Nature* **170**, 164.

Gibor, A., and Granick, S. (1962). *J. Protozool.* **9**, 327.

Goldemberg, S. H., and Maréchal, L. R. (1963). *Biochim. Biophys. Acta* **71**, 743.

Goldemberg, S. H., Maréchal, L. R., and De Souza, B. C. (1966). *J. Biol. Chem.* **241**, 45.

Granick, S., and Mauzerall, D. (1958). *Federation Proc.* **17**, 233.

Gross, J. A., and Wolken, J. J. (1960). *Science* **132**, 357.

Gurr, M. I., and Bloch, K. (1966). *Biochem. J.* **99**, 16c.

Haigh, W. G., and Beevers, H. (1962). *Plant Physiol.* **37**, (Suppl.), lx.

Haigh, W. G., and Beevers, H. (1964). *Arch. Biochem. Biophys.* **107**, 147.

Hill, R. (1954). *Nature* **174**, 501.

Hudock, G. A., and Fuller, R. C. (1965). *Plant Physiol.* **40**, 1205.

Hunter, F. R., and Lee, J. W. (1962). *J. Protozool.* **9**, 74.

Hurlbert, R. E., and Rittenberg, S. C., (1961). *Bacteriol. Proc.* **61**, 191.

Hurlbert, R. E., and Rittenberg, S. C. (1962). *J. Protozool.* **9**, 170.

Hutner, S. H., Bach, M. K., and Ross, G. I. M. (1956). *J. Protozool.* **3**, 101.

Hutner, S. H., Zahalsky, A. C., Aaronson, S., and Smillie, R. M. (1966). *In* "The Biochemistry of Chloroplasts" (T. W. Goodwin, ed.), Vol. II, p. 703. Academic Press, New York.

Huzisige, H., and Satoh, K. (1960). *Biol. J. Okayama Univ.* **6**, 71.

Kahn, V., and Blum, J. J. (1965). *J. Biol. Chem.* **240**, 4435.

Karali, E. F., and Price, C. A. (1963). *Nature* **198**, 708.

Katoh, S. (1959). *J. Biochem.* (*Tokyo*) **46**, 629.

Katoh, S., and Takamiya, A. (1965). *J. Biochem.* (*Tokyo*) **58**, 396.

Keister, D. L., San Pietro, A., and Stolzenbach, F. E. (1960). *J. Biol. Chem.* **235**, 2989.

Kempner, E. S., and Miller, J. H. (1965). *Biochemistry* **4**, 2735.

King, J., and Waygood, E. R. (1963). *Proc. Soc. Can. Plant Physiol.* **4**, 23.

Kornberg, H. L. and Krebs, H. A. (1957). *Nature* **179**, 988.

Krebs, H. A. (1964). *Proc. Roy. Soc.* **B159**, 545.

Krinsky, N. I. (1964). *Biochim. Biophys. Acta* **88**, 487.

Lazzarini, R. A., and San Pietro, A. (1963). *In* "Studies on Microalgae and Photosynthetic Bacteria," p. 453. Japan. Soc. Plant Physiologists, Univ. of Tokyo Press, Tokyo.

Lazzarini, R. A., and Woodruff, M. (1964). *Biochim. Biophys. Acta* **79**, 412.

Levedahl, B. H. (1965). *Exptl. Cell Res.* **39**, 233.

Lewis, S. C., Schiff, J. A., and Epstein, H. T. (1961). *Biochem. Biophys. Res. Commun.* **5**, 221.

Lewis, S. C., Schiff, J. A., and Epstein, H. T. (1965). *J. Protozool.* **12**, 281.

Lipmann, F., Jones, M. E., Black, S., and Flynn, R. M. (1952). *J. Am. Chem. Soc.* **74**, 2384.

Lynch, V. H., and Calvin, M. (1953). *Ann. N. Y. Acad. Sci.* **56**, 890.

Malkoff, D. B., and Buetow, D. E. (1964). *Exptl. Cell Res.* **35**, 58.

Manners, D. J., and Taylor, D. C. (1965). *Biochem. J.* **94**, 17P.

Maréchal, L. R., and Goldemberg, S. H. (1963). *Biochem. Biophys. Res. Commun.* **13**, 106.

Maréchal, L. R., and Goldemberg, S. H. (1964). *J. Biol. Chem.* **239**, 3163.

Marzullo, G., and Danforth, W. F. (1964). *J. Gen. Microbiol.* **34**, 21.

Meeuse, B. J. D. (1964). *Basteria* **28**, 67.

Millerd, A., and Bonner, J. (1954). *Arch. Biochem. Biophys.* **49**, 343.

Nagai, J., and Bloch, K. (1965). *J. Biol. Chem.* **240**, 3702.

Nagai, J., and Bloch, K. (1966). *J. Biol. Chem.* **241**, 1925.

Nishimura, M. (1959). *J. Biochem. (Tokyo)* **46**, 219.

Norris, L., Norris, R. E., and Calvin, M. (1955). *J. Exptl. Botany* **6**, 64.

Ohmann, E. (1963). *Naturwissenschaften* **50**, 578.

Ohmann, E. (1964). *Biochim. Biophys. Acta* **82**, 325.

Olson, J. M., and Smillie, R. M. (1963). *In* "Photosynthetic Mechanisms of Green Plants," Publ. 1145, p. 56. Natl. Acad. Sci.—Natl. Res. Council, Washington, D. C.

Perini, F., Kamen, M. D., and Schiff, J. A. (1964a). *Biochim. Biophys. Acta* **88**, 74.

Perini, F., Schiff, J. A., and Kamen, M. D. (1964b). *Biochim. Biophys. Acta* **88**, 91.

Peterkofsky, A., and Racker, E. (1961). *Plant Physiol.* **36**, 409.

Price, C. A. (1962a). *Science* **135**, 46.

Price, C. A. (1962b). *Biochem. J.* **82**, 61.

Price, C. A. (1966). *In* "Zinc Metabolism" (A. S. Prased, ed.). Thomas, Springfield, Illinois.

Raacke, I. D., and Allen, M. B. (1960). *Exptl. Cell Res.* **21**, 236.

Racker, E., and Schroeder, E. A. R. (1958). *Arch. Biochem. Biophys.* **74**, 326.

Rao, G. A., Hansen, I. A., and Bachhawat, B. K. (1961). *J. Sci. Ind. Res. (India)* **20C**, 284.

Reeves, H. C., Kadis, S., and Ajl, S. (1962). *Biochim. Biophys. Acta* **57**, 403.

Rosen, O. M. (1966). *Arch. Biochem. Biophys.* **114**, 31.

Rosen, O. M., Rosen, S. M., and Horecker, B. L. (1965). *Arch. Biochem. Biophys.* **112**, 411.

Russell, G. K., and Gibbs, M. (1966). *Plant Physiol.* **41**, 889.

Rutner, A. C., and Price, C. A. (1964). *Abstr. Intern. Congress Biochem., 6th, New York.*

Rutter, W. J., (1964). *Federation Proc.* **23**, 1248.

Salas, M., Vinuela, E., Salas, J., and Sols, A. (1964). *Biochim. Biophys. Res. Commun.* **17**, 150.

Saltman, P. (1953). *J. Biol. Chem.* **200**, 145.

San Pietro, A., and Lang, H. M. (1958). *J. Biol. Chem.* **231**, 211.

Shah, V. C., and Lyman, H. (1966). *J. Cell Biol.* **29**, 174.

Shapiro, D. M. (1961). Ph. D. Thesis, Johns Hopkins, Univ. Baltimore, Maryland.

Smillie, R. M. (1960a). *Nature* **187**, 1024.

Smillie, R. M. (1960b). *Plant Physiol.* **35** (Suppl.), xx.

Smillie, R. M. (1962). *Plant Physiol.* **37**, 716.

Smillie, R. M. (1963). *Can. J. Botany* **41**, 123.

Smillie, R. M. (1964). *In* "Fructose-1, 6-diphosphatase and Its Role in Gluconeogenesis" (R. W. McGilvery and B. M. Pogell, eds.), p. 31. Am. Inst. Biol. Sci., Baltimore, Maryland.

Smillie, R. M. (1965). *Biochem. Biophys. Res. Commun.* **20**, 621.

Smillie, R. M., and Fuller, R. C. (1960). *Biochem. Biophys. Res. Commun.* **3**, 368.

Smillie, R. M., Rigopoulos, N., and Kelly, H. (1962). *Biochim. Biophys. Acta* **56**, 612.

Smillie, R. M., Evans, W. R., and Lyman, H. (1963). *In Brookhaven Symp. Biol.* **16**, 89.

Sommer, J. R., and Blum, J. J. (1965). *J. Cell Biol.* **24**, 235.

Stern, A. I. (1962). Ph. D. Thesis, Brandeis Univ., Waltham, Massachussetts.

Stern, A. I., and Avron, M. (1966). *Biochim. Biophys. Acta* **118**, 577.

Taketa, K., and Pogell, B. M. (1965). *J. Biol. Chem.* **240**, 651.

Tocher, R. D. (1962). Master's Thesis, Univ. of Washington, Seattle, Washington.

Trown, P. W. (1965). *Biochemistry* **4**, 908.

Webster, D. A., and Hackett, D. P. (1965). *Plant Physiol.* **40**, 1091.

Weissbach, A., Horecker, B. L., and Hurwitz, J. (1956). *J. Biol. Chem.* **218**, 795.

Wiessner, W., and Kuhl, A. (1962). *Vortr. Gesamtgebiet Botan., Deut. Botan. Ges.* **1**, 102.

Wolken, J. J. (1961). "*Euglena*, an Experimental Organism for Biochemical and Biophysical Studies." Inst. Microbiol. Rutgers, The State University, New Brunswick, New Jersey.

Wolken, J. J., and Gross, J. A. (1963). *J. Protozool.* **10**, 189.

CHAPTER 2

RESPIRATION

William F. Danforth

I. Introduction

Since the present chapter will deal with studies on members of only two genera, *Euglena* and *Astasia*, it is worth pointing out that the respiratory metabolism of other phytoflagellates belonging to at least two other orders (Phytomonadida and Cryptomonadida) is similar in many respects (Danforth, 1963). Thus, with a few exceptions, the metabolic features emphasized here are characteristic of a large group of "acetate flagellates" (Hutner and Provasoli, 1951, 1955), rather than unique to the euglenoids.

As a group, these flagellates are characterized by the ability to use photosynthesis and heterotrophic oxidative assimilation as interchangeable and essentially equivalent sources of carbon and energy. The degree of interchangeability varies from species to species. *Euglena gracilis* var. *bacillaris* cultured autotrophically in the light or heterotrophically on any of several single-carbon compounds grow equally well, while the Vischer strain of *E. gracilis* grows more rapidly in light than on any organic substrate so far tested (Cramer and Myers, 1952). At one extreme are found obligate photo-autotrophs such as *E. pisciformis* (Lwoff, 1951), at the other such obligate heterotrophs as *Astasia* and the "bleached" strains of *Euglena*.

Photosynthetic metabolism is considered elsewhere in this book (Chapter 3). This chapter will be concerned with the heterotrophic functional equivalent of photosynthesis, the metabolism of organic compounds serving as major carbon and energy sources. In these flagellates, the metabolism of such compounds is a process of *oxidative assimilation* (Barker, 1936; Griffiths, 1965) in which a single substrate provides both energy and carbon for growth. As will become apparent, the oxidative and assimilative processes are inseparably related.

It is humbling to note that practically all that is known about the respiratory metabolism of euglenoids is derived from experiments with a few strains of *E. gracilis* and two species of *Astasia*, although over 150 species have been described within the genus *Euglena* alone (Gojdics, 1953).

II. Electron Transfer and Oxidative Phosphorylation

Von Dach (1942) reported the presence in *Astasia klebsii* of absorption bands at approximately 605, 565, and 555 mμ, corresponding roughly to the positions of the bands for the a, b, and c groups of cytochromes respectively. The bands responded to aeration and to cyanide in the manner expected of the cytochromes. Concentrations of cyanide as low as 10^{-5} M greatly inhibited the respiration on acetate, while the endogenous respiration was relatively insensitive to cyanide concentrations as high as 10^{-3} M. Low concentrations of azide inhibited the respiration on acetate but increased the rate of respiration in the absence of substrate.* Other investigators (Nishimura, 1959; Gross and Wolken, 1960; Wolken and Gross, 1963; Butler and Baker, 1963; Smillie, 1963; Webster and Hackett, 1965; Perini *et al.*, 1964a,b) have found that the absorption band corresponding to c-type cytochromes can be further resolved into two bands, one with a maximum at 552 mμ and the second with a maximum at 556 mμ. Thus, there is evidence for four cytochrome pigments in *Euglena*, cyto-chrome c (552, *Euglena*), cytochrome type c (556, *Euglena*), cytochrome b

---

* This stimulation by azide probably results from the uncoupling action of azide on oxidative phosphorylation (Lehninger, *et al.*, 1959) rather than from an effect on cytochrome.

(561, *Euglena*), and cytochrome type a (605, *Euglena*).* Of these four, however, only two can be considered components of the respiratory electron-transport system, since cytochrome c (552) and cytochrome b (561) are localized in the chloroplasts and are not present in nonphotosynthetic strains or in dark-grown cells of photosynthetic *Euglena* (Perini *et al.*, 1964a,b; Gross and Wolken, 1960; Wolken and Gross, 1963; Smillie, 1963).

The shape of the absorption band of *Astasia* cytochrome type a (605) differs from that in green algae (including the flagellates, *Polytoma* and *Polytomella*) and in higher plants (Webster and Hackett, 1965). The respiration of *Euglena* is only slightly inhibited by carbon monoxide (Perini *et al.*, 1964b), and the carbon monoxide difference spectrum of *Astasia* cytochrome type a is much weaker than that of typical cytochrome a (Webster and Hackett, 1965).[†] Extracts of *Astasia* do not oxidize mammalian cytochrome c (Webster and Hackett, 1965). Taken together, these findings strongly suggest that the a-type cytochrome of euglenoids differs from those of conventional cytochrome systems and that conventional cytochrome oxidase is absent.

Similarly, the respiratory cytochrome type c (556) seems to differ in important respects from typical cytochrome c. The midpoint oxidation–reduction potential of the *Euglena* enzyme is $+310–320$ mV, as compared to $+240–260$ mV for mammalian cytochrome c, and to approximately $+290$ mV for mammalian cytochrome a (Perini *et al.*, 1964a; Wolken and Gross, 1963). Such a high oxidation–reduction potential does not seem consistent with the position of cytochrome c in the classic electron-transfer chain, and suggests a position much nearer the oxidizing end of the chain. The *Euglena* pigment, unlike mammalian cytochrome c, is autoxidizable by air (Perini *et al.*, 1964b). The *Euglena* enzyme will interact with yeast mitochondria; it is reduced by the mitochondria plus succinate, and the mitochondria accelerate its oxidation by air (Perini *et al.*, 1964b).

Most studies have given no indication of any respiratory b-type cytochrome in euglenoids, since there is strong evidence that cytochrome b (561, *Euglena*) is photosynthetic in function and is confined to the chloroplasts. However, Von Dach (1942) and Webster and Hackett (1965) observed a b-type absorption band (563–565 mμ) in nonphotosynthetic *Astasia*, and the same band was present, although with reduced intensity, in the mitochondrial fractions prepared by differential centrifugation (Webster and Hackett, 1965). Whether these observations indicate the presence of a mitochondrial b-type cytochrome in *Astasia* or contamination of the mitochondrial fractions with the rudiments of a nonfunctional photosynthetic system deserves further investigation.

---

* The nomenclature used here for *Euglena* cytochromes is that of Perini *et al.* (1964a).
† This weakness in the carbon monoxide difference spectrum might be an effect of contamination by a second CO-binding pigment, however.

Buetow and Buchanan (1964, 1965) have studied the oxidative phosphorylation coupled with electron transfer in isolated *Euglena* mitochondria.
Although the isolated mitochondria were capable of phosphorylation, the
coupling between electron transfer and phosphorylation was not "tight";
that is, substrate oxidation and electron transfer to oxygen occurred at the
same rate whether or not phosphorylation was blocked by the absence of a
phosphate acceptor. In other organisms, "tight coupling" seems to play
an important part in the regulation of respiratory metabolism (Chance, 1961;
Lehninger, 1964), limiting the rate of substrate utilization to match the
rate at which phosphate acceptor is freed by energy-consuming reactions.
If "loose coupling" is characteristic of *Euglena* mitochondria *in vivo*, as well
as *in vitro,** this regulatory mechanism presumably is not available to
Euglena. The ratio of phosphate molecules esterified to oxygen atoms
consumed (P:O ratio) approached 1.0 for succinate and 2.0 for various
substrates of NAD-linked dehydrogenases. In each case, these values
indicate one less phosphorylation per electron pair than is found with
mammalian mitochondria. Since the electron-transfer chain in *Euglena* is
almost certainly different from that in mammals, it is not unlikely that
one less phosphorylation site might be present in *Euglena*.

With exogenous NADH as substrate, phosphorylation occurred with a
P:O ratio of approximately 0.4, as compared to about 2.0 for NAD-linked
intermediary metabolites. The difference may reflect the commonly observed
fact that extramitochondrial NAD reacts differently with the electron-
transfer system than does the "bound" NAD of the mitochondria. Exogenous
NADPH was oxidized, but without phosphorylation.

The effects of 2,4-dinitrophenol, amytal, antimycin A, and rotenone on
Euglena mitochondria were similar to those found with mitochondria of
higher plants and animals, suggesting that despite apparent differences,
the oxidative phosphorylation system of euglenoids has a number of reactions
in common with that of multicellular organisms.

III. Pathways of Oxidation and Oxidative Assimilation

Insofar as they have been determined or may reasonably be inferred from
experimental studies, the major metabolic pathways involved in oxidative
assimilation are those shown in Fig. 1. With a few exceptions, the enzymes
responsible for the reactions shown in Fig. 1 have been demonstrated

---

* Partial or complete uncoupling in mammalian mitochondria is one of the earliest
signs of damage during isolation or incubation *in vitro*. It is thus possible that the loose
coupling *Euglena* mitochondria is an artifact of isolation.

to be present in *Euglena* or *Astasia* or both (Chapter 1). For present purposes it is convenient to consider these reactions as composed of three functional pathways (Fig. 2); oxidation of reserve carbohydrate (paramylon), oxidation

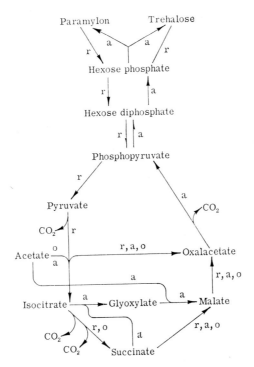

Fig. 1. Enzymic pathways believed to participate in the respiratory metabolism of *Euglena*. Acetate is assumed to be the exogenous substrate. r, Reactions of the "reserve oxidation" pathway; o, reactions of the "substrate oxidation" pathway; a, reactions of the "substrate assimilation" pathway.

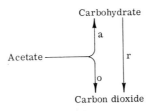

Fig. 2. Schematic diagram of the main routes of carbon flow during acetate utilization by *Euglena*. The letters r, o, and a have the same significance as in Fig. 1, which should be compared. Routes a plus o constitute the "primary substrate metabolism" defined in Section V,B.

of low molecular weight substances (acetate, ethanol, Krebs-cycle intermediates), and assimilation of low molecular weight substrates. Metabolism
of exogenous carbohydrates is discussed elsewhere (Chapter 7) and will be
considered only incidentally here.

The presence of the conventional Embden–Meyerhof–Parnas pathway
has been demonstrated (Hurlbert and Rittenberg, 1962) in *Euglena*. The
hexose monophosphate shunt, a possible alternative pathway, is also present
(Hurlbert and Rittenberg, 1962) but tracer studies (Barry, 1962) indicate
that exogenous carbohydrate is oxidized almost entirely through the
Embden–Meyerhof–Parnas pathway, and it seems likely that the same is
true for endogenous carbohydrate. The pyruvate thus formed is further
oxidized to carbon dioxide via the Krebs tricarboxylic acid cycle (Danforth,
1953; Hunter and Lee, 1962; Danforth and Wilson, 1961). There are two
possible routes by which the pyruvate might enter the Krebs cycle. Pyruvate
might be decarboxylated to acetaldehyde, as in yeast, the acetaldehyde
oxidized to acetate, and the acetate then converted to acetyl-CoA. Alternatively, as in animal tissues, pyruvate might be oxidatively carboxylated
yielding acetyl-CoA in a single complex enzymic reaction. The enzymes for
the yeastlike pathway have been detected in *Euglena* (P.R. Erve, unpublished;
Ohmann, 1964); those of the animallike pathway have not so far been
demonstrated.

When acetate is the exogenous substrate, it is converted to acetyl-CoA
via the acetate thiokinase reaction (Ohmann, 1964). The alternative route of
acetyl-CoA formation via acetate kinase is apparently not present in *Euglena*.
Ethanol probably follows the same pathway after conversion to acetate
by alcohol dehydrogenase and acetaldehyde dehydrogenase, although this
route has not been experimentally confirmed.

In the case of acetate, initial stages of substrate assimilation almost
certainly occur via the glyoxylate cycle, which may be regarded as a "by-pass"
on the Krebs cycle. The effect of the glyoxylate cycle is to convert two
molecules of acetate to one molecule of oxalacetate, which may then be
decarboxylated and phosphorylated to form phosphopyruvate. The
phosphopyruvate is probably converted to carbohydrate by what is, in the
main, a reversal of the glycolytic pathway (Krebs and Kornberg, 1957).
For energetic reasons an exact reversal of glycolysis is impossible; to drive
the overall process in the synthetic direction, alternative reactions are
required at the three steps of the glycolytic pathway that involve the
greatest energy changes. Tracer studies of the distribution of acetate carbon
during oxidative assimilation (Danforth, 1961) are consistent with this
pathway for acetate assimilation. Very little is known about the assimilatory
pathways for substrates other than acetate.

The degree of overlap between these three pathways is striking. The

Krebs cycle occurs in both the reserve oxidation and the substrate oxidation pathways, and all but two of its reactions are also components of the glyoxylate-cycle portion of the substrate assimilation pathway. Similarly, many of the glycolytic enzymes that function in substrate oxidation probably also take part in substrate assimilation.

Except for the unusual carbohydrate reserve, paramylon, these pathways are entirely conventional. The presence of trehalose as a secondary carbohydrate reserve, and of a yeastlike pyruvate carboxylase, suggest a possible special affinity with the fungi. In forming acetyl-CoA from acetate by the acetate thiokinase reaction, *Euglena* differs from such algae as *Chlorella* and *Scenedesmus* (Ohmann, 1964).

IV. Endogenous Respiration

When incubated in the absence of substrate, *Euglena* and *Astasia* exhibit an endogenous respiration of approximately 10 μl oxygen per million cells per hour at 25°–28° C. Higher rates, ca. 20–25 μl per million cells per hour, were found with *E. gracilis* Z at 30° C (Cook and Heinrich, 1965). The absolute rates vary with the culture age and probably with other aspects of the past history of the cells. Typically, the rate of endogenous respiration declines 25–50% over the first hour or two after harvesting, reaching a constant level which is then maintained for many hours (Von Dach, 1942; Danforth and Wilson, 1961). The endogenous respiratory rate is essentially independent of pH over a wide range (Von Dach, 1942; Danforth, 1953), and of the nature of the growth medium (Danforth and Wilson, 1961).* Wilson (1962; Wilson and James, 1963) grew *Astasia longa* at temperatures ranging from 15° to 28° C and measured respiration at the temperature of growth. Over this entire range of temperatures, the endogenous respiratory rate varied only from 6 to 8.4 μl oxygen per million cells per hour. Since the rates of enzymic reactions would be expected to increase 2- or 3-fold with temperature over this range, it seems likely that cells grown at low temperature compensate by synthesizing higher levels of the enzymes responsible for endogenous respiration. If so, the compensation is much less effective in the case of substrate metabolism, since the respiration of the same cells on acetate was several times greater at the highest temperature than at the lowest (see also Buetow, 1963). Unlike the respiration

---

* An exception to this statement is the finding of Boehler (1966) that the endogenous respiration of *E. gracilis* var. *bacillaris* grown on a glucose–tryptone medium was about twice as great as that of acetate-grown cells. Cook and Heinrich (1965), using defined media, found no such difference between glucose-grown and acetate-grown *E. gracilis* Z.

on acetate (see below), the endogenous respiration of *A. longa* was almost independent of population density (Wilson, 1962).

In *Astasia* cultures whose division had been synchronized by temperature cycling, the endogenous respiratory rate at the high temperature (28.5° C) was almost double that of cells grown exponentially at the same temperature, while the low temperature (14.8° C) rate was slightly less than that of low-temperature grown exponential cells (Wilson and James, 1963).

The respiratory quotient of the endogenous metabolism is very close to 1.0 for *A. klebsii* (Von Dach, 1942) and *E. gracilis* var. *bacillaris** (Danforth and Wilson, 1961), suggesting that the main endogenous substrate is carbohydrate in nature. This is supported by the finding that the carbohydrate[†] content of *E. gracilis* decreases more rapidly than either protein or RNA during carbon starvation (Blum and Buetow, 1963; Kempner and Miller, 1965c). After transfer from acetate medium to endogenous medium (with carry-over of a certain amount of acetate), the cells underwent 4 to 5 divisions, then survived without dividing for about 13 days after division ceased. Nearly 50% of the carbohydrate disappeared during the prestarvation divisions (Blum and Buetow, 1963) and by the time division ceased, paramylon granules were no longer visible in electron micrographs (Malkoff and Buetow, 1964). It is reasonable to assume, therefore, that paramylon, and probably trehalose (Marzullo, 1965), are the main substrates during the early phases of endogenous metabolism.

Danforth and Wilson (1961) produced evidence that the carbohydrate reserves most recently formed by substrate assimilation are (at least on the average) the first to be reoxidized via the reserve oxidation pathway, and proposed that a "labile reserve" consisting of the most recently assimilated carbohydrate exchanged material only very slowly with the much larger pool of "stable reserves." Trehalose (Marzullo, 1965) may account for at least a part of the "labile reserve." However, the trehalose content was 6 to 10 times smaller than the estimated capacity of the "labile reserve," so it is likely that paramylon also contributes to the "labile reserve." Since paramylon occurs in the cell as dense, insoluble granules, it is possible that the surface layers of the granules are the last portions to be synthesized and the first to be used.

---

* The endogenous respiratory quotient of glucose-grown *E. gracilis* var. *bacillaris*, however, was found to be around 0.65 (Boehler, 1966).

† The disappearing carbohydrate is called paramylon in the publications cited, although the anthrone method used for determination would respond to nearly all carbohydrate. By far the largest part of the carbohydrate of unstarved *Euglena* is paramylon, but this may no longer be true after prolonged starvation.

V. Utilization of Exogenous Substrates

A. GENERAL CONSIDERATIONS

The ability of euglenoids to use exogenous substrate as carbon and energy sources is limited, and varies greatly between species and strains (Cramer and Myers, 1952; Baker *et al.*, 1955; Hutner *et al.*, 1956). Many substrates that stimulate respiration of *E. gracilis* var. *bacillaris* (Danforth, 1953) cause no stimulation in *A. klebsii* (Von Dach, 1942, 1953) or *A. longa* (Hunter and Lee, 1962). The peculiarities of sugar utilization (Chapter 7) further illustrate the differences between strains. Among the commonly used laboratory strains of euglenoids, the Mainx and Vischer strains of *E. gracilis*, *A. longa*, and *A. klebsii* utilize relatively few substrates, while *E. gracilis* var. *bacillaris* and *E. gracilis* Z utilize many more.

While no single explanation seems fully adequate to account for the specificity of substrate utilization in any given strain, or for the differences between strains, cellular permeability is undoubtedly one of the more important factors limiting substrate availability. The available literature (Cramer and Myers, 1952; Hutner and Provasoli, 1951; Danforth, 1953; Von Dach, 1942, 1953; Hunter and Lee, 1962) indicates that, as a rule of thumb, the most readily utilized substrates are acetic and butyric acids and the corresponding alcohols; dicarboxylic acids are used only by the more versatile strains, while the tricarboxylic acids are used by none. With acidic substrates, respiratory stimulation is usually slight in neutral media but increases as the pH is lowered (Danforth, 1953; Hunter and Lee, 1962; Wilson *et al.*, 1959), presumably because the un-ionized acid molecules penetrate the cell more rapidly than the more polar anions. At still lower pH, the weakest acids are markedly toxic (Danforth, 1953). Utilization of nonionic substrates like ethanol is almost independent of pH (Eshlman and Danforth, 1964). All of these results are consistent with the general rule that small, weakly polar molecules penetrate cellular membranes more readily than large or highly polar molecules (Davson and Danielli, 1952; Danforth, 1953, 1963; Wilson *et al.*, 1959).

There are a number of cases of substrate specificity that cannot be accounted for on the basis of the simple rules of diffusive permeability. The very peculiar limitations on sugar utilization (Chapter 7) are a striking example. Danforth and Wilson (1957) found evidence for two mechanisms of acetate penetration into *E. gracilis* var. *bacillaris*, one conforming to the "rules" discussed above for weak acids, the other at least partially inducible and characterized by enzymelike kinetics. It was proposed that the second mechanism is a "permeaselike"-transport system specific for acetate anions. Since most strains of *Euglena* and *Astasia* use acetate readily at pH 7-8 (where acetate is 96–99% ionized), it is likely that acetate ion–transport systems are present in all the common laboratory strains. Probably similar systems occur that are specific for other substrates.

In nature, these permeability limitations may be ecological adaptations to habitats that are highly acidic or rich in fermentation products (Hutner and Provasoli, 1951).

B. Oxidative Assimilation of Acetate

Acetate is readily utilized by all strains of *E. gracilis* and *Astasia* whose respiration has been studied. Typically, addition of acetate stimulates the respiration of *Euglena* or *Astasia* to a rate three to eight times the endogenous respiratory rate. The ability to utilize acetate appears to be an inducible property of *Euglena* (Danforth and Wilson, 1957; Cook and Heinrich, 1965). In the case of *E. gracilis* var. *bacillaris*, adaptation to acetate appeared to involve the induction of a transport system for acetate anions. Rates of respiration ranging from about 20 to 60 μl oxygen per million cells per hour have been reported for acetate-grown cells respiring on acetate at about 25° C. The range of rates is about the same for *A. longa*, *A. klebsii*, and *E. gracilis* var. *bacillaris*. For *E. gracilis* Z, at 30° C, the rate was about 90 μl per million cells per hour (Cook and Heinrich, 1965). Culture age (Von Dach, 1942), pH (Danforth and Wilson, 1957), testosterone (Buetow and Levedahl, 1961), centrifugation (Buetow, 1961a), and cell concentration (Wilson, 1963) all influence the respiratory rate.

Early studies with synchronized populations of *Astasia* (Wilson and James, 1963) indicated that the respiratory rate per cell on acetate was constant over almost the entire cell cycle, suggesting that synthesis (or activation) of new respiratory machinery was limited to a short period at the approximate time of cytokinesis. Later investigations with improved techniques (James, 1965; Wilson and James, 1966) supported the conclusion that changes in the respiratory rate were abrupt, rather than continuous, although the time at which these changes occurred varied from culture to culture for reasons not fully understood.

Carbon-balance studies of acetate metabolism are complicated by the fact that oxidation of endogenous reserves continues during acetate metabolism. This fact creates difficulties which are most apparent in experiments with radioactively labeled acetate. In very short-term experiments of this type, the CO_2 produced is composed of two fractions, one derived from acetate, and hence labeled, the other derived from nonlabeled endogenous reserves. Meanwhile, however, acetate is being used to synthesize new (radioactive) intracellular reserves. As the duration of the experiment is increased, more and more of the reserves are derived from labeled acetate, and more and more of the CO_2 produced by the reserve oxidation contains radioactive carbon. If such an experiment could be continued indefinitely, eventually all of the intracellular reserve and all of the CO_2 produced would be derived from the labeled acetate, even though no change occurs in the underlying metabolic processes.

This situation is greatly clarified if we consider the metabolism of *Euglena* on acetate to be made up of two independent processes occurring simultaneously (Fig. 2). One of these, the *primary substrate metabolism*, consists of the direct oxidation of a portion of the acetate to CO_2 and assimilation of the remaining portion into intracellular reserves. The second, *reserve oxidation*, consists of the oxidation of the intracellular reserves to CO_2, and is practically equivalent to the endogenous metabolism that would occur if acetate were not present. In calculating the carbon balance of the primary substrate metabolism, the CO_2 produced and the oxygen consumed in reserve oxidation should not be included. In practice this can be achieved by subtracting the respiration of an endogenous control from the respiration in the presence of acetate. This method gives a sort of short-term, or gross, efficiency of acetate utilization. For long-term steady-state growth on acetate, however, the net efficiency (the fraction of the acetate carbon retained permanently within the *Euglena* cells) will be lower, because, in the long run, the carbon lost through the reserve oxidation pathway will also be derived from acetate. In estimating this net efficiency, the total respiration from both acetate oxidation and reserve oxidation should be included in the calculations. The distinction between the two efficiency measures has not always been clearly expressed in the literature (Blumenthal *et al.*, 1957; Wilson, 1963; Eshleman and Danforth, 1964).

The concepts just outlined are appropriate only in cases in which primary substrate metabolism and reserve oxidation occur simultaneously and with essentially no interference. This assumption cannot be taken for granted, but must be tested experimentally for each organism and for each substrate[*] (Danforth, 1963; Wilson, 1963; Griffiths, 1965). In the case of acetate utilization by *Euglena*, the results of tracer studies, combined with respirometric carbon balances cannot be accounted for by any other reasonable model (Wilson and Danforth, 1958; Danforth and Wilson, 1961; Danforth, 1961). The data indicate that there is essentially no competition and no exchange of intermediates between the reserve oxidation pathway and the pathways of oxidative assimilation of acetate, except by the way of reserve

---

[*] There is evidence (Boehler, 1966) that oxidation of reserves is partially inhibited during glucose utilization by *E. gracilis* var. *bacillaris*. The experiments of Kempner and Miller (1965b) suggest that reserve oxidation is completely inhibited during growth on glutamate since *E. gracilis* Z grown on radioactive glutamate lose almost none of their radioactivity during further growth on unlabeled glutamate.

carbohydrate. Similar studies on *A. longa* are in agreement with those on *Euglena* (Wilson, 1963).

In experiments designed to study the primary substrate metabolism, it was found that 42% of the acetate carbon consumed appeared as CO_2, while 58% was assimilated (Wilson and Danforth, 1958; Danforth, 1961; Marzullo and Danforth, 1964b). The same ratio was found with *A. longa* at temperatures ranging from 15° to 28° C. As long as acetate is the sole carbon source present, this ratio has proved invariant under all experimental conditions tested, including conditions that greatly modify the rate of acetate consumption.

About 81% of all the acetate carbon assimilated by *Euglena* can be recovered in the glucose units of paramylon (Marzullo and Danforth, 1964b). A large proportion of the remainder is in the form of the soluble oligosaccharide, trehalose (Marzullo, 1965). Thus, to a first approximation, CO_2 and carbohydrate, in constant ratio, may be considered the sole products of primary acetate utilization.

When *Euglena* are killed and fractionated with ethanol after incubation with radioactive acetate, the ethanol-insoluble fraction consists mainly of paramylon (Marzullo and Danforth, 1964b), while the soluble fraction contains trehalose, Krebs-cycle and glycolytic intermediates, and related compounds (Marzullo, 1965). During the first hour after addition of acetate, the radioactivity of the soluble fraction rises to a plateau, while that of the insoluble fraction starts slowly and accelerates (Marzullo and Danforth, 1964a). Kinetic analysis suggests that during this time the soluble fraction behaves like a well-mixed pool of fixed size which is the precursor of the insoluble fraction. After about another hour, the soluble radioactivity rises again to a higher plateau value. This second batch of soluble material does not behave like a precursor of the insoluble fraction. It was proposed that the second group of soluble substances are intermediates in the reserve oxidation pathway, derived indirectly from acetate via the carbohydrate reserves. Chromatographic analysis (Marzullo, 1965) showed that the two "steps" of the soluble fraction, and the same fraction after exhaustion of the acetate, contained the same substances in practically the same relative amounts. If the interpretation of the kinetics is correct, this is direct evidence for the chemical similarities (p. 68) between substrate metabolism and reserve oxidation.

A rather surprising feature of these kinetic studies was the finding of γ-aminobutyric acid as one of the earliest intermediates of acetate utilization. This compound was already known as a metabolic product in *Euglena* (McCalla, 1963), but its precise role remains undetermined.

It is evident that the primary substrate metabolism of acetate follows a remarkably simple and stereotyped pattern. The only variable feature of the entire process seems to be the rate at which acetate is utilized, which is influenced by environmental variations and by adaptive responses of the organism.

C. OXIDATIVE ASSIMILATION OF ETHANOL

Like acetate, ethanol can serve as sole carbon and energy source for the growth of most euglenoids. Respiratory rates on ethanol fall in the same range as those on acetate; depending on the past history of the cells, the respiratory rate on ethanol may be greater than, equal to, or less than that on acetate (Danforth and Wilson, 1957; Eshleman and Danforth, 1964). The respiratory rate of ethanol-grown *Astasia* on ethanol was about 17% higher than that of acetate-grown cells on acetate, other conditions being held constant (Buetow and Padilla, 1963). The rate of ethanol utilization is essentially independent of pH, but is rather strongly dependent on ethanol concentration; 10 mM ethanol is required to give maximum respiratory rates, approximately 1 mM supports half-maximal respiration. Acetate-grown and ethanol-grown *Euglena* were similar in these characteristics (Eshleman and Danforth, 1964).

The available evidence suggests that as with acetate, oxidation of intracellular reserves continues during ethanol metabolism. Carbon-balance studies indicate that for each mole of ethanol consumed, 0.97 moles of oxygen are used and 0.29 moles of CO_2 produced. This stoichiometry cannot be accounted for on the assumption that all of the ethanol carbon assimilated is converted to carbohydrate. Considerable amounts of products more reduced than carbohydrates are required to balance the equation (Wilson and Danforth, 1958; Eshleman and Danforth, 1964). There is evidence that some acetaldehyde is released during ethanol metabolism (J. J. Blum, personal communication) but the amounts of acetaldehyde produced are not enough to account for the carbon balance (J. N. Eshleman, unpublished). It is tempting to assume that an appreciable portion of the ethanol carbon is assimilated into lipid reserves, but direct evidence is lacking and the lipid content of ethanol-grown *Astasia* was actually less than that of acetate-grown cells (Buetow and Padilla, 1963). The CO_2 production from ethanol is less than that which would be expected even if all the ethanol were assimilated via the glyoxylate cycle. Thus, if the glyoxylate cycle functions at all in ethanol metabolism, hardly any ethanol can be oxidized via the Krebs cycle. It seems likely that the Krebs cycle is "shut off" entirely during ethanol utilization. This suggestion is supported by the results of experiments on the effects of ethanol on acetate metabolism. In the presence of ethanol, 75% of the acetate carbon (rather than the usual 58%) was assimilated (Danforth, 1961). This is the ratio expected if all the acetate went through the glyoxylate cycle and none through the Krebs cycle. The rate of oxygen consumption on ethanol plus acetate is usually, although not always, higher than that on either substrate alone, but less than the sum of the rates on the two substrates individually (Buetow, 1961b; Eshleman, 1963), while the rates of acetate utilization (Danforth, 1961) and of ethanol utilization (Eshleman, 1963) are the same as in the absence of the other substrate.

VI. Some Outstanding Problems

A. Regulation of Oxidation–Assimilation Ratios

Perhaps the most striking feature of the primary acetate metabolism is the constancy of the oxidation–assimilation ratio. Clearly, some regulatory mechanism must be present to maintain this ratio in the face of environmental changes that alter enzymic rates.

The constancy of the ratio suggests a stoichiometric coupling between the two pathways, in which a product of one pathway is a required substrate for the other, rather than feedback effects on enzymic rate constants. "Respiratory control" of mammalian mitochondria by the ADP produced in energy-consuming reactions (Chance, 1961) is a well-known example of such a stoichiometric control mechanism, since ADP is an essential respiratory substrate for tightly coupled mitochondria. The lack of tight coupling in *Euglena* mitochondria (p. 58), and experiments with phosphorylation inhibitors (Danforth and Kaplan, 1964) raise doubts as to the importance of this particular mechanism for control of the oxidation–assimilation ratio in *Euglena*.

B. Relation between Substrate Metabolism and Reserve Oxidation

The continued oxidation of intracellular reserves parallel with but independent of acetate and ethanol metabolism, and the lack of any pooling of intermediates of the two processes are difficult to account for. As has already been pointed out, the two pathways have many enzymes and intermediates in common and would be expected to interact at many levels. Lack of interaction, under these circumstances, suggests that the processes may be spatially separated. Since many of the reactions in both pathways are known to occur in mitochondria, it is tempting to suggest that any individual mitochondrion may be active in reserve oxidation or in substrate metabolism but not in both. This might be a matter of localization, mitochondria near paramylon granules carrying on reserve oxidation, and mitochondria near the cell surface acting on substrate.

C. RELATIONSHIP OF OXIDATIVE ASSIMILATION TO GROWTH

The discovery that carbohydrates are practically the sole direct products of acetate assimilation raises serious problems concerning the relationship of the oxidative assimilation process to cell growth. Acetate is known to serve as sole carbon source for balanced growth of *Euglena* populations. In order to do so, acetate carbon must ultimately be converted into all the organic constituents of *Euglena* cells, in the proportions in which these occur in the normal cell. For periods of acetate metabolism up to 6 hours (Marzullo and Danforth, 1964b), far more paramylon and far less protein and lipid are formed than would be required for balanced growth. If this were the only process involved in growth, the cells would soon be converted into little bags of almost pure paramylon. While these short-term experiments are performed under somewhat artificial conditions, identical oxidation-assimilation ratios have been obtained under growth conditions (Wilson, 1963). Probably, therefore, all the acetate carbon assimilated is converted to paramylon, and the paramylon is later "reworked" to form other cellular constituents. In terms of Fig. 2, this would mean that the raw materials for synthesis of protein, lipid, etc., are bled off the reserve oxidation pathway rather than the primary substrate pathways.

Such a seemingly awkward arrangement may, in fact, have adaptive advantage. Although the ability of phytoflagellates to thrive in extremely metabolite-rich environments has been emphasized (Hutner and Provasoli, 1951), they show remarkable abilities to survive starvation (Blum and Buetow, 1963). These contrasts suggest adaptation to circumstances of alternating feast and famine. If so, the primary substrate metabolism may be a mechanism for capturing substrates quickly while they are available, and storing them for future use. Certainly the respiratory rates associated with acetate and ethanol metabolism are much higher than are necessary to support good growth. Substrates such as succinate (Wilson *et al.*, 1959) and glucose (Cook and Heinrich, 1965; Boehler, 1966) support optimal growth without stimulating respiration significantly above the endogenous rate. Indeed, there is little or no correlation between respiratory rate and growth rate. Careful materials-balance studies of steady-state growth are needed in order to clarify these apparent paradoxes. The studies of Kempner and Miller (1965a,b) are a valuable beginning in this direction. Similar long-term studies on acetate utilization would be especially helpful, since so much comparative data is available on the products of short-term acetate metabolism.

References

Baker, H., Hutner, S. H., and Sobotka, H. (1955). *Ann. N. Y. Acad. Sci.* **62**, 349.
Barker, H. A. (1936). *J. Cellular Comp. Physiol.* **8**, 231.
Barry, S. C. (1962). *J. Protozool.* **9**, 395.
Blum, J. J., and Buetow, D. E. (1963). *Exptl. Cell Res.* **29**, 407.
Blumenthal, H. J., Koffler, H., and Heath, E. C. (1957). *J. Cellular Comp. Physiol.* **50**, 471.
Boehler, R. A. (1966). M. S. Thesis, Illinois Inst. Tech., Chicago, Illinois.
Buetow, D. E. (1961a). *Anal. Biochem.* **2**, 242.
Buetow, D. E. (1961b). *Nature* **190**, 1196.
Buetow, D. E. (1963). *Nature* **199**, 196.
Buetow, D. E., and Buchanan, P. J. (1964). *Exptl. Cell Res.* **36**, 204.
Buetow, D. E., and Buchanan, P. J. (1965). *Biochim. Biophys. Acta* **96**, 9.
Buetow, D. E., and Levedahl, B. H. (1961). *Arch. Biochem. Biophys.* **94**, 358.
Buetow, D. E., and Padilla, G. M. (1963). *J. Protozool.* **10**, 121.
Butler, W. L., and Baker, J. E. (1963). *Biochim. Biophys. Acta* **66**, 206.
Chance, B. (1961). *Cold Spring Harbor Symp. Quant. Biol.* **26**, 289.
Cook, J. R., and Heinrich, B. (1965). *J. Protozool.* **12**, 581.
Cramer, M., and Myers, J. (1952). *Arch. Mikrobiol.* **17**, 384.
Danforth, W. (1953). *Arch. Biochem. Biophys.* **46**, 164.
Danforth, W. F. (1961). *J. Protozool.* **8**, 152.
Danforth, W. F. (1963). *In* "Physiology and Biochemistry of Algae" (R. A. Lewin, ed.), pp. 99–123. Academic Press, New York.
Danforth, W. F., and Kaplan, J. H. (1964). *J. Protozool.* **11** (Suppl.), 26.
Danforth, W. F., and Wilson, B. W. (1957). *J. Protozool.* **4**, 52.
Danforth, W. F., and Wilson, B. W. (1961). *J. Gen. Microbiol.* **24**, 95.
Davson, H., and Danielli, J. F. (1952). "The Permeability of Natural Membranes," 2nd ed. Cambridge Univ. Press, London and New York.
Eshleman, J. N. (1963). M. S. Thesis, Illinois Inst. Tech., Chicago, Illinois.
Eshleman, J. N., and Danforth, W. F. (1964). *J. Protozool.* **11**, 394.
Gojdics, M. (1953). "The Genus Euglena." Univ. of Wisconsin Press, Madison, Wisconsin.
Griffiths, D. J. (1965). *Sci. Progr. (London)* **53**, 553.
Gross, J. A., and Wolken, J. J. (1960). *Science* **132**, 357.
Hunter, F. R., and Lee, J. W. (1962). *J. Protozool.* **9**, 74.
Hurlbert, R. E., and Rittenberg, S. C. (1962). *J. Protozool.* **9**, 170.
Hutner, S. H., and Provasoli, L. (1951). *In* "Physiology and Biochemistry of Protozoa" (A. Lwoff, ed.), Vol. I, pp 27–128. Academic Press, New York.
Hutner, S. H., and Provasoli, L. (1955). *In* "Physiology and Biochemistry of Protozoa" (S. H. Hutner and A. Lwoff, eds.), Vol. II, pp. 17–43. Academic Press, New York.
Hutner, S. H., Bach, M. B., and Ross, G. I. M. (1956). *J. Protozool.* **3**, 101.
James, T. W. (1965). *Exptl. Cell Res.* **38**, 439.
Kempner, E. S., and Miller, J. H. (1965a). *Biochim. Biophys. Acta* **104**, 11.
Kempner, E. S., and Miller, J. H. (1965b). *Biochim. Biophys. Acta* **104**, 18.
Kempner, E. S., and Miller, J. H. (1965c). *Biochemistry* **4**, 2735.
Krebs, H. A., and Kornberg, H. L. (1957). *Ergeb. Physiol. Biol. Chem. Exptl. Pharmakol.* **49**, 212.
Lehninger, A. L. (1964). "The Mitochondrion," pp. 132–139. Benjamin, New York.
Lehninger, A. L., Wadkins, C. L., and Remmert, L. F. (1959). *In* "The Regulation of Cell Metabolism" (G. E. W. Wolstenholme and C. M. O'Connor, eds.), Ciba Foundation Symp., pp. 130–149. Little, Brown, Boston, Massachusetts.

Lwoff, A., ed. (1951). In "Physiology and Biochemistry of Protozoa," Vol. I, pp. 1–26. Academic Press, New York.

McCalla, D. R. (1963). J. Protozool. 10, 491.

Malkoff, D. B., and Buetow, D. E. (1964). Exptl. Cell Res. 35, 58.

Marzullo, G. (1965). Ph. D. Thesis, Illinois Inst. Technol., Chicago, Illinois.

Marzullo, G., and Danforth, W. F. (1964a). J. Gen. Microbiol. 34, 9.

Marzullo, G., and Danforth, W. F. (1964b). J. Gen. Microbiol. 34, 21.

Nishimura, M. (1959). J. Biochem. (Tokyo) 46, 219.

Ohmann, E. (1964). Biochim. Biophys. Acta 82, 325.

Perini, F., Kamen, M. D., and Schiff, J. A. (1964a). Biochim. Biophys. Acta 88, 74.

Perini, F., Kamen, M. D., and Schiff, J. A. (1964b). Biochim. Biophys. Acta 88, 91.

Smillie, R. M. (1963). Can. J. Botany 41, 123.

Von Dach, H. (1942). Biol. Bull. 82, 356.

Von Dach, H. (1953). Federation Proc. 12, 149.

Webster, D. A., and Hackett, D. P. (1965). Plant Physiol. 40, 1091.

Wilson, B. W. (1962). Ph. D. Thesis, Univ. of California, Los Angeles, California.

Wilson, B. W. (1963). J. Cellular Comp. Physiol. 62, 49.

Wilson, B. W., and Danforth, W. F. (1958). J. Gen. Microbiol. 18, 535.

Wilson, B. W., and James, T. W. (1963). Exptl. Cell Res. 32, 305.

Wilson, B. W., and James, T. W. (1966). In "Cell Synchrony" (I. L. Cameron and G. M. Padilla, eds.), pp. 236–255. Academic Press, New York.

Wilson, B. W., Buetow, D. E., Jahn, T. L., and Levedahl, B. H. (1959). Exptl. Cell Res. 18, 454.

Wolken, J. J., and Gross, J. A. (1963). J. Protozool. 10, 189.

CHAPTER 3

PHOTOSYNTHESIS IN *EUGLENA*

William R. Evans

I. Introduction

The use of *Euglena* in studies on photosynthesis has been primarily devoted to compositional changes associated with the transition from an animal-type metabolism in the dark to a photosynthetic plant-type metabolism in the light. As a result of this dual existence, questions concerning the localization of a substance in the chloroplast can generally be answered with *Euglena*. Consequently, a large amount of literature is available on studies of this nature and I have attempted to review this work. However, a paucity of information exists on the biochemistry of photosynthesis in *Euglena*, with the majority of these studies being published within the past year. Nevertheless, a significant observation has been obtained from these studies relative to the role of cytochrome f in the electron-transport pathway of photosynthesis.

II. Components of *Euglena* Chloroplasts Concerned with Photosynthesis

A. PIGMENTS

The forms of chlorophyll *in vivo* in *Euglena* have been reviewed (Smith and French, 1963; Bogorad, 1962; Brody and Brody, 1963; Wolken, 1963; French, 1966; see also Chapter 9). Suffice it to say that *Euglena* contains the 650-mμ absorption form of chlorophyll b and the 670- and 680-mμ absorption forms of chlorophyll a. A third form of chlorophyll a, with an absorption maximum at 695-mμ, develops when the cells are grown under low light intensity (ca. 200 ft-c). Brown (1963) suggested that, under these conditions, perhaps some of the 670-mμ form of chlorophyll a is converted into the 695-mμ absorption form in order to take advantage of additional light energy.

Olson (1963) presented evidence for an oriented far-red pigment which he assumed to be an energy-trapping form of chlorophyll a. By virtue of spectral measurements of dichroism and bifluorescence this pigment was related to chlorophyll a 705 (Butler, 1961); to P700 (Kok and Hoch, 1961); and to chlorophyll a 695 (Brown and French, 1961).

The existence of two functional pigment systems has been inferred from action spectra of cytochrome oxidation–reduction reactions (Olson and Smillie, 1963). The nomenclature of Duysens and Amez (1962) is used here; i.e., system I refers to the long-wavelength chlorophyll a absorbing at 683 mμ and the other pigments that function with it. System II refers to the shorter wavelength-absorbing pigments, chlorophyll b and chlorophyll a 670, as well as those accessory pigments that feed light energy into chlorophyll a 670 mμ. The Emerson enhancement effect (Emerson *et al.*, 1957), indicative of two separately acting pigment systems, is barely detectable in *Euglena*. Brown and French (1961) suggested that the low amount of chlorophyll b relative to chlorophyll a may account in part for the lack of a significant enchancement effect. The failure to find any substantial enchancement between 695-mμ and shorter wavelengths in cells that have considerable absorption at 695 mμ, suggests that chlorophyll a 695 is not a part of the functional long-wavelength chlorophyll system, but may be an accessory pigment (Brown, 1963). Bergeron and Sybesma (1963) have suggested that a fluorescent species of the pigment with a maximum at 710 mμ might be the energy sink for system II. French (1966) believes this 710-mμ fluorescent species to be due to the chlorophyll a component absorbing at 695 mμ.

The carotenoid composition of both dark-grown and light-grown cells has been determined by Krinsky *et al.* (1964). Neoxanthin is found only in light-grown cells and the sequence of neoxanthin formation and development of photosynthetic competence during greening of dark-grown cultures strongly suggest an intimate role for this carotenoid in photosynthesis. Krinsky (1966) has proposed that an epoxide cycle, involving zeaxanthin and antheraxanthin, could protect cells against lethal photosensitized oxidations. Using lyophilized powders he has shown that epoxidation of zeaxanthin takes place only under conditions (light and oxygen) that can lead to photosensitization. Zeaxanthin is then regenerated by a dark enzymic de-epoxidation of antheraxanthin.

B. LIPIDS

Information relative to the role that lipids play in photosynthesis, in regard both to structure and function of the chloroplast, has been obtained from a comparison of the lipid patterns of etiolated cells and green cells (for example, see Chapter 6). The most profound difference between them is the percent of the total lipid fraction associated with the phospholipids and the galactolipids. In autotrophically grown cells, 70% of the total lipids is found in the "pigment fraction," which is comprised mainly of galactosyl glycerides; whereas, in dark-grown heterotrophs, only 6% of the total lipids is associated with this fraction. In contrast, the total phospholipid content of etiolated cells is 74% of the total lipids compared to only 21% in autotrophic cells (Hulanicka *et al.*, 1964). Moreover, the "pigment fraction" in dark-grown cells was completely devoid of galactose-containing lipids (Hulanicka *et al.*, 1964). Carter *et al.* (1961) had previously observed the absence of this type of lipid in heterotrophic cells. However, Rosenberg (1963) showed that there are galactose-containing lipids in both dark-grown and permanently bleached cells, although the dark-grown cell contained only 17% as much galactose in the total lipid fraction as the green cell.

The sulfolipid, 6-sulfoquinovosyl(1-1′)diglyceride, has been detected in both etiolated and green cultures (Rosenberg and Parker, 1964, Davies *et al.*, 1965; Benson *et al.*, 1962; Abraham and Bachhawat, 1963). In etiolated cells the bulk of the sulfolipid is found in the 105,000-g pellet while in green cells the sulfolipid segregates with the chlorophyll, suggesting that the major portion is located in the chloroplasts (Davies *et al.*, 1965). Rosenberg and Parker (1964) have shown that the quantity of sulfolipids trebled during the total greening process. The major function of these surfactant lipids, such as the galactosyl glycerides and sulfolipids, is presumed to be the stabilization of lipoprotein membranes (Weier and Benson, 1966).

The fatty acid pattern of total lipids from cells cultivated in the dark and light have been determined by Carter *et al.* (1961), Rosenberg and Parker (1964), Erwin and Bloch (1963), Hulanicka *et al.* (1964), Haverkate and Van Deenen (1965), and Korn (1964). One pertinent observation from these studies was the direct relationship between α-linolenic acid content and oxygen-producing capacity. In dark-grown cells the α-linolenic content of the total fatty acids amounts to only 0.8% while in autotrophically grown cells this particular fatty acid accounts for 32% of the total fatty acids (Erwin and Bloch, 1963). Approximately 70% of the α-linolenate found in green cells is associated with the galactosyl glycerides (Hulanicka *et al.*, 1964) and over 85% of the α-linolenate was localized in the chloroplasts (Erwin and Bloch, 1963). The amount of α-linolenate found is a function not only of the dark or light growth conditions but also of the concentration of CO_2 used during autotrophic growth (Erwin and Bloch, 1964). Cells grown in 5% CO_2 in air contained four times the amount of α-linolenate as those grown in 0.5% CO_2 in air. Although the chlorophyll content was essentially the same for both types of cells, chloroplasts prepared from the cells grown in 5% CO_2 in air evolved oxygen at a rate 2.6 times as fast as cells grown in 0.5% CO_2 in air.

trans-Δ³-Hexadecenoic acid is another fatty acid found only in green cells (Van Deenen and Haverkate, 1966) esterfied exclusively to phosphatidyl glycerol. A specific association between phosphatidyl glycerol and the *trans-Δ³*-hexadecenoic acid appears to occur only in those organisms in which photosynthesis is of the type found in green plants.

Involvement of α-linolenate, and other polyenic fatty acids, and *trans-Δ³*-hexadecenoic acid in the reactions that lead to oxygen evolution have been seriously discounted by studies of the fatty acid composition of the blue-green algae *Anabena variablis* and *Anacystis nidulans*. Recent studies by Nichols *et al.* (1965) demonstrated that although *A. variablis* produces α-linolenic acid, no *trans-Δ³*-hexadecenoic acid was found. Furthermore, Holton *et al.* (1964) and Allen *et al.* (1966) have shown that in *A. nidulans* the fatty acid composition is similar to the photosynthetic bacteria in lacking α-linolenic and other polyunsaturated acids. Holton *et al.* (1964) suggested that the polyunsaturated acids are probably integral components of the chloroplast membrane and their function is one of a structural nature rather than being related to a specific biochemical reaction.

Plastoquinone, α-tocopherol, α-tocopherolyl quinone, and plastoquinone c have been isolated from autotrophically grown cells (Threfall and Goodwin, 1964). Intracellular distribution studies of the quinones indicated that all four of these quinones were localized in the chloroplasts. Earlier work by Fuller *et al.* (1961) had shown the absence of plastoquinone in streptomycin-bleached cells and the presence of coenzyme Q_8 in both the light-grown and streptomycin-bleached cells.

C. PROTEINS

1. *Electron-Transport Carriers*

Davenport and Hill (1950) first observed that acetone preparations obtained from *Euglena* exhibited spectra of nonautoxidizable components which, in the reduced state, possessed broad absorption bands with maxima at 552–553 mμ. It was supposed that these maxima represented mixtures of those for cytochrome c and for cytochrome f. Nishimura (1959) later showed that the maximum that occurred at 552 mμ was not a composite of c-type and f-type bands but arose from a single c-type cytochrome. This c-type cytochrome was absent in dark-grown cells and appeared with chlorophyll during the development of the chloroplast. Gross and Wolken (1960), in an investigation of a complex, "chloroplastin," obtained from light-grown cells by treatment with digitonin, found a soluble heme protein, identical to that reported by Nishimura, with an α-band at 552 mμ. Smillie (1963) found another cytochrome in light-grown cultures which was a b-type heme protein, particle-bound and localized in the chloroplast. Smillie (1963) also showed that cytochrome 552 was associated with the chloroplast. The c-type cytochrome with absorption maximum for the α-band at 552 mμ has been completely characterized by Perini *et al.* (1964a). It exhibits a characteristic high midpoint potential, +370 ± 5 mV at pH 7, and a acid isoelectric point. Unlike other algal and plant c-type cytochromes, this cytochrome has a symmetrical α-band.

Determination of the chlorophyll and cytochrome-552 composition of cells during chloroplast development indicated that functional units in the chloroplast are built containing constant ratios of 350 chlorophyll molecules per molecule of cytochrome 552 (Perini *et al.*, 1964b).

NADP-reductase (NADP-reductase is synonymous with NADPH-diaphorase) activity has been shown to be present in *Euglena* by Lazzarini and San Pietro (1963), Smillie (1963), Perini (1963), and Nagai and Bloch (1966). Evidence that the function of this enzyme is to transfer electrons from reduced ferredoxin to NADP has been summarized by San Pietro and Black (1965). There appears to be a significant basal level of this enzyme in dark-grown and permanently bleached cells. The enzyme from both types of cells, as well as that from green cells, is cross-reactive to an antiserum prepared against the reductase obtained from spinach (Lazzarini and San Pietro, 1963). Smillie *et al.* (1963) presented evidence, by measurement of NADPH-diaphorase activity changes during greening, which might indicate the presence of two NADPH-diaphorases, one activity being soluble and the other associated with the chloroplast fraction.

The presence of ferredoxin has been demonstrated by Shapiro (1961), Smillie (1963), Perini *et al.* (1964a), and Nagai and Bloch (1966). Spectra of the isolated protein are similar to those reported for the ferredoxins from spinach and parsley (San Pietro, 1963, Tagawa and Arnon, 1962; Bendall *et al.*, 1963). No data is available as to the content of heme iron and "labile sulfur" or amino acid composition of the *Euglena* ferredoxin. Ferredoxin has been shown by Nagai and Bloch (1966) to be an essential component of the stearyl acyl carrier protein desaturase system. The role of ferredoxin in photoreduction reactions has recently been reviewed by San Pietro and Black (1965).

To the author's knowledge there have been no reports in the literature on the presence or isolation of plastocyanin in *Euglena*.

2. CO_2-Fixation Enzymes

Euglena was one of the organisms employed by Peterkofsky and Racker (1961) in their study of the enzyme activities of the reductive pentose phosphate cycle in cell-free extracts. All of the pentose phosphate cycle enzymes were found to be present. However, the activities of ribulose-diphosphate carboxylase, fructose diphosphatase, and sedoheptulose diphosphatase were inadequate to support the measured rate of CO_2 fixation in the intact cells of *Euglena*, as well as those of *Chlorella*. Pedersen *et al.* (1966) showed that the reactions catalyzed by these enzymes are the same reactions, along with photophosphorylation, that are inhibited by fatty acids and methyl octanoate during CO_2 fixation in *Chlorella*. One possible effect of the fatty acids and the ester was proposed to be "some reversible physicochemical effect on the photosynthetic apparatus which interferes with its function" (Pedersen *et al.*, 1966). These same substances when added to *Chlorella*, at the same concentrations used to inhibit CO_2 fixation, caused a large light-induced increase in light scattering as compared to control cells which did not appear to undergo appreciable light-induced scattering changes. The tentative conclusion was reached that "the fatty acids and the ester altered the properties of the lamella in such a way that photophosphorylation is blocked and a light-induced conformational change occurs" (Pedersen *et al.*, 1966). Since the diphosphatases and the ribulose carboxylase were also inhibited by these lipophilic substances it was suggested that these enzymes might be components of an organized system which may include the lamellar surface, photophosphorylation, and the diphosphatase and carboxylation reactions. The possibility that the enzymes with the intact cell might operate in an organized manner was recognized by Peterkofsky and Racker (1961), and Bassham (1964) suggested that this phenomenon might result in increased activity of some enzymes in the intact cell.

Smillie (1963) showed by fractionation in a nonaqueous medium that all of the enzymes involved in the Calvin photosynthetic cycle (Bassham *et al.*, 1963), except phosphopento-ketopimerase and sedoheptulose diphosphatase which were not assayed, occurred in the chloroplast. Enzymes that convert fructose 6-phosphate to UDPG, namely, phosphohexisomerase, phosphoglucomutase, and UDPG pyrophosphorylase, were not localized in the plastid fraction. Therefore, sucrose cannot be one of the main photosynthetic products of the chloroplast in *Euglena* as is the case for higher plants.

Leech (1966) has suggested that a NAD-dependent malic dehydrogenase is located in the chloroplasts of *Vicia faba* L. This situation might also be true for *Euglena*. Chancellor-Madison and Noll (1963) have shown that autotrophically grown cells contain a malic dehydrogenase lacking in heterotrophically grown cells. It was pointed out that the additional form of the enzyme might be due to its production by photosynthetic mechanisms or that the additional form may be repressed in the heterotrophs due to the presence of malate in the media.

Labeling patterns obtained with $^{14}CO_2$ fixation indicated that dark fixation resembled that obtained in the light (Lynch and Calvin, 1953). This was interpreted as a fixation via the photosynthetic pathway utilizing energy from dark respiration. However, no label could be detected in the sugar diphosphate area of the radioautograms. An alternate conclusion was suggested by Moses *et al.* (1959) in which the label found in the sugar monophosphates during dark fixation could have originated from the carboxylation of ribulose 5-phosphate to yield 6-phosphogluconic acid, which in turn could yield glucose 6-phosphate.

III. Characteristics of the Hill Reaction

Olson and Smillie (1963) analyzed spectroscopically the light-driven cytochrome reactions both in whole cells and chloroplast fragments. Action spectra of cytochrome-552 oxidation in whole cells indicated that a pigment with an absorption peak at 705 mμ was considerably more effective than chlorophyll a in oxidizing the cytochrome. The action spectra also showed that chlorophyll a was effective in both system I and system II, so chlorophyll b apparently does not play a unique role in sensitizing system II in *Euglena* as has been suggested in other instances of green plant photosynthesis (Myers and French, 1960; Allen *et al.*, 1962). The addition of $5 \times 10^{-5}M$ carbonyl cyanide-*m*-chlorophenylhydrazone to whole cells permitted the light-induced oxidation of cytochrome b_6 to be observed initially without any concomitant cytochrome-552 oxidation. After 40 minutes incubation the cytochrome-552 reaction reappeared almost completely without any appreciable change in the cytochrome-b_6 reaction by 1,10-phenanthroline.

Olson and Smillie (1963) had indicated that chloroplast fragments prepared from older cells in tris buffer contained very little cytochrome 552. Katoh and San Pietro (1967a) showed that chloroplasts lacking cytochrome 552 could be prepared in phosphate buffer from cells in the midlog phase of autotrophic growth. A difference spectrum, reduced minus oxidized, of an aqueous suspension of an acetone powder of chloroplasts showed an absorption maximum around 560 mμ, indicative of b-type cytochrome, but no appreciable absorbance indicative of cytochrome 552. In these chloroplast preparations both dichlorophenolindophenol (DPIP) and ferricyanide were efficient electron acceptors for the Hill reaction. In contrast, the photoreduction of NADP, cytochrome c, and methyl viologen was very low even in the presence of excess ferredoxin. However, on addition of cytochrome 552 the photoreduction of NADP, cytochrome c, and methyl viologen was restored. Some restoration of NADP photoreduction was also observed with *Porphyra tenera* cytochrome 553, but not with *Euglena* cytochrome 556 or horse heart cytochrome c. Attempts were made to prepare chloroplasts that still retained cytochrome 552 in various media, but in all instances the cytochrome 552 was localized in the soluble fraction of the preparation. It would appear that with *Euglena* chloroplasts only the photoreductions catalyzed by system II are detectable until cytochrome 552 is restored; it then couples system II to system I and the photoreduction of NADP can be observed.

The addition of cytochrome 552 was also essential for NADP photoreduction to be observed with the ascorbate–DPIP couple (Vernon and Zaugg, 1960). These results are not consistent with the data of Avron and Chance (1966) which suggested that cytochrome f was not involved in the electron transfer from reduced DPIP to NADP. Similarly, Gorman and Levine (1965) proposed that reduced DPIP functions at a site between cytochrome f and system I because a *Chlamydomonas* mutant lacking cytochrome f was still capable of photoreducing NADP with ascorbate and DPIP.

Further work by Katoh and San Pietro (1967b) showed that *Euglena* chloroplasts catalyzed either photo-oxidation or photoreduction of cytochrome 552 depending upon the reaction conditions. Oxidized cytochrome 552 was not photoreduced by a system inhibited by atrazine or DCMU. However, photo-oxidation of reduced cytochrome 552 was observed in the same system, with either atrazine or DCMU, which could photoreduce NADP concurrently in a stoichiometric manner. During a steady-state NADP Hill reaction, the ratio of oxidized to reduced cytochrome 552 remained constant and corresponded to about 90% reduction regardless of the redox state of the cytochrome 552 added initially.

Heating of *Euglena* chloroplasts for 5 minutes at 40° C completely abolished the Hill reaction with ferricyanide or DPIP (Katoh and San Pietro, 1967c). However, no significant inhibition of NADP photoreduction occurred with reduced cytochrome 552, or, in the presence of cytochrome 552, with reduced DPIP or the electron donor. The addition of ascorbate alone restored the ability of the heated chloroplasts to photoreduce NADP and this ascorbate-supported NADP photoreduction was still sensitive to various poisons of the oxygen evolution system whereas the ascorbate–DPIP system was not. Katoh and San Pietro propose that the oxygen-evolving system in these heated chloroplasts could still be relatively intact but seemingly nonfunctional and unable to produce continually a reductant because the necessary removal or reduction of an oxidant by water is no longer possible. However, the oxidant could possibly react with substances more reducing than water, such as ascorbate, and thus support a continued production of reductant by facilitating removal of the oxidatant. In other words, Katoh and San Pietro suggest that ascorbate can serve in place of water as the ultimate electron donor for the oxygen-evolving system in these heated chloroplast preparations. As a result of these observations Katoh and San Pietro propose that two separate mechanisms are involved in the inhibition of the Hill reaction by heat and poisons such as DCMU and atrazine. It was suggested that heating preferentially destroys the capacity of the chloroplasts to oxidize water but still permits the oxidation of substances more reducing than water, such as ascorbate. The inhibition by the poisons, observed in the presence of ascorbate, was proposed to be due to a block in the transfer of electrons from system II to cytochrome 552.

IV. Photophosphorylation

The first report of photophosphorylation in *Euglena* was by Eversole and Wolken (1958). By utilizing digitonin extracts of chloroplasts, a light-catalyzed conversion of inorganic phosphate into labile phosphate was observed over a 1-hour period in an anaerobic system containing 6 cofactors and adenosine monophosphate. By using a glucose–hexokinase trap, 80–90% of the inorganic phosphate that disappeared was accounted for as labile phosphate. Dark controls reportedly converted only 3–4% of that found in the light. No further reports of this type of photophosphorylation have appeared in the literature. An interval of 8 years ensued until a further report of photophosphorylation in *Euglena* chloroplasts was described. Kahn (1966) reported that isolated chloroplasts were able to catalyze noncyclic photophosphorylation with ferricyanide and cyclic photophospho-rylation with pycoanine. However, the rates reported were at best only 10–20% of those obtained with spinach chloroplasts. Kahn indicated that chloroplasts isolated from either autotrophically or heterotrophically grown cells gave the same low rate of phosphorylation. Apparently, the low rates observed were due to a slow rate of electron transport and not due to uncoupling.

Chang and Kahn (1966) have recently reported the isolation of a possible coupling factor for photophosphorylation from chloroplasts. This protein from *Euglena* differs in some major aspects from that isolated from spinach by Vambutas and Racker (1966). Apparently, the *Euglena* enzyme can act as a coupling factor and a Ca^{2+}-dependent ATPase concurrently, while the spinach enzyme loses its ability to couple phosphorylation when the ATPase activity is activated by trypsin digestion. The coupling factor from *Euglena* was much more effective in restoring photophosphorylation to uncoupled spinach chloroplasts as compared to uncoupled *Euglena* chloroplasts.

V. Summary

One observation which is pertinent to the overall scheme of photosynthesis has been obtained by the studies of Olson and Smillie (1963) and Katoh and San Pietro (1967a) on *Euglena*, namely, that their results are consistent with a scheme of photosynthesis consisting of two photoreactions connected by an electron-transfer chain involving cytochrome as proposed by Hill and Bendall (1960). The recoupling of system II to system I by cytochrome 552 clearly seems to substantiate this scheme. The high solubility of cytochrome 552 found in *Euglena* as compared to that of cytochrome f in higher plants permitted these observations to be made.

One question that arises from the above studies is whether or not the chloroplasts capable of photophosphorylation (Kahn, 1966) contained any cytochrome 552. Presumably the phosphorylation obtained with the ferricyanide would require no cytochrome 552 for electron transport, but if pycoanine is reduced only by system I cytochrome 552 should be required for electron transport. Once the proper techniques are acquired to prepare *Euglena* chloroplasts that consistently show reasonable rates of photophosphorylation it should be possible to establish whether photophosphorylation occurs only in system I or system II or in both light reactions.

The inconsistency between the results of Avron and Chance (1966) and Gorman and Levine (1965) versus those of Katoh and San Pietro (1967a) as to the site of cytochrome f in the electron-transport chain might possibly be due to the different organisms employed in the respective studies. It would seem to be important to establish whether or not plastocyanin is actually present in *Euglena*. If plastocyanin is not present the results obtained by these investigations would not appear to be incompatible.

Nagai and Bloch's (1966) observation that ferredoxin is an essential component of the fatty acid desaturase system suggests another metabolic function for the reductive aspect of photosynthesis. It would seem quite feasible that the ferredoxin reduced via photosynthesis could function in the desaturase system as well as that reduced by the *in vitro* system employed by Nagai and Bloch (1966).

ACKNOWLEDGMENT

The author wishes to thank Dr. S. Katoh and Dr. A. San Pietro for permitting him to examine their manuscripts prior to publication and Dr. San Pietro for reviewing this chapter.

References

Abraham, A., and Bachhawat, B. K. (1963). *Biochim. Biophys. Acta* **70**, 1–4.

Allen, C. F., Hirayama, O., and Good, P. (1966). In "Biochemistry of Chloroplasts" (T. W. Goodwin, ed.), Vol. I, p. 195. Academic Press, New York and London.

Allen, M. B., Prette, L. R., and Murchio, J. C. (1962). *Biochim. Biophys. Acta* **60**, 539.

Avron, M., and Chance, B. (1966). In "Currents in Photosynthesis" (J. B. Thomas and J. C. Goodher, eds.), p. 455. Ad. Donker, Rotterdam, The Netherlands.

Bassham, J. A. (1964). *Ann. Rev. Plant. Physiol.* **15**, 101.

Bassham, J. A., Benson, A. A., Kay, L. D., Harris, A. Z., Wilson, A. T., and Calvin, M. (1953). *J. Am. Chem. Soc.* **76**, 1760.

Bendall, D. S., Gregory, R. P. F., and Hill, R. (1963). *Biochem. J.* **88**, 29p.

Benson, A. A., Cook, J. R., and Yagi, T. (1962). *Plant Physiol.* **37** (Suppl.), 446.

Bergeron, J. A., and Sybesma, C. (1963). *Federation Proc.* **22**, 588.

Bogorad, L. (1962). In "Physiology and Biochemistry of Algae" (R. A. Lewin, ed.), p. 385. Academic Press, New York.

Brody, S., and Brody, M. (1963). In "Photosynthetic Mechanisms of Green Plants," p. 455. Publ. 1145. Nat. Acad. Sci.—Natl. Res. Council, Washington, D. C.

Brown, J. S. (1963). *Photochem. Photobiol.* **2**, 159.

Brown, J. S., and French, C. S. (1961). *Biophys. J.*, **1**, 539.

Butler, W. L. (1961). *Arch. Biochem. Biophys.* **93**, 413.

Carter, H. E., Ohno, K., Nojima, S., Tipton, C. L., and Stanacev, N. Z. (1961). *J. Lipid Res.* **2**, 215.

Chancellor-Madison, J., and Noll, C. R. (1963). *Science* **142**, 61.

Chang, I. C., and Kahn, J. S. (1966). *Arch. Biochem. Biophys.* **117**, 282.

Davenport, H. E., and Hill, R. (1950). *Proc. Roy. Soc.* **B139**, 327.

Davies, W. H., Mercer, E. D., and Goodman, T. W. (1965). *Phytochemistry* **4**, 741.

Duysens, L. N M., and Amesz, J. (1962). *Biochim. Biophys. Acta* **64**, 243.

Emerson, R., Chalmers, R., and Cederstrand, C. N. (1957). *Proc. Natl. Acad. Sci. U.S.* **43**, 133.

Erwin, J. A., and Bloch, K. (1963). *Biochem. Z.* **338**, 496.

Erwin, J., and Bloch, K. (1964). *Science* **143**, 1006.

Eversole, R. A., and Wolken, J. J. (1958). *Science* **127**, 1287.

French, C. S. (1966). In "Biochemistry of Chloroplasts" (T. W. Goodwin, ed.), Vol I., p. 377. Academic Press, New York.

Fuller, R. C., Smillie, R. M., Rigopoulos, N., and Young, V. (1961). *Arch. Biochem. Biophys.* **95**, 197.

Gorman, D. S., and Levine, R. P. (1965). *Proc. Natl. Acad. Sci. U. S.* **54**, 1665.

Gross, J., and Wolken, J. J. (1960). *Science* **132**, 357.

Haverkate, F., and Van Deenen, L. L. M. (1965). *Koninkl. Ned. Akad. Wetenschap, Proc. Ser. B* **68**, 141.

Hill, R., and Bendall, F. (1960). *Nature* **186**, 136.

Holton, R. W., Blecker, H. H., and Onor, M. (1964). *Phytochemistry* **3**, 595.

Hulanicka, D., Erwin, J., and Bloch, K. (1964). *J. Biol. Chem.* **239**, 2778.

Kahn, J. S. (1966). *Biochem. Biophys. Res. Commun.* **24**, 329.

Katoh, S., and San Pietro, A. (1967a). *Arch. Biochem. Biophys.* **118**, 488.

Katoh, S., and San Pietro, A. (1967b). *Arch. Biochem. Biophys.* **121**, 211.

Katoh, S., and San Pietro, A. (1967c). *Arch. Biochem. Biophys.* **122**, 144.

Kok, B., and Hoch G. (1961). *In* "A Symposium on Light and Life" (W. D. McElroy and B. Glass, eds.), p. 397. Johns Hopkins Press, Baltimore, Maryland.

Korn, E. D. (1964). *Biochem. Biophys. Res. Commun.* **14**, 1.

Krinsky, N. I. (1966). *In* "Biochemistry of Chloroplasts" (T. W. Goodwin, ed.), Vol I., p. 423. Academic Press, New York.

Krinsky, N. I., Gordon, A., and Stern, A. I. (1964). *Plant Physiol.* **39**, 441.

Lazzarini, R. A., and San Pietro, A. (1963). *In* "Studies on Microalgae and Photosynthetic Bacteria," p. 453. Japan. Soc. Plant Physiologists, Univ. of Tokyo Press, Tokyo.

Leech, R. M. (1966). *In* "Biochemistry of Chloroplasts" (T. W. Goodwin, ed.), Vol. I, p. 65. Academic Press, New York.

Lynch, V. H., and Calvin, M. (1953). *Ann. N. Y. Acad. Sci.* **56**, 890.

Moses, V., Holm-Hansen, O., and Calvin, M. (1959). *J. Bacteriol.* **77**, 70.

Myers, J., and French, C. S. (1960). *J. Gen. Physiol.* **43**, 723.

Nagai, J., and Block, K. (1966). *J. Biol. Chem.* **241**, 1925.

Nichols, B. W., Harris, R. V., and James, A. T. (1965). *Biochem. Biophys. Res. Commun.* **20**, 256.

Nishimura, M. (1959). *J. Biochem.* **46**, 219.

Olson, J. M., and Smillie, R. M. (1963). *In* "Photosynthetic Mechanisms of Green Plants," p. 56. Publ. 1145. Natl. Acad. Sci.—Natl. Res. Council, Washington, D. C.

Olson, R. A. (1963). *In* "Photosynthetic Mechanisms of Green Plants," p. 545. Publ. 1145. Natl. Acad. Sci.—Natl. Res. Council, Washington, D. C.

Pedersen, T. A., Kirk, M., and Bassham, J. A. (1966). *Biochim. Biophys. Acta* **112**, 189.

Perini, F. (1963). *In* "Photosynthetic Mechanisms of Green Plants," p. 291. Publ. 1145. Natl. Acad. Sci.—Natl. Res. Council, Washington, D. C.

Perini, F., Kamen, M. D., and Schiff, J. A. (1964a). *Biochim. Biophys. Acta* **88**, 74.

Perini, F., Kamen, M. D., and Schiff, J. A. (1964b). *Biochim. Biophys. Acta* **88**, 91.

Peterkofsky, H., and Racker, E. (1961). *Plant Physiol.* **36**, 409.

Rosenberg, A. (1963). *Biochemistry* **2**, 1148.

Rosenberg, A., and Parker, M. (1964). *Biochemistry* **3**, 254.

San Pietro, A. (1963). *In* "Methods in Enzymology" (S. P. Colowick and N. O. Kaplan, eds.) Vol. 6, p. 439. Academic Press, New York.

San Pietro, A., and Black, C. C. (1965). *Ann. Rev. Plant Physiol.* **16**, 155.

Shapiro, D. M. (1961). Ph. D. Thesis, Johns Hopkins Univ. Baltimore, Maryland.

Smillie, R. M. (1963). *Can. J. Botany* **41**, 123.

Smillie, R. M., Evans, W. R., and Lyman, H. (1963). *Brookaven Symp. Biol.* **16**, 89.

Smith, J. H. C., and French, C. S. (1963). *Ann. Rev. Plant Physiol.* **14**, 181.

Tagawa, K., and Arnon, D. (1962). *Nature* **195**, 537.

Threfall, D. R., and Goodwin, T. W. (1964). *Biochem. J.* **90**, 40 p.

Vambutas, V. K., and Racker, E. (1966). *J. Biol. Chem.* **240**, 2660.

Van Deenen, L. L. M., and Haverkate, F. (1966). *In* "Biochemistry of the Chloroplasts" (T. W. Goodwin, ed.), Vol. I, p. 117. Academic Press, New York.

Vernon, L. P., and Zaugg, W. S. (1960). *J. Biol. Chem.* **235**, 2728.

Weier, T. E., and Benson, A. A. (1966). *In* "Biochemistry of Chloroplasts" (T. W. Goodwin, ed.), p. 91. Academic Press, New York.

Wolken, J. J. (1963). *In Photosynthetic Mechanisms of Green Plants,"* p. 515. Publ. 1145. Natl. Acad. Sci.—Natl. Res. Council Washington, D. C.

CHAPTER 4

HETEROTROPHIC
CO_2 FIXATION IN *EUGLENA*

B. H. Levedahl

I. Introduction

Lynch and Calvin (1953) were the first to point out that *Euglena* may be a somewhat unique organism as regards to its ability to fix carbon dioxide. They state (p. 891) "The radioactive products formed during dark CO_2 fixation in *Euglena gracilis* were strikingly different from those of any other microorganism, either photosynthetic or nonphotosynthetic, that has been investigated." They state further, "not only were the characteristic dark CO_2 fixation products (malic, citric, aspartic, and glutamic acids) formed, but many of the phosphorylated compounds typical of CO_2 fixation in the light were observed."

Unfortunately, there has been very little "follow-up" of the problems posed with nonphotosynthetic CO_2 fixation in *Euglena*.

This paper will review what *is* known about nonphotosynthetic CO_2 fixation in *Euglena*, attempt to determine how this information relates to heterotrophic* CO_2 fixation in other organisms and, finally, suggest what

---

* Defined here as growth in the presence of one or more essential metabolites with the energy provided entirely by dark chemical reactions, for example, oxidation of exogeneous organic substances. Thus, the growth of bleached *Euglena* can be described as chemo-organo-heterotrophic (Fogg, 1953).

additional information may be necessary to clarify the role and the
mechanism of heterotrophic CO_2 fixation in this flagellate.

II. Heterotrophic CO_2 Fixation

In their original studies of dark fixation of CO_2 in the green form of the
flagellate *E. gracilis* var. *bacillaris*, Lynch and Calvin reported the results
of a kinetic study of the fixation. They determined that the early appearance
of labeled phosphorylated compounds was not explainable in terms of a
"preillumination effect," but instead represented a real difference between

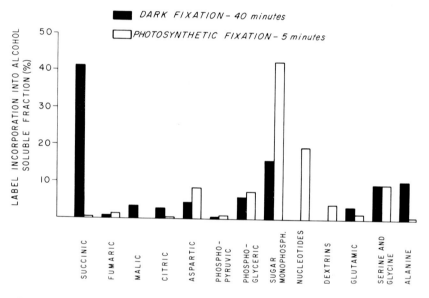

Fig. 1. A comparison of the distributions of ^{14}C from CO_2 fixation in *Euglena gracilis*
var. *bacillaris* under conditions of photosynthetic and dark fixation (data from Lynch
and Calvin, 1953). □ Dark fixation products after 40 minutes; ■ photosynthetic fixation
products after 5 minutes.

dark fixation of CO_2 in *Euglena* and in other organisms they had investigated
(Lynch and Calvin, 1953). The difference in the incorporation of CO_2 into
Euglena under light and dark conditions is shown in Fig. 1, adapted from
the data of Lynch and Calvin (1953). Although the time of incorporation
was different for the dark and light fixation (40 minutes as compared to
5 minutes) and the results therefore are not quantitatively comparable,
they do show two major qualitative differences.

First, under conditions of photosynthetic fixation a large percentage of alcohol soluble activity appears in sugar monophosphates, nucleotides, and dextrins; and second, a much greater percentage of soluble activity appears in succinate, malate, citrate, glutamate, and alanine under conditions of dark fixation. The data presented did not eliminate the possibility that the dark fixation of CO$_2$ into phosphorylated sugars occurred in *Euglena* through the same pathways defined for the photosynthetic fixation. The presence of lipids was not reported under any of the experimental conditions for dark-adapted organisms. The implication then was that CO$_2$ could enter the phosphorylated compounds by incorporation directly into phosphoglyceric acid with the energy source being provided by respiration or fermentation. The enzyme necessary for this reaction has been identified in numerous nonphotosynthetic organisms (Fuller, 1957) and in *E. gracilis* strain Z (Peterofsky and Racker, 1961; Smillie, 1963; Hudock and Fuller, 1965).

However, Moses *et al.* (1959), after comparing the nonphotosynthetic CO$_2$ incorporation into *Chlorella pyrenoidosa*, *Nostoc muscorum*, and *Zygorrhynchus moelleri*, suggested that the incorporation of ^{14}C during dark fixation into the sugars of *Euglena* might better be explained by the reaction through phosphogluconic acid rather than through carboxylation of ribulose diphosphate to form phosphoglyceric acid.

The characteristics of the patterns of incorporation of ^{14}CO$_2$ in *Z. moelleri* and *E. gracilis* suggested that in these two forms, the label that appeared in the phosphorylated sugars did not arise by the reversal of glycolysis as had been proposed for the algae investigated (Moses *et al.*, 1959). In *Z. meolleri*, label appeared within 4 seconds in phosphogluconic acid and later in hexose monophosphates without appearing in diphosphate sugars. In *Euglena* (Lynch and Calvin, 1953), ^{14}C from ^{14}CO$_2$ entered the hexose monophosphates early and no activity was observed in the sugar diphosphate in periods up to 40 minutes.

Because their organisms were grown in the presence of both light and acetate, Lynch and Calvin (1953) also carried out preliminary investigations of acetate-2-^{14}C incorporation into *Euglena*. Acetate-2-^{14}C was incorporated principally into lipid (47% soluble activity) in the presence of light, and to a lesser extent into lipid in the dark (18%). Figure 2 shows a comparison of these results with those of Cook (1965) who studied acetate incorporation into *E. gracilis* strain Z, and Levedahl (1966) who used a streptomycin-bleached strain (SML-1) of *E. gracilis* var. *bacillaris*.

It is apparent from the data that incorporation of acetate into lipids is increased under the influence of light in the photosynthetic organism. The presence of CO$_2$ fixed heterotrophically in the bleached organism (Levedahl, 1966) does not influence the incorporation of acetate in a similar manner. It would appear that either CO_2 fixation in the green form is not related to acetate conversion to lipid, or else the method of fixation is different in the bleached form. This light-enhanced reaction of acetate conversion to lipid is not unique for *Euglena*, but has also been observed in *Scenedesmus* (a green algae) (Calvin *et al.*, 1951), *Rhodospirillum rubrum* (a purple bacteria) (Glover *et al.*, 1952) and *Chlamydomonas mundana* (Eppley *et al.*, 1963). There do not seem to be comparable studies of the influence of CO_2 on acetate incorporation under nonphotosynthetic conditions in other forms.

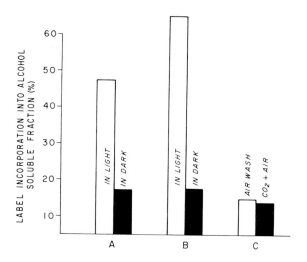

Fig. 2. Acetate incorporation into lipids of *Euglena*. A, Results from Lynch and Calvin (1953) using *E. gracilis* var. *bacillaris* (green form); B, results from Cook (1965) using *E. gracilis* strain Z; C, results from Levedahl (1966) *E. gracilis* var. *bacillaris* (streptomycin-bleached).

If one accepts the explanation (Moses *et al.*, 1959) of $^{14}CO_2$ incorporation into the phosphorylated sugars of *Euglena*, there still remains the problem of the mechanism of entrance of this $^{14}CO_2$ into the compounds of the Krebs cycle and related acids. The suggestion (Moses *et al.*, 1959) that the principal carboxylation was of pyruvic acid provides only one possible alternative for the explanation of the results. A number of carboxylation reactions could yield the observed results, and in *Euglena* the mechanism has not yet been completely identified. There are, however, some interesting speculative considerations.

Since the original description by Wood and Werkman (1936), fixation of CO_2 has been shown to result in the formation of C_4 dicarboxylic acids by different enzyme systems (Flavin and Ochoa, 1957; Ochoa *et al.*, 1947;

Utter and Kurahashi, 1954; Bandurski and Greiner, 1953; Sui and Wood, 1962).

These possible routes of entry of CO_2 can be described as follows:

$$\text{Propionyl–CoA} + CO_2 + \text{ATP} \xrightarrow{\text{Propionyl-CoA carboxylase}} \text{methylmalonyl–CoA} + \text{ADP} + P_i \quad (1)$$

$$(\text{Methylmalonyl–CoA} \underset{\text{Isomerase}}{\rightleftharpoons} \text{succinyl–CoA} \longrightarrow \text{succinate})$$

$$\text{Pyruvate} + CO_2 + \text{TPHH} \xrightarrow{\text{Malic enzyme}} \text{L–malate} + \text{TPH}^+ \quad (2)$$

$$\text{Phosphoenolpyruvate} + CO_2 + \text{GDP} \xrightarrow{\text{PEP carboxykinase}} \text{oxalacetate} + \text{GTP} \quad (3)$$

$$\text{Phosphoenolpyruvate} + CO_2 + H_2O \xrightarrow{\text{Phosphopyruvate carboxylase}} \text{oxalacetate} + P_i \quad (4)$$

$$\text{Phosphoenolypyruvate} + CO_2 + P_i \xrightarrow[\text{carboxytransphosphorylase}]{\text{Phosphenolpyruvic}} \text{oxalacetate} + P_iP_i \quad (5)$$

The only necessary enzyme from the above reactions that has been identified in *Euglena* is the malic enzyme in strain Z (Smillie, 1963). Care should be taken, however, not to assume (no matter how tempting) simply because the enzyme is present that it plays an important role, or indeed any role, in the heterotrophic CO_2 fixation in the organism.

The malic enzyme and its characteristics have been rather extensively investigated. Some of these characteristics may be of importance in considering whether or not this enzyme is important in the CO_2 fixation reactions in *Euglena*.

Ochoa (1951) reported that with pigeon liver enzyme, the production of malate from pyruvate can be accelerated by increasing the concentration of CO_2. Walker (1960) has reported similar results with malic enzyme from *Kalanchoë crenata* If malic enzyme from *Euglena* were to behave similarly, one would expect that *Euglena* grown with pyruvate as the sole carbon source should respond to increased concentrations of CO_2. We have examined this possibility in our laboratory and the data are given in Table I. The results show that neither the rate of growth nor the peak populations reached are different when pyruvate is the carbon source and CO_2-enriched air is bubbled through the growing culture.

Utter (1959) has reported that in fractionation studies using chicken liver, malic enzyme is almost completely localized in the supernatant fraction while PEP carboxykinase is found mainly in the mitochondrial fraction. In bleached *Euglena* it has been shown (Levedahl, 1966) that under conditions that would pellet the mitochondria of *Euglena* homogenate, both pellet and supernatant are needed to fix CO_2, and that supernatant alone is not effective.

Table I

EFFECT OF CO_2-ENRICHED AIR ON GROWTH OF *Euglena* ON
DIFFERENT CARBON SOURCES

	Pyruvate (10 mM)			Propionate (10 mM)		
	Air	5% CO_2	10% CO_2	Air	5% CO_2	10% CO_2
Generation time (hours)	17	18	17	26	26	27
Peak population ($\times 10^{-3}$)	260	250	260	270	250	260
Final pH	7.80	7.90	7.85	7.65	7.60	7.50

[a] Organisms were grown on the medium of Cramer and Myers (1952) at 25°C, pH 6.8 for at least three transfers using the appropriate carbon compounds as the sole carbon source for growth. Growth studies were then performed as described by Tremmel and Levedahl (1966) using gas flush rates of 0.5 liters per hour per flask.

If CO_2 were fixed in *Euglena* primarily by propionyl-CoA carboxylase, one would expect that the growth characteristics of *Euglena* adapted for growth on propionate would be affected by additional CO_2 especially since acetate thiokinase has been shown to be present in *Euglena* (Abraham and Bachhawat, 1962). Again, the results given in Table I show this not to be the case, at least with gas washes with as much as 10% CO_2–90% air.

The remaining enzymes possibly involved in CO_2 fixation (PEP carboxykinase, phosphopyruvate carboxylase, and PEP carboxytransphosphorylase) have not to date been reported in *Euglena*. However, if one assumes the presence of one (or all) of these enzymes their presence could be used to help to interpret the effects of CO_2 on succinate metabolism (Levedahl, 1967) in *Euglena*.

When succinate-2-3-^{14}C is metabolized by *Euglena*, approximately 47% of the succinate carbon appears in lipids within 15 minutes if air is bubbled through the incubation mixture. However, if 5% CO_2–95% air is used as the wash, the carbons of succinate are distributed in a very different manner. In general, the presence of CO_2 results in the carbons of succinate being distributed into those compounds observed to fix ^{14}C from CO_2. Table II shows the results adapted from Levedahl (1967). If acetate is the sole carbon source for *Euglena*, the presence of CO_2-enriched air does not influence the acetate-2-^{14}C distribution during the first hour of incubation (Levedahl, 1967).

The effects of CO_2 on the succinate metabolism of *Euglena* may, of course, result from its influence on many separate reactions within the organism and no explanation can be more than a guess at this point. If one were to assume, however, that CO_2 is fixed principally through some pathway

Table II

SUCCINATE-2-^{14}C INCORPORATION INTO *E. gracilis* IN THE PRESENCE OF AIR OR 5% CO$_2$–95% AIR

Compound	5 Minutes		15 Minutes		30 Minutes		60 Minutes		120 Minutes		240 Minutes	
	Air	CO$_2$	Air	CO$_2$	Air	CO$_2$	Air	CO$_2$	Air	CO$_2$	Air	CO$_2$
Citric	1.3	0.8	0.8	—	0.6	1.4	0.3	1.3	0.1	1.8	0.2	1.7
Fumaric	—	0.8	0.3	0.5	0.1	0.8	—	0.9	—	0.1	—	0.4
Malic	0.9	7.5	1.0	6.6	0.5	5.5	0.3	4.0	0.1	3.0	0.2	3.7
Succinic	49.7	41.3	20.1	17.0	14.1	25.0	10.8	15.9	2.1	4.8	2.8	5.6
Alanine	—	7.7	1.5	6.2	0.7	6.7	0.4	7.1	0.6	6.3	0.5	5.8
Aspartic	1.0	1.3	—	1.2	—	0.3	—	0.8	—	0.3	—	0.6
Glutamic	13.3	19.3	5.2	29.2	6.2	19.3	5.4	18.8	0.3	24.5	2.2	21.6
Leucine–isoleucine	—	—	—	1.0	—	—	—	—	—	—	—	—
Threonine	4.7	1.3	3.4	7.0	5.1	9.0	1.8	14.2	4.5	3.3	0.6	1.6
Valine	—	—	2.1	0.1	0.3	4.0	0.9	3.7	—	1.9	—	—
Dissacharides	0.9	—	3.5	2.2	1.6	2.6	2.0	4.2	2.1	5.1	0.8	6.1
Nucleotides	—	2.4	1.2	3.6	2.8	5.3	4.3	5.8	2.5	8.7	3.0	14.4
Lipids	14.0	—	47.5	—	54.4	—	67.4	4.6	82.8	10.6	84.6	8.7
Monophosphates	10.3	15.0	8.0	17.4	8.5	16.7	4.2	15.8	2.3	25.3	3.3	26.7
Unidentified	1.5	—	3.2	2.5	2.0	0.2	0.4	0.2	0.7	0.9	0.7	0.9

[a] Values are in percentage of total incorporation in alcohol extraction.
[b] Data adapted from Levedahl (1967).

Table III

CO$_2$ FIXATION IN DIFFERENT ORGANISMS[a,b]

Organism	Citric	Fumaric	Malic	Succinate	Latic	Alanine	Aspartic	Glutamic	Leucine-isoleucine	Threonine	Valine	Serine-glycine	Phospho-pyruvic	Alanine
E. gracilis var. bacillaris[e] green	2.7	0.8	3.4	41.2	—	10.5	4.6	3.4	—	—	—	9.6	0.3	—
E. gracilis var. bacillaris (streptomycin-bleached)[d]	1.8	1.6	13.0	4.3	—	12.4	3.1	4.8	1.2	11.3	1.8	—	—	—
Rhodopseudomonas capsulatus	2.1	—	1.8	—	—	2.3	5.6	34.5	—	2.6	—	8.6	—	—
Chlorella pyrenoidosa	1.6	3.0	15.7	1.7	—	2.0	26.9	35.2	—	—	—	1.1	—	—
Nostoc muscorum	2.5	—	0.3	—	—	2.3	40.5	24.8	—	2.6	—	—	—	—
Zygorrhynchus moelleri	6.1	4.0	46.1	—	—	0.52	4.1	13.8	—	0.36	0.3	0.85	—	—
Scenedesmus D$_3$	14.0	0.4	7.0	0.7	—	—	34.0	44.0	—	—	—	—	—	—
Synechococcus cedorum	—	2.0	16.00	18.0	18.0	12.0	—	15.0	36.0	—	—	—	—	—
Hansenula anomala	4.0	—	6.0	26.0	—	5.0	25.0	25.0	—	—	—	—	—	—
Tetrahymena gelei	—	1.0	8.0	63.0	2.0	2.0	4.0	13.0	—	—	—	—	—	—
Allomyces arbuscula	2.0	2.0	6.0	4.0	—	0.4	22.0	13.0	—	—	—	2.0	—	—
Blastocladia pringsheimii	1.0	5.0	15.0	5.0	2.0	4.0	32.0	28.0	—	—	—	2.0	—	—
Azotobacter agile	3.0	—	1.0	—	18.0	—	1.0	8.0	—	—	—	—	—	—
Butyribacterium rettgeri	2.0	—	23.0	—	—	—	5.0	6.0	—	—	—	—	—	22.0
Clostridium kluyveri	—	—	1.0	—	—	78.0	5.0	2.0	—	—	—	—	—	—
Physarum polycephalum	—	7.0	24.0	—	—	—	20.0	13.0	—	—	—	—	—	—
Tobacco leaves	10.7	5.3	1.1	59.8	4.5	—	13.5	8.0	—	—	—	—	0.6	—
Entobdella bumpusi[f]	—	4.3	9.0	54.9	18.1	—	—	—	1.5	—	—	—	—	—
Fucus vesiculosus craigie	—	21.6	—	2.9	3.2	—	4.2	15.9	30.8	—	—	—	—	—
Polysiphonia lanosa	—	—	—	—	—	—	3.1	64.4	18.4	—	—	—	—	—
Prototheca coptii cirferri	—	30.0	8.0	25.0	8.0	—	—	29.0	—	—	—	—	—	—
Chlamydomonas mundara	—	0.3	—	0.5	—	—	0.8	1.1	3.6	—	—	—	—	—
Barley seedlings leaves	—	6.0	—	31.0	—	—	2.2	28.0	17.0	—	—	—	4.7	—

Organism	Tyrosine	α-Keto-glutarate	Methionine sulfoxide	Phosphoglyceric	Phos-phoenol-pyruvic	Disaccharides	Nucleotides	Lipids	Mono-phosphate	Poly-saccharides	Glutamine	Citralline	Proline	Asparagine	Ref.
E. gracilis var. *bacillaris* green	—	—	—	—	—	2.5	5.6	17.3	16.0	—	—	—	—	—	1
E. gracilis var. *bacillaris* (streptomycin-bleached)[d]	0.6	—	—	—	—	—	—	—	15.6	—	—	—	—	—	2
Rhodopseudomonas capsulatus	—	0.8	2.6	8.4	0.8	—	—	—	19.6[e]	—	3.2	—	—	—	3
Chlorella pyrenoidosa	—	—	—	0.47	0.2	—	—	—	1.2	—	—	—	—	—	4
Nostoc muscorum	—	—	—	1.1	—	—	—	—	5.0	—	1.7	7.0	—	—	4
Zygorrhynchus moelleri	0.05	—	—	0.05	—	1.1	—	—	0.59	—	4.4	1.2	1.1	—	4
Scenedesmus D$_3$	—	—	—	—	—	—	—	—	—	—	—	—	—	—	5
Synechococcus cedorum	—	—	—	—	—	—	—	—	—	—	—	—	—	—	5
Hansenula anomala	—	—	—	—	—	—	—	—	—	—	—	—	—	—	5
Tetrahymena gelei	—	—	—	—	—	—	—	—	—	24.0	2.0	—	—	2.0	5
Allomyces arbuscula	—	—	—	—	—	—	—	—	—	6.0	2.0	—	—	1.0	5
Blastocladia pringsheimii	—	—	—	—	—	—	—	—	—	54.0	—	—	—	—	5
Azotobacter agile	15.0	—	—	—	—	—	—	—	—	—	—	—	—	—	5
Butyribacterium rettgeri	—	—	—	—	—	—	—	—	—	—	—	—	—	—	5
Clostridium kluyveri	—	—	—	—	—	—	—	—	—	—	—	—	—	2.0	5
Physarum polycephalum	—	—	—	—	—	—	—	—	—	—	1.3	—	—	—	6
Tobacco leaves	—	—	—	—	—	—	—	—	—	—	—	—	—	—	7
Entobdella bumpusi[f]	—	0.9	—	—	—	—	—	—	—	—	—	—	—	—	8
Fucus vesiculosus craigie	—	—	—	—	—	—	—	—	—	—	13.3	—	—	—	8
Polysiphonia lanosa	—	—	—	—	—	—	—	—	—	10.6[g]	3.5	—	—	—	9
Prototheca coptii citferri	—	—	—	—	—	—	—	—	—	4.1	0.1	—	0.8	—	10
Chlamydomonas mundara	—	—	—	0.4	—	38.8[h]	—	—	10.1	2.9[g]	8.2	—	—	—	10
Barley seedlings leaves	—	—	—	—	—	—	—	—	—	—	—	—	—	—	11

[a] Results are given in total incorporation from extraction procedures used by each author. Only dark or heterotrophic fixation is included. Results were obtained from the following sources:

[b] Key to references: *1*, Lynch and Calvin (1953); *2*, Levedahl (1967); *3*, Stoppani *et al.* (1955); *4*, Moses *et al.* (1959); *5*, Lynch and Calvin (1952); *6*, Kunitake *et al.* (1959); *7*, Hammen and Lum (1962); *8*, Craigie (1963); *9*, Ciferri and Sala (1962); *10*, Eppley *et al.* (1963); *11*, Benson and Calvin (1950).

[c] Forty-minute incorporation.

[d] Thirty-minute incorporation.

[e] Includes both mono and diphosphates.

[f] Acids only reported.

[g] Reported as phosphate esters.

[h] Reported as free sugars.

involving phosphoenolpyruvate that leads fairly directly to the formation of additional succinate, this might be enough to unbalance the Krebs cycle and account for the observed results.

One question arising from the work reported on dark or heterotrophic fixation of CO_2 by *Euglena* is whether the fixation in *Euglena* is something different than that observed in other organisms, or whether the fixation in *Euglena* is representative of a general pattern observed in numerous different cell types. This is a difficult point to clarify. At first glance there appears to be as many experimental conditions as there are investigators in the area of heterotrophic CO_2 fixation. Incubation times, separation methods, analytical methods, temperatures, pH, levels of $^{14}CO_2$ concentration, and presence or absence of additional carbon sources are only a few of the variables one encounters. Despite this, however, if results from a number of organisms are tabulated, any obvious similarities in fixation patterns should be forthcoming. The results of such a tabulation are given in Table III. Times of incubation have been chosen as close to the same as possible from the different literature cited and are generally in the range of 30–60 minutes. When photosynthetic organisms were used, only the results of dark fixation are listed. This listing of organisms is not intended to be exhaustive. Rather it is representative of the wide number of forms that have been studied and is limited by the method of reporting results chosen by the different authors. The effort has been made to obtain data on enough forms, however, so that the results tabulated give a cross section of the CO_2 fixation studies in the literature.

Examination of the data presented in Table III does make it appear that *Euglena* may be somewhat unique in the pattern of dark or heterotrophic CO_2 fixation. Only a few of the forms reported (an alga, *N. muscorum*, and a fungus, *Z. moelleri*) appear to have markedly similar patterns (Moses *et al.*, 1959). The pattern appears to require two direct routes of CO_2 incorporation into *Euglena*. The first would be the reaction via phosphogluconic acid (Moses *et al.*, 1959), while the second would be incorporation into oxalacetate probably through phosphoenolpyruvate.

A few words should be said about the difference between metabolism in the dark by green *Euglena* and metabolism of the streptomycin-bleached form of the same species. The first two columns of Table III show a comparison of the results of Lynch and Calvin (1953) and those of Levedahl (1967). Among the marked differences observed between the dark fixation of CO_2 in the green form and the permanently bleached form are the reduced fraction of incorporation into succinate and the increased fraction of incorporation into malate in the bleached form. Additionally, the bleached form labels threonine (11% of the soluble activity) but not glycine or serine, and significant incorporation of ^{14}C appears in both nucleotide and lipid fractions. The significance of these differences has not been assessed to date, but is is fair to assume that they represent differences in metabolism resulting from the permanent bleaching of *Euglena* with streptomycin.

Similar differences in the two forms are seen in the incorporation of labeled acetate. Table IV contains the data to permit comparison of the

Table IV

Acetate-2-^{14}C INCORPORATION IN *Euglena*[a,b]

Compound	Dark incorporation (12 minutes)	Bleached (15 minutes)
Citric	—	1.1
Fumaric	—	0.7
Malic	—	6.0
Succinic	—	1.5
Alanine	5.5	1.0
Aspartic	5.2	0.8
Glutamic	7.8	21.9
Glutamine	5.8	4.2
Leucine–isoleucine	—	3.8
Threonine	—	9.9
Dissacharides	—	5.0
Nucleotides	—	3.6
Lipids	17.3	14.0
Monophosphates	49.3	15.2
Dextrins	3.7	0
	94.6	88.7

[a] Percent of total incorporated in alcohol-soluble fraction.
[b] Data adapted from Lynch and Calvin (1953) and Levedahl (1966).

results of Lynch and Calvin (1953) and Levedahl (1967) on this point. The bleached form apparently sacrifices monophosphate compounds to form dissacharides, nucleotides, Krebs-cycle acids and different amino acids.

III. Conclusions

Data available to date show that *Euglena* is a unique organism for use in the study of heterotrophic CO_2 fixation. Two primary fixation routes are well established, but many details still remain to be worked out on the exact reactions that are involved. Once these details are known, there remains the question of other roles that CO_2 plays in the metabolism of the organism. It is clear that the presence of CO_2 modifies the metabolism of different carbon sources in different ways in *Euglena*, and only a few carbon sources have been studied. *Euglena* should be a valuable tool for further investigations of control mechanisms involving CO_2.

References

Abraham, A., and Bachhawat, B. K. (1962). *Biochim. Biophys. Acta* **62**, 376.
Bandurski, R. S., and Greiner, C. M. (1953). *J. Biol. Chem.* **204**, 781.
Benson, A. A., and Calvin, M. (1950) *J. Exptl. Botany* **1**, 63.
Calvin, M., Bassham, J. A., Benson, A. A., Lynch, V., Ouellet, C., Schou, L., Stepka, W., and Tolbert, N. E. (1951). *Symp. Soc. Exptl. Biol.* **5**.
Ciferri, O., and Sala, F. (1962). *Enzymologia* **24**, 298.
Cook, J. R. (1965). *Plant Cell Physiol.* (*Tokyo*) **6**, 301.
Craigie, J. S. (1963). *Can. J. Botany* **41**, 317.
Cramer, M., and Myers, J. (1952). *Arch. Mikrobiol.* **17**, 384.
Eppley, R. W., Gee, R., and Saltman, P. (1963). *Physiol. Plantarum* **16**, 777.
Flavin, M., and Ochoa, S. (1957). *J. Biol. Chem.* **229**, 965.
Fogg, G. E. (1953). "*The Metabolism of Algae,*" *Methuen*, London.
Fuller, R. C. (1957). *Brookhaven Natl. Lab. Rept.* **BNL-3415**.
Glover, J., Kamen, M. D., and Van Genderen, H. (1952). *Arch. Biochem Biophys.* **35**, 384.
Hammen, C. S., and Lum, S. C. (1962). *J. Biol. Chem.* **237**, 2419.
Hudock, G. A., and Fuller, R. C. (1965) *Plant Physiol.* **40**, 1205.
Kunitake, G., Stitt, C., and Saltman, P. (1959). *Plant Physiol.* **34**, 123.
Levedahl, B. H. (1966). *Exptl. Cell Res.* **44**, 393.
Levedahl, B. H. (1967). *Exptl. Cell Res.* **48**, 125.
Lynch, V. H., and Calvin, M. (1952). *J. Bacteriol.* **63**, 525.
Lynch, V., and Calvin, M. (1953). *Ann. N. Y. Acad. Sci.* **56**, 890.
Moses, V., Holm-Hansen, O., and Calvin, M. (1959). *J. Bacteriol.* **77**, 70.
Ochoa, S. (1951) *In* "The Enzymes" (J. B. Sumner and K. Myrback, eds.), Vol. II, p. 929. Academic Press, New York.
Ochoa, S., Mehler, A., and Kornberg, A. (1947). *J. Biol. Chem.* **167**, 871.
Peterkofsky, A., and Racker, E. (1961). *Plant Physiol.* **36**, 409.
Smillie, R. C. (1963). *Can. J. Botany* **41**, 123.
Stoppani, A. O. M., Fuller, R. C., and Calvin, M. (1955). *J. Bacteriol.* **69**, 491.
Sui, P. M. L., and Wood, H. G. (1962). *J. Biol. Chem.* **237**, 3044.
Tremmel, R. D., and Levedahl, B. H. (1966). *J. Cell. Physiol.* **67**, 361.
Utter, M. F. (1959). *Ann. N. Y. Acad. Sci.* **72**, 451.
Utter, M. F., and Kurahashi, K. (1954). *J. Biol. Chem.* **207**, 787.
Walker, D. A. (1960). *Biochem. J.* **74**, 216.
Wood, H. G., and Werkman, C. H. (1936). *Biochem. J.* **30**, 48.

CHAPTER 5

NUCLEIC ACIDS

George Brawerman

I. Introduction

Euglena gracilis provides a useful experimental system for the study of nucleic acid function and specificity. The cells can be grown easily, and the cultures can be subjected to a variety of physiological alterations. Numerous studies have been performed on the changes in nucleic acid content under different culture conditions. Many of the nucleic acid components of *E. gracilis* have been characterized. The failure so far to isolate intact nuclei, however, has prevented the study of the nuclear RNA. The problem of the metabolic behavior of the various nucleic acid components has remained largely untouched, primarily because of the difficulties involved in incorporating labeled precursors into the cells. Such metabolic studies should prove of great interest for the understanding of nucleic acid function.

The chloroplast system of *E. gracilis* is of particular importance for the study of nucleic acid specificity. The plastids comprise nearly one-half the total protein complement of the green cells. They have been shown to contain both DNA and RNA, and to possess a protein-synthesizing system of their own. Chloroplast development can be readily controlled in *E. gracilis*, and the replication of these organelles can be arrested by a variety of agents which leave cell multiplication largely unaffected. This provides the possibility for the study of specific components concerned with the synthesis and replication of a well-defined cell structure.

II. Nucleic Acid Content of *E. Gracilis*

A. Variations of RNA Content with Conditions of Growth

1. Amount of RNA in Cells

Most of the reported values for the RNA content of *Euglena* range between 20 and 40 μg per 10^6 cells. This is quite close to the amount of RNA in mammalian tissues (Brawerman and Shapiro, 1962). Rat liver, for instance, contains about 50 μg RNA per 10^6 cells. Aside from the variations due to the physiological state of the cells, differences in the procedures used in various laboratories for the estimation of nucleic acids must contribute substantially to the diversity of the reported values. The optimal conditions for the quantitative estimation of nucleic acids in *Euglena* have been critically evaluated by De Torres and Pogo (1965), and the values reported from their laboratory are probably most reliable.

As in many other organisms, the RNA content of *Euglena* cells can vary quite considerably with the conditions of growth. The data for stationary-phase cells grown on complex medium are listed in Table I. Cells grown

Table I

NUCLEIC ACID AND PROTEIN CONTENT OF *E. gracilis* IN THE
STATIONARY PHASE OF GROWTH IN COMPLEX MEDIUM[a]

Strain	DNA	RNA	Protein	Reference[b]
Green cells				
var. *bacillaris*	2.5	88	—	*1*
Strain Z	2.4	17	—	*2*
Strain Z	3.3	28	300	*3*
Strain Z	3.0	38	—	*4*
Dark-grown cells				
Strain Z	3.0	20	210	*3*
Strain Z	3.2	31	320	*5*

[a] Values expressed as micrograms per 10^6 cells.
[b] Key to references: *1*, Neff (1960); *2*, Smillie and Krotkov (1960); *3*, Brawerman *et al.* (1962a); *4*, De Torres and Pogo (1965); *5*, Pogo *et al.* (1966).

in the dark, which lack mature chloroplasts, have less RNA and protein than cells grown in the light. The excess protein in green cells has been shown to be associated with chloroplasts (Brawerman *et al.*, 1962a). The occurrence of chloroplast RNA, however, could only account in part for the excess RNA of the green cells. The latter also appear to have more RNA in the microsomal fraction. The large amount of RNA listed for *E. gracilis* var. *bacillaris* in Table I could represent a strain difference. It should be noted, however, that other investigators have reported a value for the RNA content of this strain similar to that of *E. gracilis* strain Z (see Table II).

Table II

VARIATIONS OF NUCLEIC ACID AND PROTEIN CONTENT WITH CONDITIONS OF GROWTH[a]

Type of cells	Conditions of growth	DNA	RNA	Protein	Reference[b]
var. *bacillaris*, bleached	Log	4.4	30	—	*1*
	Stationary	4.2	22–27	—	*1*
var. *bacillaris*, bleached	Log	4.4	30	—	*2*
	Starved of acetate	3.1	15	—	*2*
Strain Z, green	Log	—	50	—	*3*
	Stationary	3.0	38	—	*3*
Strain Z, colorless	Complex med., log	3.1	36	340	*4*
	Complex med., stationary	3.2	31	320	*4*
	Defined med., log	3.6	40	280	*4*
	Defined med., stationary	3.8	19	220	*4*

[a] Values expressed as micrograms per 10^6 cells.
[b] Key to references: *1*, Buetow and Levedahl (1962); *2*, Blum and Buetow (1963); *3*, De Torres and Pogo (1965); *4*, Pogo *et al.* (1966).

2. Variations during Growth Cycle

Euglena cells from cultures in different phases of the growth cycle show substantial changes in the RNA content. Log-phase cells have about 20–100% more RNA than the stationary-phase organisms (Table II). The nature of the growth medium appears to have a marked influence on the RNA content of cells at different stages of the growth cycle. Pogo et al. (1966) have reported that cells grown on complex medium show relatively little change in the content of RNA and protein. In a chemically defined medium, on the other hand, the stationary-phase cells show a considerable drop in the amount of RNA and protein. An understanding of the physiological basis for the variations in the RNA content will undoubtedly require some knowledge of the factors that become limiting in stationary-phase cultures. In chemically defined media, for instance, high cell densities are usually reached (Pogo et al., 1966), and oxygen could then become limiting. In the experience of this writer, cells with a limited supply of oxygen tend to have a reduced RNA content. Cells from cultures in which acetate has become limiting have also been shown to have a sharply reduced RNA content (Table II).

3. Relation of RNA Content to Rate of Growth

The rate of growth of E. gracilis can be controlled by limiting the intensity of the light supplied to autotrophic cultures (Cook, 1963). Cells from log-phase cultures with different growth rates have been studied with respect to a variety of biochemical parameters. As in many other microorganisms, the amount of RNA per cell was found to increase markedly with the rate of growth (Table III). The protein content, on the other hand, appeared to be essentially unaffected by the growth rate.

Table III

RELATION OF NUCLEIC ACID CONTENT OF E. gracilis TO RATE OF GROWTH[a]

Generation time (hours)	Rate of protein synthesis ($\times 10^{-6}$ μg/cell/hour)	DNA	RNA	Protein
29	4.2	3.35	18	178
20	8.1	3.7	29	234
14	12.0	4.1	39	242
11	15.7	4.5	43	246

[a] Cells (strain Z) grown autotrophically under limiting light intensities. Measurements made on log-phase cells. Data from Cook (1963).

4. RNA Content of Cells from Synchronized Cultures

Perhaps the most meaningful data on the nucleic acid and protein content of *Euglena* have been obtained with the use of synchronized cells. Samples from random cultures represent cells at various stages of the division cycle, and under different culture conditions the proportion of cells in the various stages may well vary. Cultures of *E. gracilis* in an inorganic medium were synchronized by alternating periods of darkness and light (Cook, 1961). The levels of RNA and protein immediately after cell division are shown in Table IV. As expected, the values are lower than those from non-synchronized cultures (compare with Tables I, II, and III). *Astasia longa*, an aplastidic counterpart of *Euglena*, has been synchronized by alternating periods of low and high temperatures (Blum and Padilla, 1962). The amounts of RNA and protein after cell division appear to be somewhat higher than in *E. gracilis* (Table IV), in spite of the fact that they lack the RNA and protein associated with the chloroplasts.

Table IV

NUCLEIC ACID AND PROTEIN CONTENT OF CELLS FROM SYNCHRONOUS CULTURES[a]

Type of cells	Growth medium	DNA	RNA	Protein	Reference[b]
E. gracilis Z	Salts, CO_2, light	2.3	23	200	*1*
E. gracilis Z	Salts, CO_2, light	2.2–2.3	—	—	*2*
Astasia longa	Defined	2.7	32	240	*3*

[a] Values expressed as micrograms per 10^6 cells, for cells immediately after division.
[b] Key to references: *1*, Cook (1961); *2*, Edmunds (1964); *3*, Blum and Padilla (1962).

B. ALTERATIONS OF DNA CONTENT

1. Amount of DNA in Euglena

In contrast to the wide variations of the RNA content, the data on the amount of DNA in *Euglena* cells show a relative uniformity. Most values are in the range of 3.0–3.3 μg per 10^6 cells. This is about one-half the value for the DNA content of mammalian cells (Brawerman and Shapiro, 1962). No significant differences are evident between cells grown in the light and in the dark (Tables I and II). Cells grown in a chemically defined medium show a tendency to a somewhat increased DNA content (Table II). Cells with higher rates of growth appear to have a somewhat higher DNA content (Table III) but it is not certain whether or not these differences are significant (Cook, 1963).

2. DNA in Synchronized Cells

Synchronized *Euglena* cells, immediately after division, show as expected a DNA content lower than that found in cells from random cultures (Table IV). The timing of DNA replication has been studied in cells subjected to alternating periods of 14 hours of light and 10 hours of darkness. The level of DNA remained constant during the first 8 hours of the light period, then doubled during the following 6 hours. In the dark period, the level of DNA remained constant while the cells were dividing (Edmunds, 1964).

3. DNA Content of Bleached Cells

Euglena gracilis appears to be susceptible to permanent alterations of its DNA content. In several instances, bleached strains obtained by growth at 34° C have been found to contain more DNA than the normal cells from which they were derived (Table V). The data reported by Neff (1960) for two different bleached strains show an increase of approximately 50%. The DNA content of *A. longa*, an aplastidic counterpart of *Euglena*, was compared to that of the bleached *Euglena* strains. The value reported by Neff (1960) for *A. longa* is considerably lower than that of *E. gracilis* (Table V). Blum and Padilla (1962), however, have found an amount of DNA in this organism somewhat higher than that of *Euglena* (Table IV).

Table V

Nucleic Acid and Protein Content of Strains Bleached by Growth at 34°C

Strain	Type of cells	DNA	RNA	Protein	Reference[b]
E. gracilis T	Green	2.7	68	—	*1*
	Bleached	4.3	53	—	*1*
Astasia longa	—	1.5	12	—	*1*
E. gracilis Z	Normal, dark-grown	3.1	20	210	*2*
	Bleached I	3.8	23	220	*2*
	Bleached II	6.9	28	330	*2*

[a] Cells from stationary-phase cultures in complex media. Values as $\mu g/10^6$ cells.
[b] Key to references: *1*, Neff (1960); *2*, Brawerman *et al.* (1960).

Brawerman *et al.* (1960) have obtained a bleached strain of *E. gracilis*, also by growth at 34° C, with twice as much DNA as the normal parent strain (Table V). The RNA and protein content of the bleached cells was also increased substantially. It was shown, however, that the increase in DNA is not an obligatory consequence of bleaching. Various bleached cell lines, obtained either by growth at 34° C or in the presence of streptomycin, showed the normal DNA content (Brawerman et al., 1960). It is possible that the increases in DNA did not occur during the bleaching process itself, but took place during subsequent subculturing.

III. The Deoxyribonucleic Acid of E. gracilis

A. PROCEDURES FOR ISOLATION

DNA has been isolated from E. gracilis by phenol extraction (Brawerman et al., 1962b). The cells, defatted by extraction with ether–ethanol, were suspended in tris–HCl buffer (pH 7.6) and the suspension treated with ice-cold phenol. The resulting aqueous phase contained most of the RNA. The DNA was obtained from the residue (interphase plus phenol phase) by extraction with tris buffer (pH 9.0). Some contaminating RNA was removed from the DNA preparation by precipitation with cold 10% NaCl. For the determination of base composition, residual RNA was removed by alkaline hydrolysis followed by dialysis.

In a subsequent study (Brawerman and Eisenstadt, 1964a), DNA was extracted separately from purified chloroplasts and from a subcellular fraction rich in fragmented nuclei. Disruption of Euglena cells in a French press under mild conditions leads to fragmentation of the nuclei, but most of the cellular DNA can be recovered from a fraction that sediments at 23,000 g. The total nucleic acids in the two fractions were obtained by phenol extraction in the presence of tris buffer (pH 9.0), and the bulk of the RNA removed by precipitation in cold 10% NaCl. Ribonuclease was used to remove the residual RNA, and the enzyme was eliminated by an additional phenol treatment.

Euglena DNA labeled with ^{32}P has been prepared by a modification of the Marmur procedure (Ray and Hanawalt, 1964). Cells extracted with ethanol were suspended in 1% dodecyl sodium sulfate, 0.1 M NaCl, 1 mM EDTA, and 1 mM tris (pH 8.0). After addition of sodium perchlorate, the extract was deproteinized with chloroform–octanol.

B. CHARACTERISTICS OF Euglena DNA

Buoyant density centrifugation of Euglena DNA yields a major component with a density in CsCl of 1.705–1.708 gm/cm³ and a thermal denaturation temperature of 89–92° C (Fig. 1 and Table VI). The density values correspond to a G + C content of 46–49 moles %. These values are in relatively good agreement with those obtained by base analysis of the isolated DNA. The

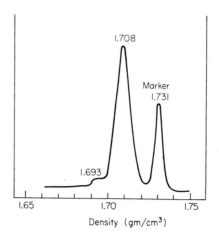

Density (gm/cm³)

Fig. 1. CsCl density gradient centrifugation pattern of nuclear DNA from *E. gracilis* strain Z. Reproduced from Brawerman and Eisenstadt (1964a).

Table VI

CHARACTERISTICS OF DNA COMPONENTS OF *E. gracilis*

Component	Strain	Buoyant density in CsCl	G–C content[a] (moles %)	T_m[b]	Reference[c]
Nuclear	var. *bacillaris*	1.705	46	90°	*1*
	Strain Z	1.708	49	89–91°	*2*
	var. *bacillaris*	1.707	48	—	*3*
	var. *bacillaris*	1.706–1.707	47–48	92°	*4*
Chloroplast	Strain Z	1.684	25	78–80°	*2*
	var. *bacillaris*	1.685	25	—	*3*
	var. *bacillaris*	1.685	25	81.5°	*4*
Other satellites	Strain Z	1.692	33	—	*2*
	var. *bacillaris*	1.690, 1.694?	31, 35?	—	*5*
	var. *bacillaris*	1.691	32	—	*6, 7*

[a] G–C content computed from buoyant density data by formula of Schidkraut *et al.* (1962b).

[b] T_m represents thermal denaturation temperature in 0.14 *M* NaCl and 0.014 *M* sodium citrate.

[c] Key to references: *1*, Schildkraut *et al.* (1962a); *2*, Brawerman and Eisenstadt (1964a); *3*, Ray and Hanawalt (1964); *4*, Edelman *et al.* (1964); *5*, Ray and Hanawalt (1965); *6*, Edelman *et al.* (1965); *7*, Edelman *et al.* (1966).

four major nucleotides are present in nearly equal amounts (Table VII). The DNA of *E. gracilis* also contains a relatively large amount of 5-methylcytidylic acid (2.3%).

Table VII

NUCLEOTIDE COMPOSITION OF NUCLEAR AND CHLOROPLAST DNA

Nucleotide	Nuclear component		Chloroplast component	
	Strain Z[a]	var. *bacillaris*[b]	Strain Z[a]	var. *bacillaris*[b]
A	24.5	22.6	37.2	38.2
G	24.8	27.7	13.0	12.3
C	23.5	23.2	14.3	11.3
T	24.7	24.4	35.5	38.1
5-Methylcytosine	2.3	2.3	None detected	>0.3

[a] Data from Brawerman *et al.* (1962b) for nuclear DNA, and from Brawerman and Eisenstadt (1964a) for chloroplast DNA. Preparation of chloroplast DNA obtained after differential lysis of purified plastids (see Fig. 4).

[b] Data from Ray and Hanawalt (1964). Values obtained by ^{32}P distribution analysis of nucleotides from labeled DNA. Components obtained by preparative CsCl density centrifugation of mixed preparation.

C. CHLOROPLAST DNA

1. *Isolation of Chloroplasts*

The possibility for the isolation from *E. gracilis* of highly purified chloroplasts in large quantities has permitted a detailed study of the nucleic acids of these organelles. The isolation procedure developed by Eisenstadt and Brawerman (1964a) involves the disruption of the cells in a French press at 1500 lb/sq inch in the presence of $MgCl_2$ and 10% sucrose buffered at pH 7.6. The Mg^{2+} concentration in this medium (4 mM) is critical, since this cation is required for the preservation of the chloroplast structure during cell disruption. An excess of $MgCl_2$, however, will cause aggregation of cytoplasmic material with the chloroplasts (Brawerman, 1963a). The crude chloroplast pellet obtained by low-speed centrifugation is resuspended in a large volume of disruption medium and the suspension is left standing for about 10 minutes. This permits the removal of membranous material that aggregates and settles to the bottom of the vessel. The resedimented chloroplasts are next subjected to flotation in concentrated sucrose. At this stage of purification, the chloroplasts are free of contamination by cytoplasmic ribosomes, and are adequate for RNA studies. An additional flotation step is necessary for studies of chloroplast DNA (Brawerman and Eisenstadt, 1964a).

2. Elimination of Nuclear Contaminant

DNA isolated from the purified chloroplasts of *E. gracilis* strain Z contains a considerable proportion of a component with a relatively low density, but the nuclear component still predominates (Fig. 2). The nuclear

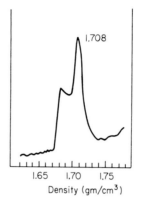

Fig. 2.   CsCl density gradient centrifugation pattern of DNA from purified chloroplasts. Reproduced from Brawerman and Eisenstadt (1964a).

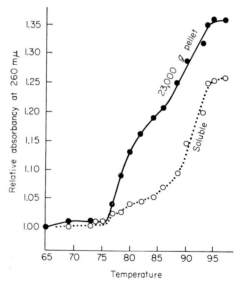

Fig. 3.   Melting profiles of DNA preparations from centrifugal fractions of chloroplasts lyzed in 0.01 M MgCl$_2$. "Soluble" refers to 100,000-g supernatant. DNA samples heated in 0.15 M NaCl and 0.01 M sodium citrate. Reproduced from Brawerman and Eisenstadt (1964a).

contaminant could be almost completely eliminated by a partial lysis of the chloroplast preparation (Brawerman and Eisenstadt, 1964a). When the plastids are treated with sodium deoxycholate in the presence of sufficient $MgCl_2$, the bulk of the chloroplast material (protein and pigment) is still in some particulate form, and it sediments at 23,000 g (Brawerman and Eisenstadt, 1964a). DNA is present both in the sediment and in the solubilized material. The melting profiles of the two DNA fractions show that the soluble material contains almost exclusively nuclear DNA, while the sediment is enriched in the low-melting component (Fig. 3). Thus it appears that nuclear fragments that contaminate the chloroplast preparations are more susceptible to the deoxycholate treatment. The localization of the low-melting DNA component in the particulate fraction rich in chloroplast material suggests that it is intimately associated with the chloroplast structure. This provides additional evidence for its identification as chloroplast DNA.

The proportion of nuclear DNA left in the partially lyzed chloroplast sediment was found to vary with the concentration of Mg^{2+} during the deoxycholate treatment. With the use of the appropriate Mg^{2+} concentration, nearly all the nuclear DNA component could be removed from the sedimentable material (Brawerman and Eisenstadt, 1964a).

3. Characteristics of Chloroplast DNA

The buoyant density centrifugation profile of the DNA obtained by differential lysis of chloroplasts from *E. gracilis* strain Z, shows a major component with a density of 1.684 gm/cm³ (Fig. 4). Measurements of

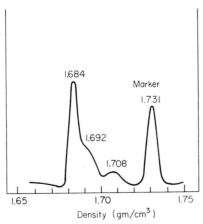

Fig. 4. CsCl density centrifugation pattern of DNA from 23,000-*g* sediment of chloroplasts lyzed in 0.005 *M* $MgCl_2$. Reproduced from Brawerman and Eisenstadt (1964a).

its thermal denaturation temperature in "standard saline citrate" give values ranging from 78 to 80° C (Table VI).

The chloroplast DNA of *E. gracilis* var. *bacillaris* has been studied by Edelman *et al.* (1964). These investigators used an enriched preparation obtained from chloroplasts purified by the procedure described in Section III,C,1. The low-density component was separated from the contaminating nuclear DNA by preparative CsCl centrifugation. The values for the buoyant density and the melting temperature of this material are essentially the same as those described for *E. gracilis* strain Z (Table VI).

In an elegant study of chloroplast DNA from *E. gracilis* var. *bacillaris*, Ray and Hanawalt (1964) used cells labeled with ^{32}P. In this manner only small quantities of purified chloroplasts were required for the isolation of the DNA. The chloroplast DNA component was also purified by preparative CsCl centrifugation, and it showed a buoyant density of 1.685 (Table VI).

Nucleotide analyses have been performed on the DNA preparations obtained after partial lysis of the chloroplasts (Brawerman and Eisenstadt, 1964a) and on the ^{32}P-labeled material recovered after preparative density centrifugation (Ray and Hanawalt, 1964). Although widely different methods of analysis were used in these two studies, the results are in close agreement (Table VII). As expected, the chloroplast DNA is very low in guanylic and cytidylic acids (24–27 moles % G + C). 5-Methylcytosine appears to be absent from the chloroplast DNA. This is of particular interest in view of the relative abundance of this component in the nuclear DNA of *Euglena*.

4. *DNA Content of Chloroplasts*

The amount of DNA per chloroplast has been estimated at approximately 1×10^{-8} μg, a value close to that for *Escherichia coli* (Brawerman and Eisenstadt, 1964a). Chloroplasts from *Chlamydomonas* and from some higher plants have been found to have a DNA content of the same order of magnitude (Brawerman, 1966).

D. OTHER DNA COMPONENTS

Euglena gracilis contains a minor DNA component with a buoyant density of 1.690–1.692 in addition to the chloroplast component with the density of 1.684–1.685. This component is evident in the CsCl density centrifugation profile of the purified chloroplast DNA preparation (Fig. 4). It also appears as a small shoulder in the buoyant density profile of the

DNA isolated from the fraction rich in fragmented nuclei (Fig. 1). It has been suggested that this component might represent mitochondrial DNA, since it is obtained from a fraction that sediments at 23,000 g, and which is essentially free of chloroplast fragments (Brawerman and Eisenstadt, 1964a).

Ray and Hanawalt (1965) have shown that the 1.690 DNA component has a relatively low sedimentation value, which corresponds to a molecular weight of 3×10^6, while the isolated chloroplast DNA component (density 1.685) has a considerably higher molecular weight ($20-40 \times 10^6$). Cells that have lost the ability to form chloroplasts no longer have any detectable amounts of the low-density, high molecular weight DNA component, but they retain the 1.690 component (Fig. 5). The absence of the chloroplast

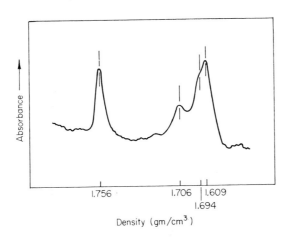

Fig. 5. CsCl density centrifugation pattern of the low buoyant density fraction of the DNA from ultraviolet-bleached *E. gracilis*, var. *bacillaris*. Hybrid 5-BU DNA from *F. coli* added as a density marker at 1.756. Reproduced from Ray and Hanawalt (1965).

DNA component from bleached cells and the occurrence of a 1.691 DNA satellite in both normal and bleached cells has also been reported by Leff *et al.* (1963) and by Edelman *et al.* (1965).

The DNA component of density 1.691–1.692 has been isolated from purified mitochondria preparations derived from bleached *E. gracilis* (Edelman *et al.*, 1966; Krawiec and Eisenstadt, personal communication). These preparations still contained a large excess of nuclear DNA, which could be removed by treatment with deoxyribonuclease. The enzyme did not appear to affect the presumed mitochondrial DNA.

IV. Ribonucleic Acids of E. gracilis

A. Procedures for Isolation

The ribonucleic acids of *E. gracilis* strain Z, have been characterized extensively. RNA was originally extracted from the defatted cells by the same procedure used for the isolation of the DNA (Brawerman *et al.*, 1962b). The bulk of the RNA was obtained by treatment of the cells with phenol at pH 7.5. High molecular weight RNA was separated from transfer RNA by precipitation in cold 10% NaCl. The extraction procedure was simplified subsequently by disrupting the cells in a French press in the presence of 0.1 M tris buffer (pH 7.6) and mixing the homogenate immediately with ice-cold phenol (Brawerman, 1963b). Pogo *et al.* (1966) have used a different procedure for RNA extraction. The cells, suspended in 1% dodecyl sodium sulfate and acetate buffer (pH 5.1), were treated with phenol at 60° C for 5 minutes. Most of the RNA was extracted after three such treatments.

B. Transfer RNA

The nucleotide composition of *Euglena* transfer RNA (Table VIII) shows the characteristics usually exhibited by this class of RNA. The A and U contents are relatively low, and pseudouridylic acid is present in substantial amounts (3 moles %). Methylated adenine and guanine derivatives have been identified. 5-Methylribocytidylic acid has also been detected. Two components tentatively identified as 2′, 5′- and 3′, 5′-guanosine diphosphate have been observed. No significant differences in nucleotide composition were observed when preparations from green and colorless cells were compared (Brawerman *et al.*, 1962b).

The transfer RNA isolated by the procedure described in Section IV,A shows amino acid–accepting activity. It also produces a considerable

Table VIII

NUCLEOTIDE COMPOSITION OF TRANSFER RNA OF *E. gracilis*[a]

Major components	Minor components
Adenylic acid 17.8 Guanylic acid 31.0 Cytidylic acid 28.9 Uridylic acid 16.6	Pseudouridylic acid 3.0 6-N-methyladenylic acid 1.2 2-N-methylguanylic acid 1.0

[a] Data from Brawerman *et al.* (1962b). Values expressed as moles per 100 moles nucleotide in RNA.

enhancement of polypeptide synthesis by cell-free systems from *E. gracilis* (Eisenstadt and Brawerman, 1964a,b). The specificity of interaction of the leucyl transfer RNA's from *E. gracilis* and *E. coli* with the activating enzymes from both organisms has been examined (Eisenstadt and Brawerman, 1966). The RNA from *E. coli* showed the same acceptor activity with the enzymes from both sources, but the *Euglena* RNA was far more active with the homologous enzyme (Table IX).

Table IX

ACCEPTOR SPECIFICITY OF LEUCYL-TRANSFER RNA FROM
E. gracilis AND *E. coli*[a]

Source of soluble enzymes	Transfer RNA[b]			Incorporation per mg RNA	
	None	From *E. coli* (215 µg/ml)	From *Euglena* (175 µg/ml)	*E. coli*	*Euglena*
E. gracilis	16	6,350	3,560	30,300	20,200
E. coli	425	7,240	1,510	31,700	6,800

[a] Transfer RNA incubated with supernatant fraction from *E. gracilis* and from *E. coli* with ATP-generating system and leucine-^{14}C. Data from Eisenstadt and Brawerman (1966).

[b] Values expressed as counts per minute per milliliter reaction.

C. RIBOSOMAL RNA

1. *Nucleotide Composition*

The overall base composition of the cellular RNA of *E. gracilis* shows a relatively high amount of guanine and cytosine (Table X). The ratio of 6-amino to 6-keto components [(A + C)/(G + U)] is near unity, as it is in most cellular RNA (Brawerman and Shapiro, 1962). The *Euglena* RNA contains substantial amounts of pseudouridylic acid and of another unidentified minor component (Brawerman and Chargaff, 1959). There are slight but significant differences in the RNA nucleotide composition of cells grown in the light and in the dark (Table X). As is shown in Section IV,D, these differences are due to the presence of chloroplast RNA in the green cells. Permanently bleached cells, on the other hand, show the same overall RNA nucleotide composition as the normal cells grown in the dark (Table X). Purified ribosomes derived from the cytoplasm of *Euglena* show the same nucleotide composition as that of the total RNA of colorless cells (Table XI), and the same values are obtained with cytoplasmic ribosomes from cells grown in the light and in the dark (Brawerman, 1963a).

Table X

NUCLEOTIDE COMPOSITION OF THE TOTAL RNA OF GREEN, COLORLESS, AND
BLEACHED *Euglena* CELLS[a]

Nucleotide	Green		Colorless		Bleached	
A	23.2	(0.2)	21.6	(0.3)	21.9	(0.1)
G	28.5	(0.5)	30.2	(0.7)	29.6	(0.5)
C	26.3	(0.5)	27.5	(0.8)	27.5	(0.5)
U	22.0	(0.3)	20.7	(0.7)	21.0	(0.4)
A/C	0.88		0.79		0.80	

[a] *Euglena gracilis* strain Z, grown in complex medium in the light (green cells) and in darkness (colorless cells). Bleached cells derived from same strain by growth at 34°C. Data from Brawerman and Chargaff (1959).

Table XI

NUCLEOTIDE COMPOSITION OF RIBOSOMAL RNA FROM THE CYTOPLASM
AND THE CHLOROPLASTS OF *E. gracilis*

Nucleotide	Chloroplast ribosomes[a]	Cytoplasmic ribosomes[b]
Adenylic acid	30.6	22.7
Guanylic acid	27.0	29.5
Cytidylic acid	17.0	27.1
Uridylic acid	25.0	19.6
Pseudouridylic acid	None detected	1.1
A/C	1.80	0.84

[a] Data from Eisenstadt, and Brawerman (1964a).
[b] Data from Brawerman (1963a).

It has been reported by Pogo *et al.* (1966) that the nature of the growth medium can influence the nucleotide composition of the high molecular weight RNA of *E. gracilis*. Normal cells grown in the dark in chemically defined medium were found to have less G and more C in their RNA than the same cells in complex medium (Table XII). This qualitative difference, in conjunction with the finding that the cells from complex medium have a considerably higher amount of RNA (Table II) could indicate that the latter cells may have additional species of RNA. Differences in the population of messenger RNA molecules in the two types of cells could hardly account for the observed shifts in the overall base composition of the cellular RNA, since they should represent only a minute fraction of total RNA. A different species of ribosomal RNA could conceivably account for the results, but heterogeneity in ribosomal RNA remains to be demonstrated.

Table XII

NUCLEOTIDE COMPOSITION OF HIGH MOLECULAR WEIGHT RNA FROM
COLORLESS CELLS GROWN IN DIFFERENT MEDIA[a]

Nucleotide	Defined medium	Complex medium
A	22.8	*23.6*
G	*27.0*	*29.0*
C	*28.8*	*27.0*
U	21.3	19.9

[a] Data from Pogo *et al.* (1966). Cells from stationary phase of growth. Significantly different values are italized.

2. Sedimentation Characteristics

The bulk RNA of *Euglena*, obtained from disrupted cells by phenol extraction at neutral pH, and freed of transfer RNA by precipitation in cold 10% NaCl, shows a single major component with a sedimentation value of approximately 19 S (Fig. 6). Ribosomal RNA usually has two components, each corresponding to one of the ribosome subunits. The failure to obtain two components from *Euglena* RNA remains to be explained. There may possibly be two ribosomal RNA components with similar sedimentation values. It is also possible that a partial fragmentation of one of the RNA components takes place during the isolation.

D. CHLOROPLAST RNA

1. Nucleotide Composition

RNA obtained from the crude chloroplast fraction of *E. gracilis* shows a nucleotide composition distinctly different from that of the total cellular RNA (Pogo *et al.*, 1962). Purification of the chloroplasts by flotation, which effectively removes contaminating cytoplasmic ribosomes (Eisenstadt and Brawerman, 1964a), leads to a considerable enhancement of these differences. The bulk of the chloroplast RNA is present in ribosomal particles (Brawerman and Eisenstadt, 1964b). The nucleotide compositions of the purified cytoplasmic and chloroplast ribosomes are compared in Table XI. The chloroplast ribosomes differ sharply from the cytoplasmic particles with respect to the content of A, C, and U. The G content remains relatively high. Thus the chloroplast RNA conforms to the general rule concerning the high guanylic acid content of ribosomal RNA. The minor components that were detected in the cytoplasmic RNA appear to be absent from chloroplast RNA.

2. Sedimentation Characteristics

Zone sedimentation of chloroplast RNA yields two components with sedimentation values of 19 S and 14 S (Fig. 6). The 19-S component does not represent contamination by cytoplasmic RNA, since its base composition is that characteristic of chloroplast RNA (Brawerman and Eisenstadt, 1964b).

An appreciable portion of the chloroplast RNA (about 20%) does not sediment with the ribosomes (Brawerman and Eisenstadt, 1964b). This "soluble" RNA appears to have the same base composition as the rest of

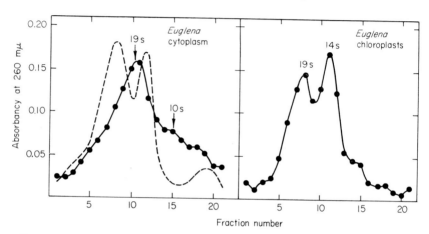

Fig. 6. Zone centrifugation patterns of cytoplasmic and chloroplast RNA of *E. gracilis*. RNA isolated from disrupted cells and from chloroplast ribosomes. Broken line, *E. coli* RNA run in a separate tube; solid lines, *Euglena* RNA. Reproduced from Brawerman and Eisenstadt (1964b).

the RNA. After zone sedimentation, it yields a single major peak which probably corresponds to the 14-S ribosomal component (Fig. 7). The nature of this RNA is further discussed in Section IV,E.

E. Template RNA

1. Phenol Extraction of RNA at Different pH Values

Some RNA fractions highly active in stimulating cell-free polypeptide synthesis have been obtained from *E. gracilis*. This property, which will be referred to as "template activity," is an important characteristic expected of messenger RNA. Thus the active components have tentatively been considered to represent messenger RNA, although it remains to be demonstrated whether or not they contain information for the synthesis of specific proteins.

After exhaustive phenol extraction of disrupted cells at pH 7.6, additional RNA components can be obtained at pH 8.0–9.0 (Brawerman, 1963b). The latter show a nucleotide composition distinctly different from that

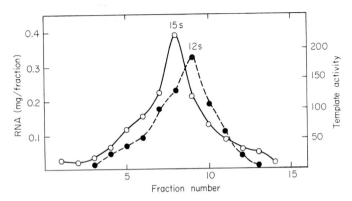

Fig. 7. Zone centrifugation patterns of RNA and template activity from soluble fraction of lyzed chloroplasts. Solid line, RNA; broken line, template activity. Reproduced from Brawerman and Eisenstadt (1964b).

of the ribosomal RNA obtained at pH 7.6 (Table XIII). The overall G + C content of these components is shifted toward the value for DNA, but the amount of A is consistently higher than that of U. Similar RNA fractions obtained from rat liver also show an elevated A content (Brawerman *et al.*, 1963), and in this case the high A content has been shown to be due to

Table XIII

NUCLEOTIDE COMPOSITION OF RNA FRACTIONS EXTRACTED FROM
Euglena AT ALKALINE pH[a]

Nucleotide	pH 7.6	pH 8.0–8.5	pH 8.5–9.0	DNA
A	21.9	28.3	27.5	24.5
G	30.1	25.0	26.9	24.8
C	27.7	21.7	22.2	26.0[b]
U(T)	20.3	25.0	23.4	24.7
A/U	1.08	1.13	1.18	0.99
$\dfrac{G + C}{A + U}$	1.37	0.88	0.97	1.03
RNA yields (mg)	104	1.7	3.8	—

[a] *Euglena gracilis* (15 ml packed cells) subjected to stepwise phenol extraction at increasing pH. Data are from Brawerman (1963b).
[b] Value represents sum of cytosine and 5-methylcytosine.

polyadenylic acid of relatively high molecular weight (Hadjivassiliou and Brawerman, 1966). Preliminary evidence indicates that polyadenylic acid may also be present in *Euglena* (Brawerman and Eisenstadt, unpublished). The effect of the *Euglena* RNA fractions obtained at alkaline pH on polypeptide synthesis by the *E. coli* cell-free system is shown in Fig. 8.

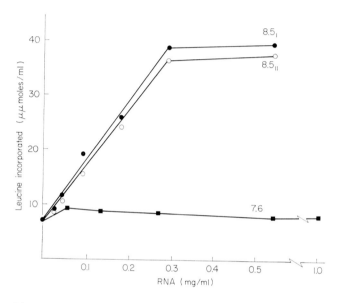

Fig. 8. Stimulation of polypeptide synthesis by RNA fractions extracted from *Euglena* at alkaline pH. RNA added to *E. coli* cell-free system; 8.5_I and 8.5_{II} represent RNA fractions obtained by first and second extraction at pH 8.5 after removal of the bulk of the RNA at pH 7.6. Brawerman and Eisenstadt (unpublished).

These fractions are far more active than ribosomal RNA, and their activity increases linearly with concentration up to 300 μg/ml. The low activity of the ribosomal RNA preparations appears to be due not to the bulk RNA, but to minor components with sedimentation values of about 22 S and 11 S (Fig. 9).

2. Template RNA in Chloroplasts

Chloroplast RNA has a far greater template activity that cytoplasmic RNA (Brawerman and Eisenstadt, 1964b). In this case also, the activity sediments as two distinct components (12 S and 22 S; see Fig. 10). The RNA from the soluble fraction of lyzed chloroplasts (see Section IV,D,2) is particularly rich in template activity, but the active component still represents

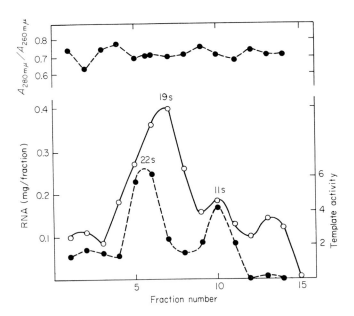

Fig. 9.   Zone centrifugation pattern of RNA and template activity of pH 7.6 RNA preparation from dark-grown cells. Solid line, RNA; broken line, template activity. Reproduced from Brawerman and Eisenstadt (1964b).

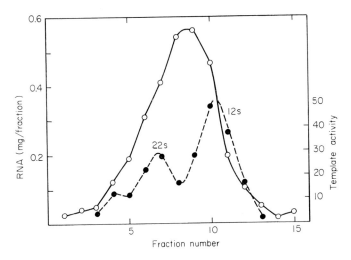

Fig. 10.   Zone centrifugation patterns of RNA and template activity from chloroplast ribosomal preparation. Solid line, RNA; broken line, template activity. Reproduced from Brawerman and Eisenstadt (1964b).

a minor portion of the total RNA, as is shown by its sedimentation characteristics (Fig. 7). The implications of the high template activity of the RNA
from the soluble fraction are discussed in Section V,B in terms of localization
of messenger RNA in these organelles.

V. Ribosomes and Polypeptide Synthesis

A. CHARACTERISTICS OF *EUGLENA* RIBOSOMES

Ribosomal particles can be isolated from the cytoplasm of *E. gracilis*
by differential centrifugation at 100,000 g, and purified by treatment with
sodium deoxycholate (Eisenstadt and Brawerman, 1964b). The purified
particles have about equal amounts of RNA and protein. The isolated
ribosomes have a sedimentation value of approximately 70 S (Fig. 11).
They are capable of promoting polypeptide synthesis, and the nascent
polypeptide sediments with the 70-S particles (Fig. 11).

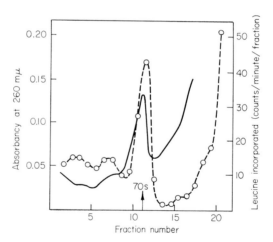

Fig. 11. Zone centrifugation of cytoplasmic ribosomes after cell-free polypeptide
synthesis. Solid line, absorbancy at 260 mµ; broken line, acid-insoluble radioactive
material. Reproduced from Eisenstadt and Brawerman (1964a).

Active ribosomes can also be obtained from purified chloroplasts after
treatment with sodium deoxycholate (Brawerman, 1963a; Eisenstadt and
Brawerman, 1964a). The chloroplast ribosomes have a sedimentation value
of 60 S (Fig. 12), distinctly lower than that of the cytoplasmic particles.
The polypeptide material synthesized by preparation from chloroplasts
sediments with the 60-S particles (Fig. 12). Thus the activity of the chloroplast

preparation can be attributed to the 60-S particles, and not to cytoplasmic ribosomes which might possibly contaminate the preparations. A 36-S component is also present in the preparation from chloroplasts (Fig. 12), but it is not known whether or not this represents a ribosomal subunit.

The two types of *Euglena* ribosomes can be readily distinguished in electron micrographs of green cells (Figs. 13 and 14). Ribosomal particles

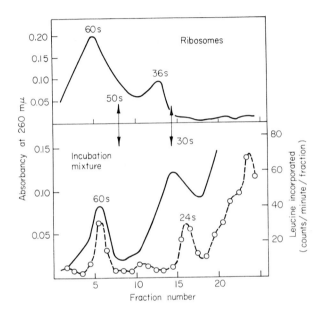

Fig. 12. Zone centrifugation of isolated chloroplast ribosomes, and of the same particles after cell-free polypeptide synthesis. Solid line, absorbancy at 260 mμ; broken line, acidinsoluble radioactive material. Reproduced from Eisenstadt and Brawerman (1964a).

are evident within the chloroplast structure and their size is clearly smaller than that of the particles in the surrounding cytoplasm. Thus the biochemical data on the size difference between cytoplasmic and chloroplast ribosomes are confirmed by direct cytological observation.

B. CELL-FREE SYSTEMS FOR POLYPEPTIDE SYNTHESIS

1. *Cytoplasmic System*

Polypeptide synthesis by isolated cytoplasmic ribosomes is greatly enhanced by factors from the high-speed supernatant fraction, and by *Euglena* transfer RNA (Table XIV). The system loses its activity after

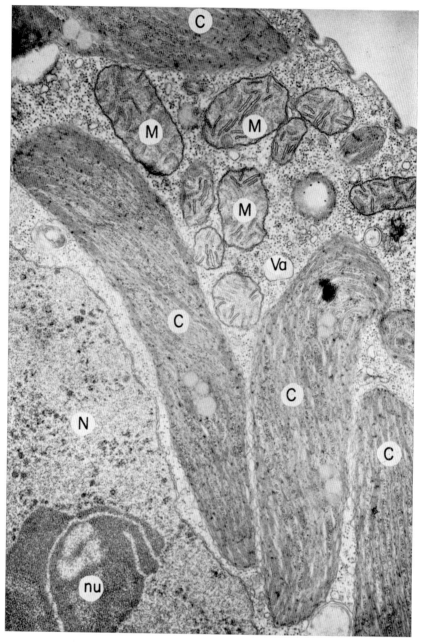

Fig. 13. Portion of the nucleus and cytoplasm of a thinly sectioned *Euglena* cell from a log-phase culture. M, mitochondrion; C, chloroplast; N, nucleus, nu, nucleolus; Va, vacuole. Note the numerous small ribosomal granules in the chloroplasts and those in the cytoplasmic matrix. ×26,000.

Preparation fixed in 1% glutaraldehyde in phosphate buffer pH 7, and postfixed in 1% OsO_4 in pH 7 phosphate buffer. Micrographs reproduced by permission from Drs. S. Dales and A. Cerami, Rockefeller University (unpublished observations).

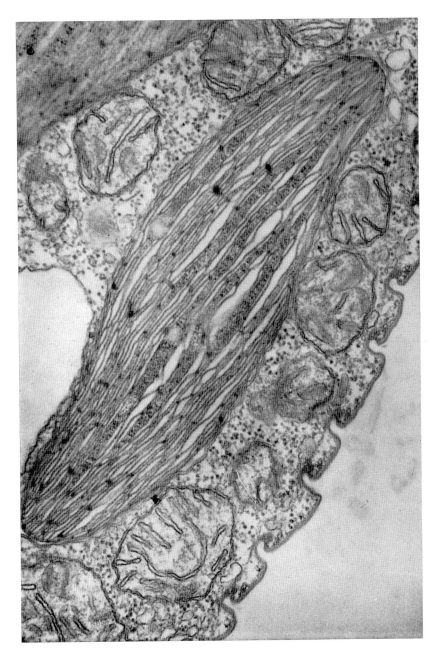

Fig. 14. Higher resolution micrograph of a segment of a cell from the same culture shown in Fig. 13. ×55,000.

Table XIV

REQUIREMENTS FOR POLYPEPTIDE SYNTHESIS BY THE CELL-FREE SYSTEM
FROM *Euglena* CYTOPLASM[a]

Conditions	Leucine incorporated ($\mu\mu$ moles/ml)
Complete system	255
No ribosomes	7
No supernatant fraction	74
No transfer RNA	120
No ATP-generating system	26
No $MgCl_2$	72
No glutathione	85
No KCl	220

[a] Data from Eisenstadt and Brawerman (1964b).

15–30 minutes of reaction. Omission of the ATP-generating system reduces the activity to a very low level. KCl, which is required by the bacterial and mammalian cell-free systems, has no effect on the activity of the *Euglena* ribosomes. Glutathione is highly stimulatory, but it cannot be replaced by β-mercaptoethanol (Eisenstadt and Brawerman, 1964b). This is in contrast with the requirements of the bacterial and mammalian systems, which are equally effective with the two reducing agents.

Ribosomes obtained from *Euglena* cultures at different growth phases have been compared with respect to synthetic activity. Surprisingly, the most active preparations were obtained from cultures beyond the exponential phase of growth (Eisenstadt and Brawerman, 1964b).

2. Chloroplast System

Purified chloroplasts show substantial activity with respect to polypeptide synthesis (Eisenstadt and Brawerman, 1964a). When the activity is expressed in terms of milligrams of RNA present in the preparation, it is about the same in the chloroplasts and in the cytoplasmic ribosomes (compare Tables XV and XVI). The characteristics of amino acid incorporation into chloroplasts are similar to those usually exhibited by ribosomal systems. The chloroplasts remain active for 15–30 minutes. They are highly dependent on supernatant factors from *Euglena*, on transfer RNA, and on an ATP-generating system (Table XV). The activity is inhibited by puromycin and ribonuclease. Phenylalanine incorporation is enhanced by polyuridylic acid.

The requirements for soluble factors are not necessarily an indication

Table XV

CHARACTERISTICS OF POLYPEPTIDE SYNTHESIS BY *Euglena* CHLOROPLASTS[a]

Conditions	Amino acid incorporated	
	Leucine ($\mu\mu$moles)	Phenylalanine ($\mu\mu$moles)
Complete system	430	192
No transfer RNA	52	127
No ATP-generating system	86	—
Added puromycin (110 μg/ml)	65	—
Added RNase (50 μg/ml)	6	—
Added polyU (120 μg/ml)	403	397
Added template RNA (100 μg/ml)	580	—

[a] Data from Eisenstadt and Brawerman (1964a). Values expressed as micromicromoles incorporated per milligram chloroplast RNA.

Table XVI

CHARACTERISTICS OF POLYPEPTIDE SYNTHESIS BY CHLOROPLAST RIBOSOMES[a]

Conditions	Leucine incorporated	
	Chloroplast ribosomes	Cytoplasmic ribosomes
Complete system	43	425
No supernatant, transfer RNA	2	8
Added ribosomal RNA (215 μg/ml)	66	—
Added template RNA (100 μg/ml)	212	423
Added puromycin (40 μg/ml)	58	—

[a] Data from Eisenstadt and Brawerman (1964a). Values expressed as micromicromoles leucine incorporated per mg ribosomal RNA.

that these factors are normally absent from chloroplasts *in vivo*. The plastids obtained from disrupted *Euglena* cells are leaky, and they tend to lose soluble enzymes during purification.

Light has a rather unexpected effect on the activity of the chloroplasts. Since plastid formation in *E. gracilis* is dependent on light, it might have been expected that illumination should lead to a stimulation of polypeptide synthesis. Light, however, is clearly inhibitory. An enhancing effect of light is observed only when the ATP-generating system is omitted from the reaction mixtures (Eisenstadt and Brawerman, 1964a).

3. Effect of Template RNA on Chloroplast Ribosomes

Ribosomes isolated from the chloroplasts are considerably less active than the intact plastids. Their activity, however, can be raised to levels approaching those of the chloroplasts and the cytoplasmic ribosomes by addition of template RNA (Table XVI). The latter material has little or no effect on the activity of both the cytoplasmic ribosomes and the intact chloroplasts.

The apparent requirement of chloroplast ribosomes for template RNA has been explained by postulating that the messenger RNA present in the chloroplast becomes separated from the ribosomes during the differential centrifugation of the lyzed plastids, and remains in the soluble fraction. This could account for the high template activity of the "soluble" chloroplast RNA (see Section IV,D). The lack of template RNA requirement by the cytoplasmic ribosomes, even when subjected to the same deoxycholate treatment, would suggest that these particles do not lose their messenger RNA as readily as the chloroplast ribosomes (Eisenstadt and Brawerman, 1964a).

4. Effect of Chloramphenicol

The effect of chloramphenicol has revealed another interesting difference between the two protein-synthesizing systems present in *E. gracilis*. Both the chloroplasts and the chloroplast ribosomes are inhibited by this antibiotic, while the cytoplasmic ribosomes remain unaffected (Table XVII). This difference in the behavior of the isolated particles is well correlated with the *in vivo* response of the protein-synthesizing systems to chloramphenicol. It has been shown by Pogo and Pogo (1965) that this antibiotic preferentially inhibits chloroplast protein synthesis in *E. gracilis*.

Table XVII

EFFECT OF CHLORAMPHENICOL ON POLYPEPTIDE SYNTHESIS BY THE
CHLOROPLAST AND CYTOPLASMIC CELL-FREE SYSTEMS[a]

Chloramphenicol (μg/ml)	Chloroplasts	Ribosomes	
		From chloroplasts	From cytoplasm
60	99	99	99
120	84	74	103
210	55	61	94
360	—	59	94

[a] Data from Eisenstadt and Brawerman (1964a). Values expressed as percent of activity in absence of chloramphenicol.

C. SPECIFICITY OF CHLOROPLAST RIBOSOMES

The ability of the chloroplast ribosomes to respond to exogenous messenger RNA is rather unique among nonbacterial cell-free systems. While most ribosomes are stimulated by some synthetic polynucleotides such as poly-U, they remain essentially unaffected by natural messenger RNA. *Euglena* chloroplast ribosomes, like the *E. coli* particles, are strongly stimulated by viral RNA. This property has permitted a direct experimental examination of the possibility that ribosomes contribute to the information for specific protein synthesis. RNA from the bacterial virus f_2 has been shown to induce the synthesis of the viral coat protein by *E. coli* ribosomes (Nathans *et al.*, 1962). The polypeptide material produced by the chloroplast ribosomes in the presence of f_2 RNA was found to be similar to that formed by the *E. coli* system (Schwartz *et al.*, 1965). Thus the ribosomes appear to have no specificity of their own with respect to determination of amino acid sequence in proteins. This result also indicates that two widely different organisms such as *E. gracilis* and *E. coli* have similar coding specificities.

VI. DNA and Chloroplast Replication*

A. ROLE OF CHLOROPLAST DNA

The occurrence of DNA in chloroplasts would seem to provide a biochemical basis for the genetic autonomy of these organelles. The precise role of the chloroplast DNA, however, remains to be determined. The primary function of DNA is commonly considered in terms of providing information for the amino acid sequences of all cellular proteins. The amount of DNA in *Euglena* chloroplasts (see Section III,C,4) is certainly sufficient to code for a large number of proteins. However, no chloroplast protein has yet been found to be under the control of a structural gene associated with the plastids. Genetic studies on various soluble enzymes associated with the photosynthetic apparatus have shown that these proteins are under nuclear control. The possibility remains that some of the plastid proteins, such as the structural proteins, are coded by the chloroplast DNA.

Biochemical evidence for the role of the chloroplast DNA in *E. gracilis* is rather scant. The chloroplast ribosomal RNA tends to resemble the plastid DNA with respect to overall base composition (Table XVIII). This suggests that the RNA may be transcribed from the chloroplast DNA.

* *Editor's Note*: This topic is further considered in Chapters 10, 11, and 12.

Table XVIII

RELATIONS BETWEEN THE NUCLEOTIDE COMPOSITION OF
DNA AND RIBOSOMAL RNA IN *E. gracilis*

Nucleotide	Ribosomal RNA		DNA	
	Chloroplasts	Cytoplasm	Chloroplasts	Nuclei
G + C (%)	44	57	25	51
A/C	1.9	0.84	2.6	0.95

The presence in the plastids of RNA with template activity (see Section IV,E), presumably messenger RNA, suggests that these organelles are capable of transcription of information for protein synthesis. This messenger RNA, however, could be conceivably derived from the nucleus. Evidence has been presented that *Euglena* chloroplast preparations possess RNA polymerase activity (Eisenstadt and Brawerman, 1964a; Shah and Lyman, 1966), but the observed activity could have been derived from contaminating nuclear material. Thus much remains to be done to determine the role of the DNA of chloroplasts.

B. DNA AND THE LOSS OF THE ABILITY TO FORM CHLOROPLASTS

Some strains of *E. gracilis* can be subjected to a variety of bleaching treatments, such as ultraviolet irradiation, exposure to streptomycin, and growth at 34° C (see Chapters 10 and 12). These treatments, which lead to the permanent loss of the ability to form chloroplasts, appear to affect a self-replicating component essential for chloroplast formation. The progressive loss of a self-replicating unit from the cells multiplying at 34° C is illustrated in Fig. 15. Return of partially bleached cultures to a lower temperature leads to a rapid recovery of the ability to form green colonies. That the self-replicating component is not the chloroplast itself, is indicated by the fact that the rate of chloroplast formation in the recovering cells remains low for a long period of time (Brawerman and Chargaff, 1960). Ultraviolet irradiation has also been shown to prevent the replication of a component essential for chloroplast formation (Lyman *et al.*, 1961). The action spectrum of ultraviolet bleaching resembles the absorption spectrum of a nucleoprotein, with maxima around 280 and 260 mμ.

It has been shown that permanently bleached cells lack the chloroplast DNA component (Ray and Hanawalt, 1965; Edelman *et al.*, 1965). Thus it is possible that the self-replicating component affected by the bleaching treatment is the DNA itself. The data on the action spectrum of ultraviolet bleaching tends to support this possibility. A particularly high sensitivity of chloroplast DNA replication toward a variety of agents cannot at present be explained in terms of its biochemical properties. The chloroplast DNA is rich in thymine, and is therefore more susceptible to ultraviolet-induced thymine dimer formation (Setlow, 1963). Because of its low G–C content, it has a relatively low thermal denaturation temperature. It is doubtful, however, that these properties can account for the high sensitivity of the chloroplast-replicating system to the slightly elevated temperature of 34° C

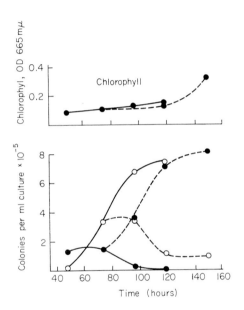

Fig. 15. Changes in the ability of *Euglena* cells to produce green colonies during bleaching and recovery. Cells grown in the light at 34.5°C; after 74 hours, a sample of the culture was placed at room temperature. Solid lines, culture at 34°C; broken lines, portion of culture returned to room temperature; solid circles, green colonies; open circles, bleached colonies. Reproduced from Brawerman and Chargaff (1960).

and to the ultraviolet treatment. The sensitivity of the chloroplast DNA could conceivably be based on its relatively low degree of methylation as compared to the nuclear DNA, but the physiological significance of methylated bases in DNA remains to be established. It is more likely, perhaps, that the sensitivity is determined either by the structural configuration of the DNA within the chloroplasts, or by a peculiar property of the DNA polymerase.

VII. Ribosomes and the Regulation of Chloroplast Protein Synthesis

A. INDUCTION AND REPRESSION OF CHLOROPLAST FORMATION

The synthesis of chloroplast proteins is readily affected by a variety of environmental factors which have essentially no effect on cell growth. Chloroplast formation in *E. gracilis* requires the continued presence of light. Removal of the light results in the cessation of synthesis of proteins associated with the chloroplasts. This includes structural proteins as well as soluble photosynthetic enzymes. The behavior of the TPN-dependent glyceraldehyde-3-phosphate dehydrogenase in the presence and absence of light is shown in Fig. 16.

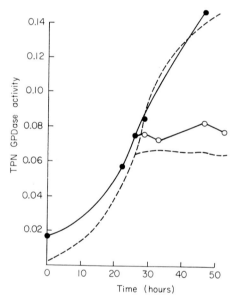

Fig. 16. Effect of light on the production of TPN glyceraldehyde 3-phosphate dehydrogenase in *Euglena*. Dark-grown cells exposed to light in a resting medium. After 26 hours, a portion of the cell suspension was returned to the dark. Solid circles, cells in the light; open circles, light removed; broken line, chlorophyll. Reproduced from Brawerman and Konigsberg (1960).

The synthesis of chloroplasts is also subject to selective repression by a variety of metabolites (App and Jagendorf, 1963). This accounts for the low chloroplast content of log-phase cultures growing in rich organic medium. Rapid chloroplast synthesis begins as the cells approach the stationary phase, presumably as a result of depletion of the repressing metabolites.

B. Regulation of Chloroplast Protein Synthesis during Bleaching

The behavior of chloroplast proteins during bleaching by growth at 34° C illustrates the strict regulatory control to which they are subject. During the early stages of the bleaching process, the chloroplasts increase at a linear rate, while the cells show the usual exponential rise. The formation of the photosynthetic enzyme, TPN glyceraldehyde-3-phosphate dehydrogenase, follows closely that of chlorophyll (Fig. 17). When the

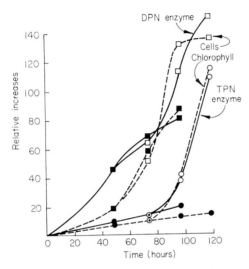

Fig. 17.   Formation of the glyceraldehyde 3-phosphate dehydrogenases during bleaching and recovery of *E. gracilis*. Cells grown in the light at 34.5°C (full circles and squares). After 49 hours, a portion of the culture was placed at room temperature (open circles and squares). Solid lines and circles, TPN enzyme; solid lines and squares, DPN enzyme; broken lines and circles, chlorophyll; broken lines and squares, cell number. Reproduced from Brawerman and Konigsberg (1960).

bleaching process is interrupted by return of the culture to a lower temperature, rapid chlorophyll synthesis resumes only after a long lag period. Again the formation of the enzyme follows that of the chlorophyll (Fig. 17). The behavior of the chloroplast structural proteins during this process has not been studied, and it should be of interest to know whether or not they follow the same pattern.

C. Significance of Specific Chloroplast Ribosomes

The occurrence of ribosomes in chloroplasts indicates that plastid proteins can be synthesized within these organelles. The possibility had been considered that these ribosomes, because of their peculiar RNA nucleotide composition, contribute to the determination of amino acid sequence in the chloroplast proteins, and thereby determine the nature of the proteins synthesized within the chloroplast structure (Brawerman, 1963a). It has been shown by Schwartz *et al.* (1965), however, that the chloroplast ribosomes do not appear to possess any coding specificity (see Section V,C). Thus the selective mechanism that determines the subcellular localization of chloroplast protein synthesis remains to be determined. One possibility is that messenger RNA molecules cannot cross the chloroplast membrane. This would insure the compartmentalization of cytoplasmic and chloroplast protein synthesis. The photosynthetic enzymes that are under the control of structural genes from the nucleus would then be synthesized in the cytoplasm, and a selective mechanism would be required for the transfer of these proteins into the chloroplasts.

The chloroplast ribosomes, with their distinct physical and biochemical properties, could play a role in the selective regulatory processes concerned with chloroplast protein synthesis. As discussed in Sections VII,A and VII,B, chloroplast formation can be strongly influenced by environmental factors that leave cytoplasmic protein synthesis largely unaffected. The synthesis of chloroplast proteins is also preferentially inhibited by chloramphenicol (Pogo and Pogo, 1965). Such selective effects on the formation of a large group of proteins could be achieved if the ribosomes concerned with the synthesis of these proteins were particularly sensitive to the regulatory agents. The effect of chloramphenicol provides a plausible model for such a mechanism, since its selective action on *in vivo* chloroplast protein synthesis can be directly accounted for by the sensitivity of the chloroplast ribosomes to this antibiotic.

References

App, A. A., and Jagendorf, A. T. (1963). *J. Protozool.* **10**, 340.
Blum, J. J., and Buetow, D. E. (1963). *Exptl. Cell Res.* **29**, 407.
Blum, J. J., and Padilla, G. M. (1962). *Exptl. Cell Res.* **28**, 512.
Brawerman, G. (1963a). *Biochim. Biophys. Acta* **72**, 317.
Brawerman, G. (1963b). *Biochim. Biophys. Acta* **76**, 322.
Brawerman, G. (1966). *In* "Biochemistry of Chloroplasts" (T. W. Goodwin, ed.), Vol. I, pp. 301–317. Academic Pres, New York.
Brawerman, G., and Chargaff, E. (1959). *Biochim. Biophys. Acta* **31**, 172.
Erawerman, G., and Chargaff, E. (1960). *Biochim. Biophys. Acta* **37**, 221.
Brawerman, G., and Eisenstadt, J. M. (1964a). *Biochim. Biophys. Acta* **91**, 477.
Brawerman, G., and Eisenstadt, J. M. (1964b). *J. Mol. Biol.* **10**, 403.
Brawerman, G., and Konigsberg, N. (1960). *Biochim. Biophys. Acta* **43**, 374.
Brawerman, G., and Shapiro, H. S. (1962). *In* "Comparative Biochemistry" (M. Florkin and H. S. Mason, eds.), Vol. IV, Part B, pp. 107–183. Academic Press, New York.

Brawerman, G., Rebman, C. A., and Chargaff, E. (1960). *Nature* **187**, 1037.
Brawerman, G., Pogo, A. O. and Chargaff, E. (1962a). *Biochim. Biophys. Acta* **55**, 326.
Brawerman, G., Hufnagel, D. A., and Chargaff, E. (1962b). *Biochim. Biophys. Acta* **61**, 340.
Brawerman, G., Gold, L., and Eisenstadt, J. M. (1963). *Proc. Natl. Acad. Sci. U.S.* **50**, 630.
Buetow, D. E., and Levedahl, B. H. (1962). *J. Gen. Microbiol.* **28**, 579.
Cook, J. R. (1961). *Biol. Bull.* **121**, 277.
Cook, J. R. (1963). *J. Protozool.* **10**, 436.
De Torres, R. A., and Pogo, A. O. (1965). *Anal. Biochem.* **13**, 281.
Edelman, M., Cowan, C. A., Epstein, II. T., and Schiff, J. A. (1964). *Proc. Natl. Acad. Sci. U.S.* **52**, 1214.
Edelman, M., Schiff, J. A., and Epstein, H. T. (1965). *J. Mol. Biol.* **11**, 769.
Edelman, M., Epstein, H. T., and Schiff, J. A. (1966). *J. Mol. Biol.* **17**, 463.
Edmunds, L. N., Jr. (1964). *Science* **145**, 266.
Eisenstadt, J. M., and Brawerman, G. (1964a). *J. Mol. Biol.* **10**, 392.
Eisenstadt, J. M., and Brawerman, G. (1964b). *Biochim. Biophys. Acta* **80**, 463.
Eisenstadt, J. M., and Brawerman, G. (1966). *Biochemistry* **5**, 2777.
Hadjivassiliou, A. G., and Brawerman, G. (1966). *J. Mol. Biol.* **20**, 1.
Leff, J., Mandel, M., Epstein, H. T., and Schiff, J. A. (1963). *Biochem. Biophys. Res. Commun.* **13**, 126.
Lyman, H., Epstein, H. T., and Schiff, J. A. (1961). *Biochim. Biophys. Acta* **50**, 301.
Nathans, D., Notani, G., Schwartz, J. H., and Zinder, N. D. (1962). *Proc. Natl. Acad. Sci. U.S.* **48**, 1424.
Neff, R. H. (1960). *J. Protozool.* **7**, 69.
Pogo, B. G. T., and Pogo, A. O. (1965). *J. Protozool.* **12**, 96.
Pogo, A. O., Brawerman, G., and Chargaff, E. (1962). *Biochemistry* **1**, 128.
Pogo, B. G. T., Ubero, I. R., and Pogo, A. O. (1966). *Exptl. Cell Res.* **42**, 58.
Ray, D. S., and Hanawalt, P. C. (1964). *J. Mol. Biol.* **9**, 812.
Ray, D. S., and Hanawalt, P. C. (1965). *J. Mol. Biol.* **11**, 760.
Schildkraut, C. L., Mandel, M., Levisohn, S., Smith-Sonneborn, J. E., and Marmur, J. (1962a). *Nature* **196**, 795.
Schildkraut, C. L., Marmur, J., and Doty, P. (1962b). *J. Mol. Biol.* **4**, 430.
Schwartz, J. H., Eisenstadt, J. M., Brawerman, G., and Zinder, N. D. (1965). *Proc. Natl. Acad. Sci. U.S.* **53**, 195.
Setlow, J. K. (1963). *Photochem. Photobiol.* **3**, 393.
Shah, V. C , and Lyman, H. (1966). *J. Cell Biol.* **29**, 174.
Smillie, R. M., and Krotkov, G. (1960). *Arch. Biochem. Biophys.* **89**, 83.

CHAPTER 6

LIPID METABOLISM*

Joseph A. Erwin

I. Introduction

The development of a new area of research is often dependent upon the discovery of the "right experimental animal," a role generally assigned in molecular biology and much of modern biochemistry to bacteria. The usefulness of bacteria as tools in research on the biosynthesis and function of lipids is limited by their inability to synthesize sterols and polyunsaturated fatty acids, compounds which are ubiquitous components of the membranes of eucaryotic cells. *Euglena* is a promising substitute since it grows well on simple and well-defined media, is richly endowed with pathways for lipid

* Preparation of this manuscript was supported by a grant from the National Science Foundation.

biosynthesis, and adapts its biochemical and physiological machinery to either a plant or animal mode of existence.

Our knowledge of lipid metabolism in euglenoids is largely confined to the results of studies on *Astasia longa*, *E. gracilis* var. *bacillaris*, and *E. gracilis* strain Z. Since most investigations have centered on *E. gracilis*, the name *Euglena* will be used without further qualification when referring to it.

Information derived from an analysis of the lipid composition of a microorganism may be considered a reliable reflection of its biosynthetic capacities only if the cells employed for analysis were grown on well-defined synthetic media. Most of the data on the lipids of *Euglena* cited here are the result of investigations that have satisfied this basic requirement, and where this is not the case it is so indicated. "Organic medium" is employed as a term for synthetic media containing sugar (Hutner *et al.*, 1956) or organic acids (Hutner *et al.*, 1949; Cramer and Myers, 1952) as carbon sources. "Mineral medium" refers to a medium often used for the photoauxotrophic growth of *Euglena*, containing vitamins, salts, and a chelator (Cramer and Myers, 1952).

It must be recognized that even when euglenoids are cultivated on lipid-free synthetic media minor variations in media composition may result in striking changes in lipid composition. The substitution of ethanol for acetate as a carbon source alters the lipid content of *Astasia* (Buetow and Padilla, 1963), and the use of less expensive grades of sucrose in the synthetic medium of Hutner *et al.* (1956) results in a large increase in the amounts of saturated C_{10} to C_{14} fatty acids in *Euglena* (D. Hulanicka and K. Bloch, personal communication). Also, it is well known that variations in the lipid composition of microorganisms arise as the result of variations in culture conditions (temperature, length of incubation, etc.). However, as there have been no systematic investigations of the effect of such parameters on the lipid composition of euglenoids, their contribution to most of the results cited in this study cannot be evaluated.

II. Lipid Composition of Euglenoids

A. FATTY ACIDS

The development of gas–liquid chromatography and other techniques that permit the rapid separation and identification of small amounts of fatty acids has permitted the accumulation of comparative data on the fatty acid composition of a variety of microorganisms, plants, and animals (see reviews: Shorland, 1962; Erwin and Bloch, 1964), and several generalizations concerning the fatty acids of eucaryotic organisms may be made from this information.

First, straight-chain saturated or unsaturated fatty acids containing 12 to 14 carbon atoms (usually an even number) predominate. Second, unsaturated fatty acids found in nature usually have the all-cis configuration. Third, the single double bond of monoenoic fatty acids is usually located between carbon atoms 9 and 10, counting from the carboxyl end of the molecule, and palmitoleic ($9\text{-}C_{16}$)* and oleic ($9\text{-}C_{18}$) acids occur most frequently. Finally, fatty acids containing multiple double bonds are found in natural sources in wide variety, their structures differing in the length of the carbon chain, the degree of unsaturation, and the location of the double bonds. The more abundant of these fatty acids have multiple double bond systems of the methylene-interrupted type and can be assigned to one of two principal categories, one represented by α-linolenic acid ($9,12,15\text{-}C_{18}$), and the other represented by γ-linolenic ($6,9,12\text{-}C_{18}$) and arachidonic ($5,8,11,14\text{-}C_{20}$) acids. Compounds of the α-linolenic type are of widespread occurrence in photosynthetic microorganisms and higher plants, while fatty acids of the γ-linolenic type are widespread in "animal-like" protists (zooflagellates, amoeba, and ciliates) and metazoa.

Table I lists the major fatty acids of *Astasia*, and wild-type and achloro-plastid mutants of both strain Z and var. *bacillaris Euglena* cells, taken from logarithmic phase cultures grown on synthetic media (Erwin and Bloch, 1962, 1963b; Hulanicka *et al.*, 1964). The identity of the fatty acids was established by gas–liquid chromatography of their methyl esters, together with information obtained by the degradation of individual components and the identification of the products (Erwin and Bloch, 1962, 1963b; Hulanicka *et al.*, 1964). A more extensive study of *Euglena* in which 61 fatty acids were identified has been made by Korn (1964).

Myristic and palmitic acids are the major saturated fatty acids and oleic and hexadecenoic acids are the major monounsaturated fatty acids in *Astasia* and all *Euglena* strains (Table I). *Euglena* can synthesize substantial amounts of all the common C_{18} and C_{20} polyenoic fatty acids (Table I) of both plants and animals, a trait previously demonstrated in several species of the chrysomonad *Ochromonas* (Haines *et al.*, 1962; Erwin *et al.*, 1964) A number of C_{22} polyenes from *Euglena*, including $7,10,13,16\text{-}C_{22}$, $4,7,10,13,16\text{-}C_{22}$, $7,10,13,16,19\text{-}C_{22}$, and $4,7,10,13,16,19\text{-}C_{22}$, have also been identified

---

* The subscript number refers to the number of carbon atoms in the fatty acid and each prefix number refers to a double bond and its localization (counting from the caboxyl end of the molecule); thus $9\text{-}C_{18}$ and $9,12\text{-}C_{18}$ would both be fatty acids containing 18 carbon atoms but the former would have a single double bond between carbon atoms 9 and 10, while the latter would have two double bonds, one between carbon atoms 9 and 10 and a second between carbon atoms 12 and 13.

Table I

MAJOR FATTY ACIDS OF EUGLENOIDS[a]

Fatty Acid	E. gracilis Z					E. gracilis var. bacillaris grown in light on organic medium			Astasia longa
	Wild type			Bleached mutant grown in light on organic medium		Wild type	Bleached mutant		
	Light-grown		Dark-grown						
	Inorganic medium	Organic medium		WZXL	W₂ZSL		W₃BUL	W₈BHL	
Myristic	7.2	7.4	11.6	11.8	13.0	12.8	2.3	3.0	15.2
Palmitic	13.9	14.7	19.4	23.5	29.2	14.2	23.1	8.8	16.7
Hexadecenoic	6.0	5.9	16.0	3.1	4.0	4.0	3.3	3.3	3.8
7,10-Hexadecadienoic	2.8	0	0	0	0	0	0	0	0
4,7,10,11-Hexadecatetraenoic	16.0	Trace	0	0	0	0	0	0	0
Stearic	0.6	6.7	1.8	0.8	1.3	7.4	1.1	0.8	4.5
Oleic	10.0	7.4	7.2	6.6	7.2	7.5	9.1	5.4	7.4
Linoleic	3.6	5.0	2.2	1.4	3.1	2.6	2.0	1.5	1.4
α-Linolenic	31.5	21.4	2.2	1.6	Trace	15.8	1.1	0.7	0
Total C_{20} + C_{22} + C_{24} Polyenoic	8.3	25.4	40.6	35.4	34.4	15.7	42.4	64.9	32.0
11,14-Eicosadienoic	—	—	3.1	—	—	—	—	—	4.8
8,11,14-Eicosatrienoic	—	—	1.1	—	—	—	—	—	4.4
11,14,17-Eicosatrienoic + arachidonic	3.3	—	10.0	—	—	—	—	—	17.6
8,11,14,17-Eicosatetraenoic	—	—	2.6	—	—	—	—	—	—
5,8,11,14,17-Eicosapentaenoic	2.3	—	9.7	—	—	—	—	—	4.3
C_{22} + C_{24} Polyenoic	2.2	—	13.0	—	—	—	—	—	—

[a] From data in Erwin and Bloch (1962, 1963b), Hulanicka et al. (1964).

(Korn, 1964). *Euglena* differs from *Ochromonas* in synthesizing several polyunsaturated C_{16} fatty acids of a type previously reported only in algae and higher plants (Klenk and Knipprath, 1959; Allen *et al.*, 1964). *Astasia* and achloroplastid mutants of both *Euglena* strains synthesize only the animal type of polyenoic acids (Table I). The effects of environmental conditions on the fatty acid composition of *Euglena* will be discussed below (Section IV,A).

B. GLYCEROL ESTERS OF FATTY ACIDS

The bulk of the fatty acids found in cells are usually components of one of two classes of glycerol esters. Neutral glycerides in which glycerol is esterified with one to three fatty acid residues (mono-, di-, and triglycerides) constitute one type. A second series consists essentially of a diglyceride linked to some more polar moiety, usually either a phosphate ester or a sugar.

1. *Neutral Glycerides*

Euglena contains substantial amounts of either di- or triglycerides, depending on culture conditions. It has been suggested that the first are primarily intermediates in glycolipid formation and the second primarily a carbon reserve (Hulanicka *et al.*, 1964).

2. *Phospholipids*

The common phospholipids consist of a diglyceride esterified with phosphate, which in turn is linked to choline (phosphatidyl choline or lecithin), or to ethanolamine (phosphatidyl ethanolamine), or to the amino acid serine (phosphatidyl serine), or to inositol (phosphatidyl inositol). All of these phospholipids appear to be present in *Euglena* (Rosenberg, 1963; Hulanicka *et al.*, 1964), but have not been unequivocally identified.

3. *Glycolipids*

a. Galactolipids. It is known, primarily from the work of Benson and Shibuya (1962), that monogalactosyl diglyceride and digalactosyl diglyceride are major and typical lipids of photosynthetic organisms. Hence it is not surprising that galactolipids are synthesized by *Euglena* (Carter *et al.*, 1961; Rosenberg, 1963; Hulanicka *et al.*, 1964).

b. Sulfolipids. Glycolipids in which a sulfate group is attached to the sugar moiety are widespread in nature, particularly in photosynthetic organisms (Benson and Shibuya, 1962). The presence of sulfolipids in *Euglena* and their incorporation of radioactive sulfate has been reported (Abraham and Bachhawat, 1963; Rosenberg, 1963; Davies *et al.*, 1966). The structure of the *Euglena* sulfolipid has been identified as (6-sulfoquinovosyl)-1-diglyceride, and thus is identical with that found in green algae and higher plants (Davies *et al.*, 1965). Enzymic studies of the formation of the *Euglena* sulfolipid have been carried out (Abraham and Bachhawat, 1963; Davies *et al.*, 1966), and a pathway for its biosynthesis proposed (Davies *et al.*, 1966).

4. Waxes

Old (10–14 days) cultures of *Euglena* have been reported to accumulate large amounts of a wax, consisting of simple esters of satured odd- and even-chain alcohols and saturated odd- and even-chain fatty acids predominantly of myristyl myristate (Rosenberg, 1963; Guehler *et al.*, 1964).

C. STEROLS

Ergosterol has been shown to be the major sterol of *Euglena*, accounting for 0.05–0.1% of the total dry weight of the organism. The identification of the sterol was made on the basis of its chromatographic behavior on alumina, its ultraviolet spectrum, its reaction with the Liebermann–Burchard reagent and the melting point and infrared spectrum of its acetate derivative (Stern *et al.*, 1960). Both light- and dark-grown cells of strain Z and var. *bacillaris* plus several achloroplastid mutants derived from these two strains contain ergosterol. No significant amounts of other sterols have been detected (Stern *et al.*, 1960).

Ergosterol has also been identified by gas–liquid chromatography and ultraviolet spectrophotometry in extracts of *Astasia ocellata* and *Peranema trichophorum* (Williams *et al.*, 1966). Large amounts of cholesterol were found in *Peranema* extracts; however, since both of these organisms were grown on crude medium it is probable that the cholesterol was of exogenous origin.

The presence of ergosterol in *Euglena* is not surprising since it is the common sterol of a variety of phyto- and zooflagellates (Aaronson and Baker, 1961; Halvey and Sarel, 1965; Kusel and Weber, 1965; Williams *et al.*, 1966; Meyer and Holz, 1966).

D. CAROTENOIDS AND OTHER FAT-SOLUBLE COMPONENTS

The carotenoids of euglenoids and other phytoflagellates have been the subject of a thorough review (Goodwin, 1964), and therefore the subject will be only briefly summarized here. The major carotenoids of light-grown *Euglena* (both strain Z and var. *bacillaris*) have been identified as antheraxanthin (3,3′-dihydroxy-5,6-epoxy-β-carotene), β-carotene, and neoxanthin (Krinsky and Goldsmith, 1960). Cryptoxanthin and γ-carotene are minor components; no astaxanthin could be detected (Krinsky and Goldsmith, 1960). The structure of neoxanthin from *Euglena* has been reported to be 3,3',5'-trihydroxy-6-hydro-5,6-epoxy-β-carotene (Schimmer and Krinsky, 1966). The carotenoids of dark-grown *Euglena* of var. *bacillaris* (Goodwin and Jamikorn, 1954) or achloroplastid mutants of the same strain (Goodwin and Gross, 1958) are drastically reduced in content and show qualitative changes in composition. *Astasia* appears to be virtually devoid of carotenoids (Blum *et al.*, 1965).

The eyespots of *Euglena* have been isolated, and the pigments present identified on the basis of their chromatographic and spectrophotometric behavior and partition coefficients. "Lutein" (probably antheraxanthin) and cryptoxanthin comprise 83% of the pigments with β-carotene and an unidentified component constituting the rest (Batra and Tollin, 1964). Again, no astaxanthin could be isolated (Batra and Tollin, 1964).

Studies on the enzymic transformation of carotenoids in *Euglena* and their possible physiological significance have also recently been reported (Bamji and Krinsky, 1965). The absence of retinene and vitamin A in both strain Z and var. *bacillaris Euglena* has been reported (Krinsky and Goldsmith, 1960).

III. Biosynthesis of Fatty Acids

A. SATURATED FATTY ACIDS*

The sequential condensation of malonyl-ACP units constitutes the principal if not the exclusive pathway for the *de novo* biosynthesis of long-chain saturated fatty acids in microorganisms, plants, and animals (Majerus *et al.*, 1964; Brooks and Stumpf, 1965). Presumably this also holds for *Euglena*, although it has not been experimentally demonstrated. Recently, however, claims have been made for the presence of an alternate pathway in *Euglena*. Extracts from *Euglena* incorporate ^{14}C-labeled acetyl-CoA into long-chain fatty acids, and evidence has been offered to show that this represents *de novo* synthesis (Cheniae, 1963, 1964; Cheniae and Kerr, 1965). The enzyme preparation required both DPNH and TPNH plus ATP and Mg^{2+} (Cheniae, 1963). Since the system did not show the inhibition by avidin nor stimulation by the addition of bicarbonate usually associated with the malonate condensation pathway in other organisms, it was suggested that an alternative pathway might be operating (Cheniae, 1963). The superiority of acetyl-CoA over malonyl-CoA as a substrate demonstrated in this

---

* Abbreviations: ACP, acyl carrier protein; CoA, coenzyme A; DPNH, reduced diphosphopyridine nucleotide; TPNH, reduced triphosphopyridine nucleotide; ATP, adenosine triphosphate.

organism was interpreted as additional evidence for this view (Cheniae, 1964; Cheniae and Kerr, 1965). However, malonyl-ACP was not tested and further investigation is required.

B. UNSATURATED FATTY ACIDS

1. *Monounsaturated Fatty Acids*

The biosynthesis of monounsaturated fatty acids constitutes an exception to the rule that basic cellular components arise by a single pathway of synthesis common to all biological systems. In some eubacteria a pathway (Fig. 1) is found which is part of a soluble fatty acid synthetase system and which synthesizes monounsaturated fatty acids via the β,γ-dehydration of medium-chain β-hydroxy acids and the subsequent chain elongation of the resulting 3-enoates (Bloch *et al.*, 1961). This pathway operates under anaerobic conditions and produces only monoenoic fatty acids (Bloch *et al.*, 1961).

A second pathway exists which requires molecular oxygen and in which acyl-CoA esters of long-chain fatty acids are desaturated to the corresponding

1. Anaerobic pathway (Bacteria)

$$C_8 \xrightarrow{+C_2} 3\text{-}C_{10} \xrightarrow{+4C_2} 11\text{-}C_{18} \text{ (Vaccenic acid)}$$

$$C_{10} \xrightarrow{+C_2} 3\text{-}C_{12} \xrightarrow{+3C_2} 9\text{-}C_{18} \text{ (Oleic acid)}$$

2. Oxidative desaturation system I (Heterotrophic *Euglena*, various protists, metazoa)

$$\text{Stearyl-CoA} \xrightarrow[\text{(Particulate system)}]{O_2 \text{ ; TPNH}} \text{Oleic acid}$$

3. Oxidative desaturation system II (Photoauxotrophic *Euglena*, green algae, metaphyta)

$$\text{Stearyl-ACP} \xrightarrow[\text{(Soluble enzymes)}]{O_2 \text{ ; TPNH}} \text{Oleic acid}$$

4. Oxidative desaturation system III [Photoauxotrophic *Euglena*, green algae (?) metaphyta (?)]

$$C_{12} \xrightarrow{O_2 (?)} 3\text{-}C_{12} \xrightarrow{+2C_2} 7\text{-}C_{16} \xrightarrow{+C_2} 9\text{-}C_{18}$$

$$C_{10} \xrightarrow{O_2 (?)} 3\text{-}C_{10} \xrightarrow{+3C_2} 9\text{-}C_{12} \xrightarrow{+C_2} 11\text{-}C_{18}$$

Fig. 1. Biosynthesis of monounsaturated fatty acids.

cis-9-monoenoic acids by particle-bound enzymes, and the same mechanism appears to be utilized for the production of polyenoic acids. This "direct (or oxidative) desaturation" pathway occurs in a variety of phylogenetic groups—in some gram-positive eubacteria, in actinomycetes, in fungi, in blue-green algae, in chrysomonads, in the "animal protist" line (amoeba, zooflagellates, and ciliates), and in metazoa (for review, see Erwin and Bloch, 1964).

A third pathway has been postulated to exist in higher plants, primarily on the basis of the negative outcome of experiments by Stumpf and his collaborators (1962) which attempted to demonstrate in plants the existence of either the direct desaturation or the anaerobic pathway. Comparative studies have indicated that the unidentified "plant pathway" operates in the "plant protist" line (green algae, phytomonads, and euglenoids) as well as in higher plants (see review, Erwin and Bloch, 1964). Recent investigations by Nagai and Bloch (1965) have partially elucidated the mechanism of the "plant pathway." From this research it appears that three distinct "oxidative desaturation" systems exist in *Euglena*, environmental conditions determining which one is operative.

System I (Fig. 1) represents a particulate enzyme preparation which can be obtained from strictly heterotropic cultures (grown on organic medium in the dark) of *Euglena*. It catalyzes the formation of oleic acid from stearyl-CoA in the presence of molecular oxygen and TPNH (Nagai and Bloch, 1965), and is presumably identical with the enzyme system responsible for the direct desaturation pathway found in animals and many protists (as described above). System I is the only mechanism for monounsaturated fatty acid biosynthesis present in heterotrophic *Euglena* and it cannot be isolated from strictly photoauxotrophic (grown on mineral medium and carbon dioxide in the light) cultures (Nagai and Bloch, 1965). Presumably, system I is also responsible for the ability of intact cells of *Astasia* to desaturate ^{14}C-labeled stearic acid to oleate (Erwin *et al.*, 1964; Hulanicka *et al.*, 1964).

System II (Fig. 1) represents a soluble enzyme system that can be isolated from strictly photoauxotrophic cultures of *Euglena* but not from strictly heterotrophic cultures (Nagai and Bloch, 1965). The system will desaturate stearyl-ACP but not stearyl-CoA to oleate, and requires TPNH and molecular oxygen (Nagai and Bloch, 1965). System II has also been isolated from higher plants (Nagai and Bloch, 1965) and is presumably present in other photosynthetic organisms reported to possess the "plant pathway" of monoenoic fatty acid biosynthesis. Apparently, in system II the thiol ester bond of stearyl-ACP produced by the malonyl-ACP condensation system is conserved, and no mechanism exists for the formation of stearyl-ACP from free stearate. System II from *Euglena* has recently been demonstrated to consist of three distinct enzymes: a desaturase that is specific for stearyl-

ACP, a TPNH oxidase, and ferredoxin. All three enzymes are required for the production of oleate (Nagai and Bloch, 1966). It is of interest that *Euglena* grown on organic medium in the light contains enzymes of both system I and system II (Nagai and Bloch, 1965).

There is probably yet a third mechanism in *Euglena* for the biosynthesis of monoenoic fatty acids. Enzymes for the postulated pathway represented by system III (Fig. 1) have not been isolated from *Euglena*, but the suggested intermediates have (Nagai and Bloch, 1965). System III represents essentially an aerobic version of the bacterial mechanism in that monoenoic acids are produced by the chain elongation of β,γ-unsaturated intermediate chain-length fatty acids. Unlike system I and II this mechanism yields several isomers of palmitoleic acid (Fig. 1), and these would provide the requisite starting material for the biosynthesis of the C_{16} polyenes found in photo-auxotrophic *Euglena* (Hulanicka *et al.*, 1964), green algae (Klenk and Knipprath, 1959), and higher plants (Allen *et al.*, 1964). System III apparently exists only in *Euglena* grown as strict photoauxotrophs (Nagai and Bloch, 1965).

The possibility that hydroxy acids may be intermediates in the formation of unsaturated fatty acids in the oxidative desaturation type of mechanism has been tested in system II isolated from *Euglena*, and several ACP acyl esters of hydroxystearate, acetoxystearate and epoxystearate were shown not to be precursors of oleate under the experimental conditions employed (Gurr and Bloch, 1966). Either 9 or 10 hydroxystearyl-ACP derivatives were desaturated to their keto form (oxostearate) but not to olefinic acids (Gurr and Bloch, 1966).

2. Polyunsaturated Fatty Acids

The ability to continue the desaturation of oleic acid to form multiple unsaturated fatty acids appears to be a property of almost all organisms, bacteria being the sole exeption (Erwin and Bloch, 1964). Although the mechanism appears to be basically similar to that employed for monoenoic fatty acid formation, little is known about the enzymology of polyenoic fatty acid biosynthesis (see review, Erwin and Bloch, 1964), except that additional coenzymes may be required (Meyer and Bloch, 1963).

As has been indicated above (Section II,A) there are two different categories of polyunsaturated fatty acids, and these are the result of the fact that further desaturation of oleic acid can proceed in two different directions. In one sequence (the α-linolenate or "plant pathway"), oleate is progressively desaturated toward the methyl end of the molecule, producing linoleic and α-linolenic acids. In the second sequence, linoleate is also formed initially but all subsequent double bonds are placed between the 9,10-position and the carboxyl end of the molecule. This carboxyl or γ-linolenate type of desaturation in conjunction with chain elongation leads to the formation of arachidonate and other C_{20} and C_{22} polyunsaturated fatty acids (see review, Erwin and Bloch, 1964).

It is evident from the fatty acid composition of *Euglena* (Table I) that the organism contains the enzymes for both pathways (Erwin and Bloch, 1962, 1963b; Rosenberg, 1963; Korn, 1964; Hulanicka *et al.*, 1964). Direct evidence for the existence of several pathways of polyenoic acid biosynthesis and an estimate of their relative rates of operation has been obtained by employing "double labeling" experiments in which a ^{14}C-labeled intermediate of one pathway and an ^{3}H-labeled intermediate of a second were fed to *Euglena* simultaneously (Hulanicka *et al.*, 1964). Figure 2 outlines the major pathways of polyenoic fatty acid biosynthesis demonstrated to be operative in *Euglena* (Hulanicka *et al.*, 1964) (several interconversions that form minor pathways are not listed). Apparently arachidonic acid can be synthesized by *Euglena* (Fig. 2) from linoleic acid by two routes: either by way of $6,9,12$-C_{18} (γ-linolenic acid) and $8,11,14$-C_{20} (homo-γ-linolenic acid), which is the major route demonstrated in vertebrates (Mead, 1960), or by initial chain elongation to $11,14$-C_{20} followed by two carboxyl-directed desaturations, a pathway shown to be a minor route in rat liver (Stoffel, 1963).

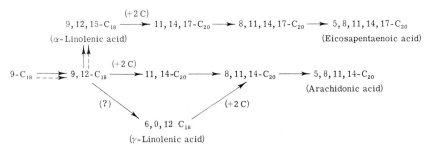

Fig. 2. Major pathways of polyunsatured C_{18} and C_{20} acids in *Euglena*. Arrows with dotted lines indicate major pathways in photoauxotrophic, and those with solid lines indicate major pathways in heterotrophic cells.

IV. Physiological and Environmental Influences on Lipid Biosynthesis

A. Effects of Light and Dark Growth

1. On Fatty Acid Biosynthesis

Comparative studies have indicated that an evolutionary trend exists toward biochemical specialization in lipid biosynthesis. This is reflected in the conservation of the α-linolenate pathway by higher plants and of the γ-linolenate pathway by animals, thus suggesting that structural differences in polyenoic acids may be of physiological importance (Erwin and Bloch, 1964; Erwin *et al.*, 1964). *Euglena* possesses the genetic capacity to produce the enzymes of both pathways and mimics the "animal" and "plant" modes of life by growing photoauxotrophically in the light and adapting to growth on organic media in the dark by surpressing the development of its photosynthetic organelles. Thus it offers the opportunity to test experimentally the question of a correlation between physiological activity and fatty acid (or lipid) structure.

The results of such an experiment are shown in Table I. *Euglena* grown in the light on organic medium contains large amounts of α-linolenic acid (Erwin and Bloch, 1962, 1963b) while *Euglena* grown in the dark contains virtually no α-linolenate but greatly increased amounts of C_{20}, C_{22}, and C_{24} polyenoic acids of the γ-linolenate type (Table I). This effect is correlated with the existence of a functional chloroplast, since achloroplastid mutants grown in the same medium in the light have a fatty acid spectrum similar to dark-grown wild-type cells (Table I) (Erwin and Bloch, 1962, 1963b). Illumination of logarithmic-phase dark-grown cells produces a steady increase in α-linolenate content and a decrease in the C_{20}, C_{22}, and C_{24} polyenoic acids, as the cells become progressively more green (Erwin and Bloch, 1962, 1963b). Illumination of stationary-phase *Euglena* resuspended in a non-nutrient medium also produces greening, accompanied by an increase in α-linolenate content. Apparently this takes place primarily at the expense of the wax that accumulates in older *Euglena* cultures (Rosenberg, 1963). If *Euglena* is cultured as a strict photoauxotroph, α-linolenate accounts for one-third of the total cellular lipid (Table I), and only very small amounts of C_{20}, C_{22}, and C_{24} polyenoic acids can be detected. Furthermore, photosynthetic *Euglena* grown on mineral media, in contrast to those grown on organic media, synthesize substantial amounts of C_{16} polyenes characteristically found only in green algae and photosynthetic tissues of higher plants (see Section II,A and Table I). Thus, although *Euglena* possesses the genetic information necessary for making both the α- and γ-linolenate families of polyenoic acids, only the former accumulate in *Euglena* dependent upon photosynthesis for its energy supply, while only the latter are found in *Euglena* dependent upon organic carbon sources for energy. Less dramatic but essentially similar results have been obtained in comparable experiments on *Chlamydomonas* mutants (Erwin and Bloch, 1962, 1963b), on a mutant of *Scenedesmus* (Erwin and Bloch, 1963b), and on the leaves of bush beans (Wallace and Newman, 1965). Additional evidence for different physiological functions for polyenoic fatty acids of the α- and γ-linolenate type is provided by the finding that α-linolenate is almost exclusively a chloroplast constituent in photosynthetic *Euglena*

(Erwin and Bloch, 1962, 1963b; Rosenberg et al., 1965) as is also true of other photosynthetic systems (Debuch, 1961; Zill and Harmon, 1962; Levin et al, 1964). In contrast, arachidonic acid is localized in the limiting membrane of the cell and in the outer membrane of the undifferentiated plastids in heterotrophic Euglena (Rosenberg et al., 1965).

The absence of significant quantities of α-linolenate in heterotrophic Euglena is apparently not due to a cessation of α-linolenate synthesis. Experiments employing radioactive tracers indicate that when Euglena is grown in the dark, α-linolenate continues to be formed at a significant rate, but instead of accumulating it enters an "animal-type" pathway of polyenoic acid synthesis in which there is chain elongation and desaturation toward the carboxyl end of the molecule (Fig. 2) to yield primarily eicosapentanoic acid, a prominent component of heterotrophic cells (Hulanicka et al., 1964).

2. On Lipid Biosynthesis

In Euglena adaptation from a photosynthetic to a heterotrophic mode of life is accompanied by a marked shift in the biosynthesis of intact lipids as well as fatty acids. As can be seen in Table II, the major lipids of the photosynthetic cells, galactolipids and diglycerides, are replaced by phospholipids, particularly lecithin (Hulanicka et al., 1964). The sulfolipid content is also decreased (Rosenberg, 1963; Abraham and Bachhawat, 1963; Davies et al., 1966). When heterotrophic Euglena are illuminated and chloroplast development initiated, sulfolipids appear first, followed by chlorophyll and then by galactolipids (Rosenberg and Pecker, 1964).

Table II

LIPIDS OF PHOTOAUXOTROPHIC AND HETEROTROPHIC E. gracilis Z

Lipid class	Presence of galactose	Photoauxotrophic cells		Heterotrophic cells	
		Total lipids (%)	Total α-linolenic acid (%)	Total lipids (%)	Total C_{20}, C_{22}, C_{24} polyunsaturated fatty acids (%)
Neutral lipids	0	8.2[a]	19.2	20.5[b]	1.2
Galactolipids	+	70.4	69.8	5.9	1.6
Serine and ethanolamine phospholipids	0	16.4	9.0	18.7	28.1
Choline phospholipids	0	4.5	2.0	55.6	69.1

[a] Primarily diglycerides.
[b] Primarily triglycerides.

Virtually all of the α-linolenic and C_{16} polyenoic fatty acids of photo-auxotrophic *Euglena* are found in galactolipids (Hulanicka *et al.*, 1964) and in sulfolipids (Davies *et al.*, 1965). Such a distribution is also found in algae and higher plants (Benson and Shibuya, 1962). The sulfolipids are primarily chloroplast components in green *Euglena*, but they probably are synthesized in the microsomes (Davies *et al.*, 1966). Since α-linolenic acid is localized in the *Euglena* chloroplasts (see Section IV,A), the bulk of the galactolipids must also be localized there. Again, the situation is comparable to that found in algae and higher plants (Benson and Shibuya, 1962; Levin *et al.*, 1964; Allen *et al.*, 1964).

In contrast, almost all of the C_{20}, C_{22}, and C_{24} polyenoic fatty acids of the γ-linolenate type are found in phospholipids in heterotrophic *Euglena* (Hulanicka *et al.*, 1964). This is similar to the distribution found in ciliates (Erwin and Bloch, 1963a) and in metazoa (Shorland, 1962).

B. EFFECTS OF METABOLIC INHIBITORS

Aaronson and his collaborators (1962; Aaronson and Bensky, 1965) tested the effects of a variety of hypercholesteremic agents including triparanol on *Euglena* and other protists, and reported that their growth inhibitory effects could be reversed by the addition of unsaturated fatty acids but not by sterols including ergosterol. Similar effects in experiments with triparanol on a variety of yeasts, algae, and protozoa suggest that triparanol may be an inhibitor of unsaturated fatty acid biosynthesis and, although triparanol is a potent inhibitor of cholesterol biosynthesis, that it is comparatively inactive against ergosterol biosynthesis (Rosenbaum *et al.*, 1965).

V. Conclusion

Plantlike protists and higher plants contain a class of glycolipids which have as major constituents polyenoic fatty acids containing a specific pattern of double bond arrangement—α-linolenic acid. In contrast, animal-like protists and higher animals generally synthesize polyenoic acids possessing an alternative pattern of double bond arrangement—the γ-linolenic series—and these are primarily constituents of phospholipids. This biochemical and phylogenetic distribution of polyenoic fatty acids of alternative structure might simply reflect a fortuitous loss in ancestral forms of the genetic information for the biosynthesis of one or the other type of polyunsaturated fatty acid.

The information accumulated from studies on *Euglena* suggests an alternative explanation. This phytoflagellate possesses the capacity to synthesize both types of polyenoic fatty acids, but it preferentially synthesizes one or the other type depending on the kind of metabolism that is the major energy source under the chosen experimental conditons. Organisms that derive their energy from photosynthesis seem to require α-linolenate containing glycolipids while those dependent upon a heterotrophic type of metabolism require large amounts of phospholipids containing the γ-linolenate series. The evidence is therefore strong that the α-linolenate glycolipids formed by *Euglena* grown in the light are associated with some function of the chloroplast. The localization of α-linolenate-containing glycolipids in the chloroplasts of *Euglena* and other photosynthetic organisms supports this concept.

The exact function of such lipids and the relationship of this function to their specific structure is unknown. Such glycolipids are not absolute requirements for the essential biochemical reaction of photosynthesis since all photosynthetic bacteria and some blue-green algae (Harris *et al.*, 1965) are devoid of polyenoic fatty acids. On the other hand, the ultrastructure of the photosynthetic apparatus of *Euglena*, green algae, and higher plants is considerably more complex than that of procaryotic photosynthetic organisms, and presumably this increase in complexity has some functional significance. Such an elaboration of morphological structure must result from an increase in the complexity and structural specificity on the molecular level. The specific structure of the α-linolenate containing glycolipids characteristic of green *Euglena* and other eucaryotic photosynthetic organisms may result in the formation of chloroplast lamellar membranes having a more efficient arrangement of the components responsible for photosynthetic electron transfer and photophosphorylation.

References

Aaronson, S., and Baker, H. (1961). *J. Protozool.* **8**, 274.
Aaronson, S., and Bensky, B. (1965). *J. Protozool.* **12**, 236.
Aaronson, S., Bensky, B., Shifrine, M., and Baker, H. (1962). *Proc. Soc. Exptl. Biol. Med.* **109**, 130.
Abraham, A., and Bachhawat, B. K. (1963). *Biochim. Biophys. Acta* **70**, 104.
Allen, C. F., Good, P., Davis, H. F., and Fowler, S. D. (1964). *Biochem. Biophys. Res. Commun.* **15**, 424.
Bamji, M. S., and Krinsky, N. I. (1965). *J. Biol. Chem.* **240**, 467.
Batra, P. P., and Tollin, G. (1964). *Biochim. Biophys. Acta* **79**, 371.
Benson, A. A., and Shibuya, I. (1962). *In* "Physiology and Biochemistry of Algae" (R. A. Lewin, ed.), pp. 371–383. Academic Press, New York.
Bloch, K., Baronowsky, P., Goldfine, H., Lennarz, W. J., Light, R., Norris, A. T., and Scheuerbrandt, S. (1961). *Federation Proc.* **20**, 921.
Blum, J. J., Sommer, J. R., and Kahn, V. (1965). *J. Protozool.* **12**, 202.
Brooks, J. L., and Stumpf, P. K. (1965). *Biochim. Biophys. Acta* **98**, 213.
Buetow, D. E., and Padilla, G. M. (1963). *J. Protozool.* **10**, 121.
Carter, H. E., Ohno, K., Nojima, S., Tipton, C. L., and Stanacev, N. Z. (1961). *J. Lipid Res.* **2**, 215.

Cheniae, G. M. (1963). *Biochim. Biophys. Acta* **70**, 504.
Cheniae, G. M. (1964). *Arch. Biochem. Biophys.* **105**, 163.
Cheniae, G. M., and Kerr, P. C. (1965). *Plant Physiol.* **40**, 452.
Cramer, M., and Myers, J. (1952). *Arch. Mikrobiol.* **17**, 384.
Davies, W. H., Mercer, E. I., and Goodwin, T. W. (1965). *Phytochemistry* **4**, 741.
Davies, W. H., Mercer, E. I., and Goodwin, T. W. (1966). *Biochem. J.* **98**, 369.
Debuch, H. Z. (1961). *Z. Naturforsch.* **16b**, 246.
Erwin, J., and Bloch, K. (1962). *Biochem. Biophys. Res. Commun.* **9**, 103.
Erwin, J., and Bloch, K. (1963a). *J. Biol. Chem.* **238**, 1618.
Erwin, J., and Bloch, K. (1963b). *Biochem. Z.* **338**, 496.
Erwin, J., and Bloch, K. (1964). *Science* **143**, 1006.
Erwin, J., Hulanicka, D., and Bloch, K. (1964). *Comp. Biochem. Physiol.* **12**, 191.
Goodwin, T. W. (1964). *In* "Biochemistry and Physiology of Protozoa" (S. H. Hutner, ed.), Vol. III, pp. 319–339. Academic Press, New York.
Goodwin, T. W., and Gross, J. A. (1958). *J. Protozool.* **5**, 292.
Goodwin, T. W., and Jamikorn, M. (1954). *J. Protozool.* **1**, 216.
Guehler, P. F., Peterson, L., Tsuchiya, H. M., and Dodson, R. M. (1964). *Biochim. Biophys. Acta* **106**, 294.
Gurr, M. I., and Bloch, K. (1966). *Biochem. J.* **99**, 16c.
Haines, T. H., Aaronson, S., Gellerman, J. L., and Schlenk, H. (1962). *Nature* **194**, 1282.
Halvey, S., and Sarel, S. (1965). *J. Protozool.* **12**, 293.
Harris, R. V., Wood, B. J., and James, A. T. (1965). *Biochem. J.* **94**, 22p.
Hulanicka, D., Erwin, J., and Bloch, K. (1964). *J. Biol. Chem.* **239**, 2778.
Hutner, S. H., Provasoli, L., Stokstad, E. L. R., Hoffmann. C. E., Belt, M., Franklin, A. L., and Jukes, T. H. (1949). *Proc. Soc. Exptl. Biol. Med.* **70**, 118.
Hutner, S. H., Bach, M. K., and Ross, G. I. M. (1956). *J. Protozool.* **3**, 101.
Klenk, E., and Knipprath, W. (1959). *Z. Physiol. Chem.* **317**, 243.
Korn, E. D. (1964). *J. Lipid Res.* **5**, 352.
Krinsky, N. I., and Goldsmith, T. H. (1960). *Arch. Biochem. Biophys.* **91**, 271.
Kusel, J. P., and Weber, M. M. (1965). *Biochim. Biophys. Acta* **98**, 632.
Levin, E. Y., Lennarz, W. J., and Bloch, K. (1964). *Biochim. Biophys Acta* **84**, 469.
Majerus, P. W., Alberts, A. W., and Vagelos, R. P. (1964). *Proc. Natl. Acad. Sci. U.S.* **51**, 1231.
Mead, J. F. (1960). *In* "Lipide Metabolism" (K. Bloch, ed.), pp. 41–68. Wiley, New York.
Meyer, F., and Bloch, K. (1963). *Biochim. Biophys. Acta* **77**, 671.
Meyer, H., and Holz, G. G. (1966). *J. Biol. Chem.* **241**, 5000.
Nagai, J., and Bloch, K. (1965). *J. Biol. Chem.* **240**, pc 3702.
Nagai, J., and Bloch, K. (1966). *J. Biol. Chem.* **241**, pc 1925.
Rosenbaum, N., Erwin, J. and Holz, G. G. (1965). *In* "Progress in Protozoology" Intern. Conf. Protozool., 2nd, London, 1965, pp. 273–274. Excerpta Medica Foundation, New York.
Rosenberg, A. (1963). *Biochemistry* **2**, 1145.
Rosenberg, A., and Pecker, M. (1964). *Biochemistry* **3**, 254.
Rosenberg, A., Pecker, M., and Moschides, E. (1965). *Biochemistry* **4**, 680.
Schimmer, B. P., and Krinsky, N. I. (1966). *Biochemistry* **5**, 1814.
Shorland, F. B. (1962). *In* "Comparative Biochemistry" (M. Florkin and H. S. Mason, eds.), Vol. III, p. 1. Academic Press, New York.
Stern, A. I., Schiff, J. A., and Klein, H. P. (1960). *J. Protozool.* **7**, 52.
Stoffel, W. (1963). *Z. Physiol. Chem.* **335**, 71.
Stumpf, P. K (1962). *Nature* **194**, 1158.
Wallace, J. W., and Newman, D. W. (1965). *Phytochemistry* **4**, 43.
Williams, B. L., Goodwin, T. W., and Ryley, J. F. (1966). *J. Protozool.* **13**, 227.
Zill, L. P., and Harmon, E. A. (1962). *Biochim. Biophys. Acta* **53**, 579.

CHAPTER 7

CARBOHYDRATE COMPOSITION AND METABOLISM IN *EUGLENA*

D. R. Barras and B. A. Stone

I. Introduction*

Carbohydrates may account for as much as 50% of the dry weight of *Euglena* cells. The proportion varies with the nutritional conditions and growth phase of the culture. Representative figures for the composition of *E. gracilis* cells have been collected by Kempner and Miller (1965a).

* Abbreviations used in the text, figures, and tables: ADP, adenosine diphosphate; ATP, adenosine triphosphate; ADPG, adenosine diphosphate glucose; G-1-P(α-G-1-P), glucose 1-phosphate; G-6-P, glucose 6-phosphate; P_i, orthophosphate; P-P, inorganic pyrophosphate; PAPS, adenosine 3′-phosphate-5′-phosphosulphate; RNA, ribonucleic acid; TCA cycle, tricarboxylic acid cycle; TDPG, thymidine diphosphate glucose; UTP, uridine triphosphate; UDPG uridine diphosphate glucose.

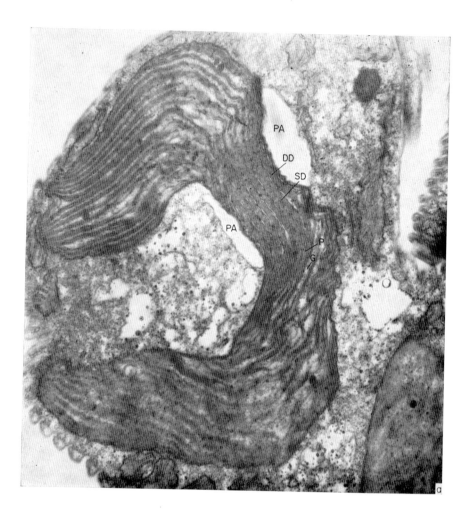

Fig. 1. Cellular location and morphology of paramylon granules. a, Granules apposed to the pyrenoid in *E. gracilis* var. *bacillaris.* DD, double disc crossing pyrenoid; G, granular chloroplast matrix; P, dense pyrenoid matrix; PA, paramylon; SD, single disc crossing pyrenoid. (Electron micrograph from Gibbs, 1960. ×41,000 in the original.) b, *Euglena spirogyra*, showing characteristic pair of large granules, above and below the nucleus; also numerous small granules scattered throughout the cytoplasm. (Anoptral contrast from Leedale *et al.*, 1965a. ×1250, in the original.) c, *Euglena acus* var. *hyalina*, showing long rod-shaped granule. (Phase contrast from Pringsheim, 1963. ×1200 in the original.) d, Granules from *P. pleuronectes.* (From Leedale *et al.*, 1965b. ×4000 in the original.) e, Granule from *E. tripteris.* (From Leedale *et al.*, 1965b. ×4000 in the original.)

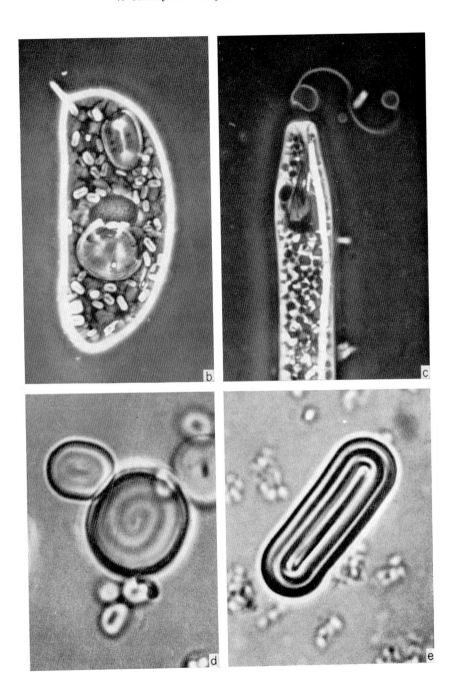

Among the carbohydrates present is an endogenous pool of sugars, oligosaccharides, and phosphorylated sugars, but quantitatively the most important carbohydrate is the polysaccharide paramylon, found in the form of granular inclusions. Carbohydrate is also associated with the galacto- and sulfolipids of the chloroplast. The secreted products of the muciferous bodies are also largely, if not entirely, carbohydrate in nature.

The occurrence, structures, metabolism, and physiological functions of these carbohydrates are discussed in the following sections. The general oxidative and endogenous metabolism of carbohydrates in *Euglena* is dealt with by Danforth (Chapter 2), the photosynthetic formation of carbohydrate by Evans (Chapter 3), and heterotrophic CO_2 fixation by Levedahl (Chapter 4).

II. Carbohydrate Composition

A. PARAMYLON GRANULES

1. *Location in the Cell and Morphology*

A distinguishing feature of photosynthetic and nonphotosynthetic members of the Euglenaceae is the presence in their cytoplasm of characteristic granules of diverse form and number. Their occurrence was first recorded by Müller in 1786. Gottlieb (1850) isolated the granules and showed that they were composed of a carbohydrate which, although isomeric with starch, was not stained with iodine. For this reason they were termed paramylon granules.

The granules appear in various locations within the cell. In many species they are scattered throughout the cytoplasm (Fig. 1b) but sometimes they seem to be confined to one end of the cell (Pringsheim, 1942). In some species, in addition to the small scattered granules, two large granules are found in fixed positions, one posterior and one anterior, e.g., in *E. spirogyra*, *E. oxyuris*, and *E. tripteris* (Pringsheim, 1956; Leedale *et al.*, 1965a), (Fig. 1b). In green forms, granules may be situated in apposition to the pyrenoid region of the chloroplasts, e.g., in *E. velata*, *E. granulata*, and *E. polymorpha* (Dangeard, 1901; Pringsheim, 1956, 1963), (Fig. 1a). (See also Figs. 9 and 10 in Ben-Shaul *et al.*, 1964.) A similar association between starch granules and the pyrenoid has been observed in other algae e.g., *Chlorella ellipsoidea* (Murakami *et al.*, 1963).

Starch granules, whatever their origin, maintain a fairly constant globular or polygonal shape; by contrast, the shape of paramylon granules varies widely within the euglenoid group. Globular, ellipsoidal, cylindrical (rod-shaped), lenticular, needle, and disc-shaped granules have been described (Fig. 1,c–e).

The size of the granules also varies. They may be as small as 2 μ in diameter or in the case of the two large granules in *E. spirogyra*, 8–15 μ long, 4–7 μ wide, and 2–3 μ thick (Leedale *et al.*, 1965a).

The distribution, shape, and size of paramylon granules is of some taxonomic significance and the monographs of Pringsheim (1942, 1956, 1963) amply illustrate the diversity of granule morphology and distribution. See also Klebs (1883), Dangeard (1901), Heidt (1937), Schiller (1952), Gojdics (1953), and Pochmann (1956, 1958).

In addition to paramylon granules, small spherical granules of unknown composition are found in the colorless forms *Menoidium*, *Rhabdomonas*, and *Astasia granulata*. They always appear at the posterior end of the cell and their number remains constant. They have not been observed in green forms (Pringsheim, 1942, 1963).

2. Chemical Composition

Investigations by Habermann (1874), Kutscher (1898), and Bütschli (1906) showed that the granular substance from a variety of euglenoid species was a polymer of glucose. Kreger and Meeuse (1952) pointed out the similarity between the X-ray powder diagram of the mixed granules from *E. viridis* and *E. geniculata* and that of yeast hydroglucan, i.e., yeast glucan boiled for 2 hours with dilute HCl. Since the main glucoside linkage in yeast glucan had been shown to be of the β-1,3-type (see Clarke and Stone, 1963 for references), Kreger and Meeuse concluded that paramylon was also a β-1,3-glucan.

Clarke and Stone (1960) examined purified paramylon granules from *E. gracilis*. On hydrolysis with hot 90% formic acid followed by refluxing with 3 N H_2SO_4 a single monosaccharide was obtained which behaved chromatographically as glucose and yielded an authentic glucose 2,5-dichlorophenylhydrazone derivative. Partial acid hydrolysis produced a series of oligosaccharides which were isolated and identified, both from their chromatographic mobilities and by the preparation of crystalline derivatives, as the β-1,3-oligoglucoside series. The material of the granules was almost completely resistant to periodate oxidation which is consistent with a 1,3-glucan structure. The glucan had an infrared spectrum with a band of moderate intensity near 890 cm^{-1} characteristic of β-linked glucopyranose units.

The paramylon granules of several other species of euglenoids have now been investigated chemically and the findings are summarized in Table I, which also includes for comparison the characteristics of some other intracellular β-1,3-glucans. In the case of *Astasia (Khawkinea) ocellata* the linear β-1,3-glucan nature of the polymer was confirmed by methylation analysis

Table I

SOURCES AND BASIC STRUCTURES OF INTRACELLULAR β-1,3-GLUCANS

Source	Organism	Structure			Reference
		1,3 linkages (%)	Other linkages or components	Degree of polymerization	
Fungi					
Sclerotan (Kinkaku glucan)	*Sclerotinia libertiana*	?	1,6 (Branched)	—	Kitahara and Takeuchi (1959)
Pachyman	*Poria cocos*	100	—	—	Warsi and Whelan (1957)
Algae					
Paramylon	*Euglena gracilis*	100	—	>150	Clarke and Stone (1960)
	Astasia ocellata	100	—	50–55	Manners *et al.* (1966)
	Peranema trichophorum	100	—	80	Archibald *et al.* (1963)
Laminarin	*Laminaria digitata*	~90	1,6 (Mannitol, 3%)	21	See Clarke and Stone (1963) and Annan *et al.* (1965a, b) for refs.
	Laminaria hyperborea ≡ *L. cloustoni*	~95	1,6 (Mannitol, 2%)	24	
	Laminaria saccharina	~90	1,6 (Mannitol, 2.5–2.7%)	28	Annan *et al.* (1965a)
Leucosin	*Eisenia bicyclis*	67	1,6	21	Handa and Nisizawa (1961)
	Ochromonas malhamensis	~90	1,6	21	Archibald *et al.* (1958)
	Mixture of diatoms	90	1,6	36–40	Beattie *et al.* (1961)
Lichens					
Lichenin	*Cetraria icelandica*	~30	1,4 (70%)	52–410	See Clarke and Stone (1963) for refs.

(Manners *et al.*, 1966). The paramylons so far studied form a closely related group of β-1,3-glucans and in the three cases comprehensively investigated appear to be unbranched but of somewhat different degrees of polymerization.

Paramylon granules from *E. gracilis* (Pringsheim, 1954a), *Trachelomonas grandis* (Singh, 1956), and a *Khawkinea* sp. (Nath *et al.*, 1960) do not stain with periodate–Schiff or the lead tetraacetate–Schiff reagents. This is consonant with the determined chemical structure of paramylon. The vicinal hydroxyl groups necessary for oxidation by the periodate or lead tetraacetate reagents are absent in β-1,3-glucans. Staining of paramylon has only been possible after sulfonation with chlorosulfonic acid using the technique of Spicer (1960) (Nath *et al.*, 1960).

Other β-1,3-glucans, notably callose, stain with resorcin blue, aniline blue, and fluorochromes isolated from aniline blue and water blue (see Clarke and Stone, 1963, for references), but no staining was observed with *E. gracilis* paramylon (Clarke and Stone, 1960). This may be due to differences in the organization of the β-1,3-glucan molecules.

3. Physical Properties

a. Solubility. Early investigators, (Gottlieb, 1850; Klebs, 1886; Kutscher, 1898; Bütschli, 1906) showed that paramylon granules were completely insoluble in cold or hot water and organic solvents but dissolved in dilute alkali and concentrated mineral acids. Formaldehyde and anhydrous formic acid are also good solvents for paramylon. Paramylon is more or less swollen by 5% calcium thiocyanate, 25% potassium iodide, saturated zinc chloride, formamide, and cuprammonium (Clarke and Stone, 1960).

The microscopic changes in paramylon granules during swelling in concentrated formaldehyde solutions, concentrated sulfuric acid and 5–7% sodium hydroxide have been followed by Bütschli (1906), Hamburger (1911), and Heidt (1937). A variety of patterns of striations and fissures, some in concentric rings and others in spirals, have been observed and may reflect an underlying organization of the paramylon within the granule.

b. Anisotropy. Under the polarizing microscope with crossed Nicol prisms, paramylon granules from some species show a cross pattern with alternating dark and light sectors similar to that shown by starch granules. This anisotropy has been the subject of many observations (Bütschli, 1906; Czurda, 1928; Haye, 1930; Deflandre, 1934).

Deflandre (1934) examined paramylon granules from a range of euglenoids and, according to their microscopic appearance under polarized light, divided them into three groups: (1) Cross very sharp, the four sectors very clear; *Phacus curvicauda, Phacus pleuronectes, Phacus longicauda, E. proxima.* (2) Cross less sharp, often two quadrants clearest; *E. spirogyra, E. fusca,*

E. granulata, Lepocinclis steinii, Astasia dangeardii, Phacus hispidula.
(3) Homogeneously anisotropic; *E. gracilis, E. oxyuris, E. acus* var. *longissima, Astasia sagittifera.* (4) Anisotropy not detected, appearance completely isotropic; *Menoidium incurvum, Distigma proteus, Petalomonas, Anisonema, Entosiphon.*

Deflandre (1934), Kamptner (1952), and Pochmann (1956, 1958) have discussed the relationship of the pattern of birefringence to the organization of paramylon within the granule.

c. X-ray Diffraction. Kreger and Meeuse (1952) showed that the paramylon from several sources *(E. viridis, E. geniculata,* and *A. ocellata)* gave patterns with fairly sharp rings. The X-ray pattern of *E. gracilis* paramylon studied by Clarke and Stone (1960) had the following spacings (Å) and relative intensities: 13.6 (vs), 7.85 (mw), 6.78 (w), 5.35 (vw), 4.45 (m dif.), 3.92 (m), 3.62 (mw), 3.45 (w), 3.00 (vw), 2.90 (w), 2.70 (vw), 2.65 (vw).

Meeuse (Leedale *et al.*, 1965b) has examined further paramylon samples and has classified them into two groups according to differences in their X-ray patterns.

Group I: *P. pleuronectes, Khawkinea (Astasia) ocellata* (1952), *E. oxyuris, E. spirogyra, E. tripteris.*

Group II: *A. longa, E. gracilis, E. acus, E. limnophila, K. ocellata* (1963), *K. pertyi.*

The X-ray pattern for *K. ocellata* paramylon taken in 1952 was distinctly different from the one taken in 1963. This suggested that the conditions of growth may alter the X-ray pattern.

Picciolo (1964) has examined the patterns of granules from the parent and a mutant strain of *A. longa.* The mutant strain had much larger granules than the parent but the X-ray patterns were almost identical, with spacings (Å) and relative intensities as follows: 12.80 (100); 6.34 (10); 5.30 (10); 4.57 (70); 4.30 (60); 3.72 (40).

4. *Electron Microscopy*

Examination of ultrathin sections of *Euglena* and *Astasia* cells by electron microscopy has failed to reveal much information regarding the internal structure of the paramylon granules. In the majority of published electron micrographs the section through the paramylon granule appears as a largely electron-transparent area although small regions of electron-scattering material can sometimes be seen (Fig. 1a; see also photographs in other papers, viz., Reger and Beams, 1954; Wolken, 1956; De Haller, 1958, 1959; Ueda, 1958, 1960; Frey-Wyssling and Mühlethaler, 1960; Gibbs, 1960; Ringo, 1963; Siegesmund *et al.*, 1962; Lefort, 1963; Blum *et al.*, 1965; Leedale *et al.*, 1965a; Sommer and Blum, 1965; Leedale, 1966).

Leedale (1966, Fig. 10, p. 31) has drawn attention to indications of helical organization in the large granules of *E. spirogyra*. In the photographs of Sommer and Blum (1965, Fig. 20, p. 247) both radial and concentric striations are apparent. There is also evidence of internal structure, possibly layering, in the photographs of Brandes *et al.* (1964, Fig. 3, p. 587). The paucity of the information obtained from the electron microscope images may be related to lack of fixation of the paramylon due to its refractory nature and the subsequent loss of material during sectioning. More information may be obtained by shadowing techniques, and unpublished photographs taken by Professor A. B. Wardrop (personal communication) of shadowed sections of paramylon granules of *E. gracilis* show fibrils running parallel to their long axis. Meeuse (Leedale *et al.*, 1965b) has reported the observation of a helical structure in electron micrographs of *E. gracilis* and *P. pleuronectes* granules prepared by a replica technique.

Electron microscopy has revealed structures at the granule–cytoplasm boundary. Gibbs (1960) reported that granules in *E. gracilis* var. *bacillaris* and strain Z, although not enclosed in a membrane, are often bordered by a denser rim of cytoplasm. Ringo (1963) reported a single 60-Å membrane associated with *A. longa* granules and Leedale *et al.* (1965a) showed a unit membrane surrounding each paramylon granule in *E. spirogyra*. Membranes are apparent in photographs of granules of var. *bacillaris* (Lefort, 1963, Fig. 5; Brandes *et al.*, 1964, Figs. 1 and 3, p. 587).

5. Enzymic Breakdown

Meeuse (1964) has tested the activity of a series of enzyme preparations, from molluscs, crustaceans, fungi, bacteria, higher plants, and euglenoids, on native paramylon granules and on the related soluble β-1,3-glucan, laminarin. Most sources hydrolyzed laminarin but hydrolysis of native paramylon was achieved only by preparations from the freshwater lamellibranchs, *Anodonta*, *Dreissena*, and *Unio* and even here the results were erratic. The molluscan enzymes gradually transformed the large, round, disc-shaped paramylon granules of *P. pleuronectes* into slender hoops by erosion outward from a central hole. Spiral structures were visible during the breakdown. The granules of *E. oxyuris* changed from the "chain link" form to a "paper clip" form.

Enzymes from the crop of the snail, *Helix pomatia*, caused only a slight etching of native granules. However, Marzullo and Danforth (1964b) were able to use snail enzymes to dissolve *E. gracilis* paramylon that had been reprecipitated from alkaline solution. Granules treated in this way may also be hydrolyzed by the *Rhizopus arrhizus* endo-β-1,3-glucan hydrolase (Archibald *et al.*, 1963; Manners *et al.*, 1966). This enzyme does not hydrolyze native granules (Meeuse, 1964). It is clear that the physical structure of the granule is highly significant in determining the degree of attack by the β-1,3-glucan hydrolases. Evidently, reprecipitation renders the paramylon molecules accessible to the *Helix* and *Rhizopus* enzymes. This is quite analogous to the situation with β-1,4-glucan hydrolases (cellulases) where it has long been recognized that the organization of the cellulose substrate determines accessibility to the enzymes (Cowling, 1963).

The ability of the lamellibranch preparations to hydrolyze native granules suggests that they may contain an extra enzymic factor lacking in most other β-1,3-glucanase preparations. In the cellulase field a similar distinction between preparations hydrolyzing both crystalline and dispersed cellulose and those hydrolyzing only dispersed cellulose is well documented. Certain fungi, e.g., *Myrothecium verrucaria* and *Trichoderma viride* possess the necessary enzymic factor for the dissolution of crystalline cellulose. The enzyme is distinct and separable from those hydrolyzing dispersed cellulose (Selby and Maitland, 1965; King, 1965).

6. *Organization of the Paramylon within the Granule*

A certain degree of organization of the molecules of paramylon is evident from the X-ray diffraction and polarized light studies. Additional evidence is provided by the observations on granules treated with swelling agents and enzymes.

The conformation of the linear molecules of paramylon is not known. Recently, Frei and Preston (1964) put forward a model describing the microfibril organization for the chemically related β-1,3-xylan from the walls of siphoneous green algae. The model accounts for the X-ray diffraction spacings, negative optical anisotropy, and density of the xylan in the walls. The model envisages helically coiled xylan chains, and the microfibrils seen in the electron microscope are thought to consist of hexagonally packed, double-stranded helices. The spacings determined for *E. gracilis* (see Section II,A,3,c) are also consistent with hexagonal cell packing (J. Fridrichsons, personal communication). A helical conformation for the paramylon in these granules may therefore be considered.

Kamptner (1952) has suggested, on the basis of birefringence studies, that the paramylon molecules are aggregated into micelles which in certain granules *(E. brevicaudata)* are oriented parallel to the long axis of the granule and to one another. This is exactly the arrangement presented by fibrils seen in shadowed sections of *E. gracilis* granules (Clarke and Stone, 1960, see also Section II,A,4). In this connection it may be noted that when amorphous yeast glucan is boiled in dilute HCl the residual material begins to show fibrils which grow in size and number as the treatment is prolonged (Houwink and Kreger, 1953). The final material (yeast hydroglucan) has the same X-ray diffraction pattern as *E. viridis* and *E. geniculata* paramylon. The data suggest that as well as having the same chemical structure (Kreger and Meeuse, 1952), the chain configuration and the packing of the chains in the micelles is also similar.

B. MUCIN AND MUCIFEROUS BODIES

Many euglenoids produce a gelatinous secretion, mucin, which may be involved in the formation both of pellicle ornamentations and of a number of gelatinous envelopes, including protective, reproductive, and resting cysts, and palmelloid stages (Günther, 1927; Dangeard, 1928; Jahn, 1946; Gojdics, 1953; Pringsheim, 1956; Diskus, 1956). A function in anchoring cells to solid substrates and in lubricating gliding movements across solid substrates has also been suggested (Diskus, 1956; Jarosch, 1962).

The production and secretion of mucin has been associated with sub-pellicular structures termed muciferous bodies, first demonstrated by Klebs (1883). Numerous studies of the morphology and staining reactions of muciferous bodies, and mucin secreted in response to chemical and mechanical stimuli, have been made using techniques of light microscopy. These studies, together with discussions of the possible function of the muciferous bodies have been extensively reviewed. (Dangeard, 1928; Hollande, 1942; Pochmann, 1953; Gojdics, 1953; Pringsheim, 1956; Diskus, 1956).

In confirmation of earlier light microscope observations, muciferous bodies closely associated with the pellicle complex of the cell have been observed in electron micrographs of *E. spirogyra* (Leedale, 1964), *E. stellata*, and *E. acus* (Mignot, 1965). A muciferous body appears in fact to be associated with each of the ridges of the pellicle complex. In *E. spirogyra* these bodies are interconnected and form a network of smooth, tubular endoplasmic reticulum which is continuous with the extensive, rough, vesiculate endoplasmic reticulum that frequently contains amorphous material. Serial sections have shown that these reticulum elements, together with the perinuclear space, are part of an interconnecting three-dimensional system in which the most peripheral elements become oriented to form muciferous bodies (Leedale *et al.*, 1965a; Leedale, 1966). An apparently similar sub-pellicular system is to be seen in *A. longa* and *E. gracilis* var. *bacillaris* (Sommer and Blum, 1965; Sommer, 1965; Blum *et al.*, 1965). Not all muciferous bodies are as closely associated with the pellicle. Large muciferous bodies, lying well within the cytoplasm have been observed in electron micrographs of *E. viridis* (De Haller, 1958, 1959) and *A. longa* (Lefort, 1963). The bodies are vesicular in shape, 0.5 μ in diameter, and contain a dense coagulum.

In the case of *A. longa* and *E. gracilis* var. *bacillaris*, mucin production may not be the only secretory role of the system. Sommer and Blum (1965) presented evidence which suggested that the system may be involved in the secretion of an induced acid phosphatase onto the surface of the pellicle. These authors also considered the possibility of a continuity between the subpellicular endoplasmic reticulum and the Golgi complex, a possibility also entertained by Leedale in the case of *E. spirogyra* (Leedale *et al.*, 1965a). The Golgi body has been found to be the site of carbohydrate transformations in plant cells (Mollenhauer and Morré, 1966).

Apart from a possible role in the formation of cyst structures, Leedale (1964; Leedale *et al.*, 1965a) has suggested that mucin may act as a lubricant in the process of "metabolic" movement, a phenomenon involving the sliding of pellicle ridges along adjacent grooves. The thin layers of mucin often seen in association with the surface of the pellicle, e.g., *E. acus* (Mignot, 1965, Plate II, Fig. 6) may represent such a lubrication layer.

Very little is known of the chemical nature of *Euglena* mucin. Staining reactions indicated that its composition was distinct from that of the pellicle (Klebs, 1883; Deflandre, 1931). Klebs was unable to detect cellulose and found the material to be swollen by acids, alkalis, and pepsin. These observations were confirmed by Bütschli (1906), who remarked upon the resistance of the material to solvents. It was dissolved when heated on a boiling water bath with 89% H_2SO_4, 37% HCl, and 35% KOH. Upon dilution with water the acid solutions formed flocculent precipitates, whereas the alkaline solution gave a precipitate only on addition of alcohol. Bütschli hydrolyzed mucin with sulfuric acid and as a result of tests on the hydrolysate concluded that it was most likely a nitrogen-free carbohydrate. The trichloracetic acid–soluble polysaccharide found by Albaum *et al.* (1950) in the fractionation of *Euglena* cells may represent the mucin component.

Mucin, isolated from cultures of *E. gracilis* var. *bacillaris*, has been found to have a carbohydrate content of at least 82%. Chromatographic analysis of acid hydrolysates of the mucin has shown the presence of glucose, galactose, mannose, xylose, fucose, and rhamnose, and small amounts of unidentified slow-moving sugars (Barras and Stone, unpublished observations). These monosaccharides are the same as those found in hydrolysates of the pellicle isolated from the same organism (Barras and Stone, 1965). It is thus probable that a large proportion of the carbohydrate found in the isolated pellicle preparation (17% dry weight) is mucin in close association with the pellicle. This is consistent with the observed association of the muciferous bodies with the pellicle in *E. gracilis*. A number of amino acids have also been detected in the acid hydrolysates of the mucin, indicating the presence of a relatively small amount of protein in the preparation, although whether this is part of the mucin structure is not yet known. The monosaccharide components found in the mucin hydrolysates are very similar to those found in the mucilages of a number of algae (O'Colla, 1962). The wall of the cysts of certain euglenoids is apparently derived from the muciferous body secretion. In a species of *Khawkinea* examined cytochemically by Nath *et al.* (1961) tests on the thick outer wall gave a negative result for chitin, protein, polysaccharide, and lipid, whereas the fine inner membrane gave positive results for protein, polysaccharide, and occasionally lipid.

C. GLYCOLIPIDS

1. *Galactosyl Glycerides*

Carter and co-workers (1961) isolated a monogalactosyl glycerol from *E. gracilis* strain Z. This appears to have been formed by deacylation of a diglyceride with the structure shown in Fig. 2a.

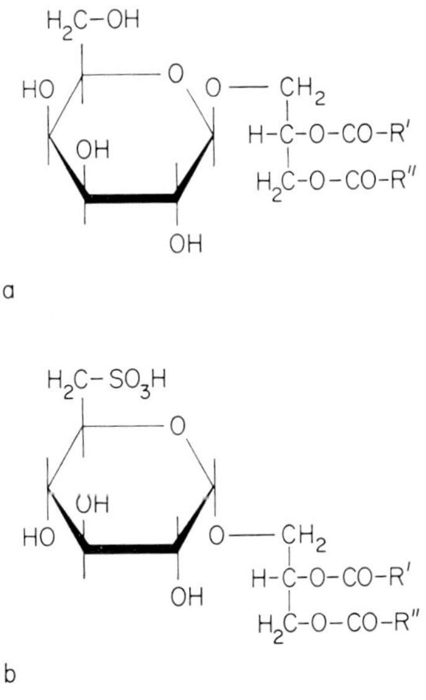

Fig. 2. Structure of glycolipids identified in *Euglena*. a, Monogalactosyl diglyceride [2,3-diacyl-1-(-D-galactopyranosyl)-D-glycerol]. b, 2,3-diacyl-1-(6-sulfo-α-D-quinovopyranosyl)-D-glycerol.

The acyl groups are derived from long-chain fatty acids, particularly polyunsaturated acids such as α-linoleic acid (Hulanicka *et al.*, 1964). A digalactosyl diglyceride has also been reported from *E. gracilis* (James and Nichols, 1966).

2. Sulfolipid

The unique sulfolipid first isolated from *Chlorella pyrenoidosa* and *Scenedesmus* D_3 by Benson *et al.* (1959) and shown to have a carbon–sulphur bond has been identified in *E. gracilis* by Rosenberg (1963). Here the diglyceride is glycosidically linked to 6-sulfo-6-deoxy-D-glucose (6-sulfo-quinivose) (Fig. 2b).

Both glycolipids are found in much greater amounts in green than in etiolated *Euglena* cells (Rosenberg, 1963) (Table II) and in the green cells they are found predominantly in the chloroplasts. These two polar lipids are probably universal constituents of plastids (James and Nichols, 1966).

Table II

ANALYSIS OF SOME LIPID FRACTIONS OF GREEN AND ETIOLATED *E. gracilis* CELLS[a]

Fraction estimated	Percent of total lipid (gm/100 gm)	
	Etiolated	Green
Galactose	1.44	8.20
Total sulfur[b]	2.86	4.16
Preformed sulfate	0.37	0.53
Inositol	0.18	0.29
Uronic acid	0.10	0.13

[a] From Rosenberg (1963).
[b] As sulfate.

Davies *et al.* (1965) found that on centrifugation of extracts of *E. gracilis* strain Z, the sulfolipid segregates with the chlorophyll in autotrophic cells, but in dark-grown cells the bulk of the sulfolipid is present in the 105,000-g fraction. This may represent sulfolipid available for transfer into the chloroplast structure.

3. Biosynthesis

The origin of the galactosyl residues of the galactolipids has not been investigated in *Euglena*. In spinach chloroplasts an enzymic transfer of the galactosyl residue from UDP-galactosyl-^{14}C to endogenous acceptors yields alkali-labile products which are similar, though not identical to the galactolipids isolated from plant material (Neufeld and Hall, 1964).

The biosynthesis of the unusual carbohydrate of the sulfolipid is of considerable interest. Shibuya *et al.* (1963) have found in *Chlorella* grown on sulfate-^{35}S, a large number of labeled sulfur compounds, including a compound tentatively identified as nucleoside diphosphate 6-sulfoquinivose. As a synthetic route they suggest the sulfonation, possibly by active sulfate (PAPS), of a nucleoside anhydro sugar derivative such as has been postulated in the formation of 6-deoxy sugars. The involvement of PAPS is also suggested by the work of Abraham and Bachhawat (1963). They found that sulfate-^{35}S was taken up and incorporated into sulfolipids of green, dark-grown, and streptomycin-bleached *Euglena* cells in the light. The incorporation was greatest in the green cells and least in the streptomycin-treated cells. Since streptomycin reduced the level of the PAPS-forming system it was suggested that the incorporation of sulfate into sulfolipid is via PAPS, possibly involving a light-dependent reduction.

Sulfolipid and chlorophyll synthesis bear a temporal relationship (Rosenberg and Pecker, 1964). In contrast, on illumination of dark-grown cells galactolipid synthesis commences at a linear rate, independent of chlorophyll level.

III. Carbohydrate Nutrition and Metabolism

A. CARBOHYDRATE NUTRITION*

The question of the ability of euglenoid species to utilize carbohydrates when grown in the dark on an otherwise nutritionally sufficient medium was not satisfactorily answered until the definitive work of Cramer and Myers in 1952. Prior to this there were conflicting reports on the growth-sustaining ability of glucose for *Euglena* and related species. The literature for this period has been reviewed on a number of occasions: Lwoff (1932, 1938); von Brand (1935); Hall (1939, 1941); Doyle (1943); Kidder (1951); Hutner and Provasoli (1951).

Cramer and Myers, using an essentially autotrophic medium (Hutner et al., 1966) based on those developed by Provasoli et al. (1948) and Hutner et al. (1949), measured quantitatively the ability of various carbon compounds to support growth. *Euglena gracilis* var. *bacillaris* grew well on glucose at pH 4.5, whereas the Vischer strain under the same conditions, was unable to use glucose. Glucose utilization was dependent on several environmental factors as well as on the strain used. Thus: (1) CO_2 tension increased growth when it was raised to values approaching 5%. This was confirmed by Hurlbert and Rittenberg (1962). (2) The pH of the medium was critical, glucose being used at pH 4.5 but not at pH 6.8. Hurlbert and Rittenberg (1962) and Cook and Heinrich (1965) have repeated this observation. In a mutant strain of *A. longa*, glucose utilization was optimal at a pH near 7 (Barry, 1962).

* *Editor's Note:* This topic is further covered in Vol. I, Chapter 6.

(3) The glucose concentration was also important. There was no growth at concentrations less than 0.2%; above this level the growth rate increased with sugar concentration up to 1%, the highest concentration tested. For *E. gracilis* var. *saccharophila* (Pringsheim, 1955) the optimum glucose concentration was 0.2%. (4) The previous history of the cells was another factor involved. Dark-grown cells from a glucose medium grew immediately on transfer to fresh glucose medium, whereas autotrophic cells took as long as 10 days to grow on glucose medium in the dark. Yaden (1965) found that the uptake of glucose-^{14}C, measured over 3 hours, by var. *bacillaris* which had been grown in the presence of 1% glucose, either in the dark or in the light, was twice as high in the dark-grown cells as in the light-grown cells. Reversal of the uptake pattern was shown in the reversible adaptation to light or darkness. Adaptation to glucose utilization is now well substantiated and is discussed in Section III,B,2.

The findings of Cramer and Myers caused a complete reappraisal of the ability of euglenoids to use glucose (see Pringsheim, 1954b). Table III summarizes the data for the growth of euglenoids on hexoses. As far as has been tested, fructose and glucose utilization are always associated. No growth on galactose, mannose, or the sugar alcohols, glycerol and mannitol, has been observed. Although sucrose has been reported as a growth substrate (Hutner *et al.*, 1956; Belsky, 1957), it is unlikely to survive autoclaving in acid media. Apart from the observation by Lwoff and Dusi (1934; discussed by Hutner and Provasoli, 1951) that *E. gracilis* can use starch, there have been no other reports of growth on polymeric carbohydrates.

In addition to the environmental factors described by Cramer and Myers and listed above, it has been found that meat extracts stimulate the growth of var. *bacillaris* and strain Z cultured on a glucose medium (Pringsheim, 1955). TCA-cycle acids and related amino acids can substitute for the meat extracts (Hutner *et al.*, 1956; Baker *et al.*, 1958; Sher and Aaronson, 1959; Hurlbert and Rittenberg, 1962).

B. CARBOHYDRATE METABOLISM

1. Pathways of Carbohydrate Metabolism

In photoautotrophic euglenoids carbon dioxide is the primary source of carbon for incorporation into cellular metabolites and structural compounds. The pathway of the reductive synthesis of carbohydrate from carbon dioxide in the chloroplast is dealt with by Evans (Chapter 3).

The colorless, obligatory heterotrophic euglenoids are able to incorporate carbon from short-chain fatty acids and alcohols, certain amino acids, and in some cases sugars, into cellular constituents, including carbohydrate,

Table III

GROWTH OF EUGLENOIDS ON HEXOSES[a]

Organism	Glucose	Fructose	Mannose	Galactose	Reference
Euglena gracilis					
var. *bacillaris*	+	+			Cramer and Myers (1952); Belsky (1957).
Vischer strain	−				Cramer and Myers (1952)
Mainx strain	+				Provasoli *et al.* (1948)
Z strain	+				Sher and Aaronson (1959)
					Cook and Heinrich (1965)
					Pringsheim (1955)
var. *saccharophila*	+	+	−	−	Leedale *et al.* (1965b)
Euglena spirogyra	−				
Astasia longa					
J strain	−				Barry (1962)
J strain mutant (X-ray)	+				
PS strain	−	−			Picciolo (1964)
PS strain mutant (ultraviolet)	−	−			
Astasia klebsii	−	−			Thayer (1949)

[a] Key: +, growth; −, no growth.

as well as to utilize these exogenous substrates in energy-yielding processes. The oxidative metabolism of these substrates is dealt with by Danforth (Chapter 2) and only aspects of their assimilation into carbohydrate components of the cell will be discussed here. The heterotrophic fixation of carbon dioxide is described by Levedahl (Chapter 4) and is mentioned only briefly.

The data available suggest that in *Euglena*, both autotrophically and heterotrophically synthesized hexose, as well as exogenous hexose, are catabolized by the ubiquitous Embden–Meyerhof and oxidative pentose phosphate pathways.

Evidence for the operation of the Embden–Meyerhof pathway has been provided by Albaum *et al.* (1950) who analyzed the nucleotide phosphates and sugar phosphates in cells of photosynthetically grown *Euglena*. Subsequently the enzymes of the sequence were identified in cell-free extracts of various strains of *E. gracilis*. In *A. longa*, hexokinase, phosphoglucomutase, and lactate dehydrogenase have been described (see Smillie, Chapter 1).

The presence of enzymes of the oxidative pentose phosphate pathway have also been reported in *E. gracilis* var. *bacillaris* and strain Z (Smillie, Chapter 1). However, in *A. longa*, glucose-6-phosphate dehydrogenase, the initial enzyme in the oxidative pentose phosphate pathway, and glucose dehydrogenase are both absent (Barry, 1962). On the basis of the equivalence of the $^{14}CO_2$ yield from glucose-1-^{14}C and glucose-6-^{14}C, Barry suggested that the Embden–Meyerhof scheme is the principal pathway of glucose catabolism in *Astasia*.

The experimental evidence for the operation of the glycolytic and oxidative pentose phosphate pathways in *Euglena* is minimal, and the evaluation of the relative roles of the two sequences has not been attempted. Evidence for the exclusion of other pathways, such as the glucuronic acid pathway, is lacking although definitive methods for their evaluation are available (Horecker, 1962; Landau and Katz, 1965). Since considerable amounts of lipid are synthesized by *Euglena* cells (Cook, 1965; Kempner and Miller, 1965a) it might be expected that the pentose phosphate pathway could be an important source of reducing equivalents for the synthesis of the constituent fatty acids (Cheniae, 1963; Cheniae and Kerr, 1965).

2. *Hexose Uptake and Utilization*

As indicated in Section III,A, the ability of euglenoid species and strains to utilize hexoses is variable. The passage of hexoses and other exogenous small molecules across the cell membrane is probably an "active" and selective process (cf. Cirillo, 1961; Taylor, 1960a,b). Even after passing this barrier the molecules will be metabolized only if the appropriate auxiliary enzyme systems for their entry into the intermediary pathways are available. The situation is further complicated since, given the genetic potential, cells that are unable to utilize a certain compound, either due to the lack of the necessary transport system at the cell membrane or of the auxiliary enzyme systems, or both, may adapt to utilize the substrate. In addition, in the case of hexoses, as has been mentioned (Section III,A) the environmental conditions in the culture may also operate in facilitating or hindering their entry and utilization.

The idea of permeability differences between strains is supported by the findings of Barry (1962) with an X-ray mutant of the J strain of *A. longa*. The mutant can utilize glucose as judged by $^{14}CO_2$ liberation from glucose-^{14}C but the parent cells cannot. Cell-free extracts of both parent and mutant strains possess hexokinase, phosphoglucomutase, and lactate dehydrogenase, the hexokinase activity being highest in the parent strain. It would seem that the mutation has caused an increase in the permeability of the membrane to glucose. In the phytoflagellate *Polytoma obtusum*, glucose and other hexoses are not utilized but hexokinase is present, also suggesting the absence of the transport system (Chapman *et al.*, 1965).

There is evidence that nonutilization of glucose may in some strains be due to the absence of hexokinase as suggested by Hutner and Provasoli (1951). Ohmann (1963) found that whole cells of *E. gracilis* strain 1224-5/25 were unable to utilize glucose or glucose 1-phosphate as judged by CO_2 production, however, fructose 1,6-diphosphate supported CO_2 production. Evidence was presented that suggested that both hexokinase and phosphofructokinase were absent from the cell-free extracts. The nonutilization of glucose can be readily understood in terms of the absence of hexokinase but the absence of phosphofructokinase is difficult to reconcile with the ability of *Euglena* to utilize endogenous hexose phosphates.

Several workers (Cramer and Myers, 1952; App and Jagendorf, 1963; Cook and Heinrich, 1965) have noted the adaptation of *E. gracilis* to the utilization of glucose after being transferred from a noncarbohydrate to a glucose medium. Hexokinase induction is probably involved in some strains, as is suggested by the observation that the hexokinase of *E. gracilis* var. *bacillaris* was "labile" in the absence of glucose (Belsky, 1957). The possibility that in other strains the adaptation is due to the induced synthesis of the transport system must also be considered.

The availability of mutant strains of *Euglena* makes possible a more systematic examination of the processes of uptake and utilization of glucose and other sugars and of the characteristics of the adaptation. When these phenomena are better understood it may be possible to explain the effects of glucose concentration, CO_2, and pH, and the presence of other substrates on glucose utilization by *Euglena*.

3. Gluconeogenesis*

a. General Pathways of Gluconeogenesis. Euglenoids have been shown to grow on a range of noncarbohydrate carbon sources (Table IV). Those most investigated have been acetate, ethanol, and succinate, and the assimilation of the carbon atoms of these substrates into carbohydrates (hexose phosphate or paramylon) has been demonstrated. The information for other substrates is often limited to quantitative or semiquantitative growth data. In these cases, however, it can be assumed that the cells have their normal chemical composition and that along with proteins, lipids, and nucleic acid, carbohydrates are formed to a greater or lesser extent from the carbon skeletons of these substrates.

Table IV shows that certain of the TCA-cycle intermediates and amino acids yielding TCA-cycle intermediates are able to support growth. Their probable routes to hexose phosphate and paramylon are shown in Fig. 3. The steps from phosphopyruvate to hexose phosphate involve the same intermediates as in the catabolic glycolytic pathway and with one exception the enzymes involved are the same. The phosphofructokinase-catalyzed reaction is irreversible and a phosphatase is required to hydrolyse the 1-phosphate ester linkage. This enzyme, the neutral fructose-1,6-diphosphatase, has been found in *E. gracilis* (Smillie, 1960, 1963, 1964).

The pyruvate → phosphopyruvate conversion is not freely reversible and in mammalian and plant tissues and in microorganisms, pyruvate is converted, directly or via malate, to oxalacetate which can then be converted to phosphopyruvate and CO_2. Nothing is yet known of the way in which phosphopyruvate is formed from pyruvate in *Euglena*.

The carbon atoms of other TCA-cycle intermediates may reach oxalacetate by way of either the normal TCA-cycle enzymes or those of the glyoxylate pathway (see below). Glutamate can be transaminated to α-oxoglutarate (Kempner and Miller, 1965b; Chancellor-Maddison and Noll, 1963) and aspartate is presumably transaminated to oxalacetate. Propionate may enter the gluconeogenic pathway via propionyl-CoA, methylmalonyl-CoA, succinyl-CoA, and succinate. This pathway is known to operate in *Ochromonas malhamensis* (Arnstein and White, 1962) and requires vitamin B_{12} for the enzymic isomerization of methylmalonyl-CoA to succinyl-CoA. Other pathways for the metabolism of propionate are known. In the colorless alga *Prototheca zopfii* it is metabolized by a multistep conversion of propionyl-CoA to acetyl-CoA and CO_2 (Lloyd and Callely, 1965).

Presumably the isomeric trioses, dihydroxyacetone and glyceraldehyde, enter the gluconeogenic pathway via triose kinase which has been reported in *E. coli* and mammalian tissues (Hers, 1962).

* *Editor's Note:* This topic is further covered in Vol. I, Chapter 6.

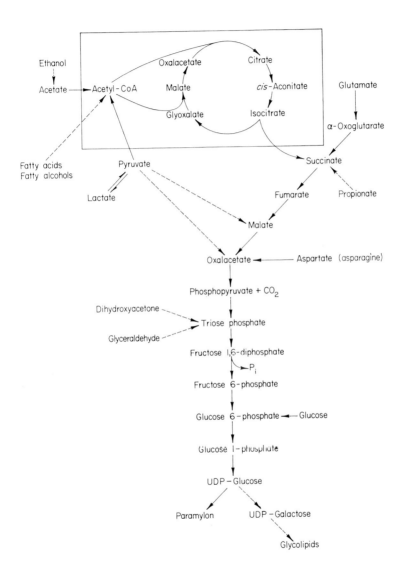

Fig. 3. General pathways of gluconeogenesis. The solid arrows represent reactions or reaction sequences known to occur in euglenoids, while the broken arrows represent reactions or reaction sequences which have not been demonstrated in euglenoids. The glyoxalate cycle is enclosed in a box.

D. R. Barras and B. A. Stone

Table IV

NONCARBOHYDRATE SUBSTRATES REPORTED TO SUPPORT GROWTH OF EUGLENOID FLAGELLATES*†

	E. gracilis							E. viridis (a)	Astasia longa (a)	Astasia quartana	Astasia chattoni	Astasia longa, ps and ms strains (k)	Astasia klebsii (n)
	var. bacillaris (b)	Vischer strain (b)	Z strain (a)	Reinhardt strain (a)	var. robusta (a)	Klebs (d)	var. urophora (d)						
Acetate (C$_2$)	+(b,h,m)	+	+(c)	+	+	+	+	+	+(a,e)	+(a,d)	+(a,d)	+	+
Propionate (C$_3$)	+(j)			-	+	+	+	+	+	+(a,d)	+(a,d)		-
n-Butyrate (n-C$_4$)	+(b)	+	+(c,g)	+	+	+	+	-	+	+(a,d)	+(a,d)		+
Isobutyrate (iso-C$_4$)				-	+	-	+	-	+	+(a)	+(a,d)		
n-C$_5$				-	+	+	+	-		±(d)	±(d)		
n-C$_6$			+(c)	+	+	+	+	+	+	+(a,d)	+(a,d)		
iso-C$_6$				+	+	±	±	-	+	+(a,d)	+(a,d)		
n-C$_7$				+	+	-	+	-	+	+(a,d)	+(a,d)		
n-C$_8$				+	+	+	+	-	+	+(a)	+(a,d)		
n-C$_9$				+	+	+	±	-	+	+(a)	+(a,d)		
n-C$_{10}$				+	+	+	±	-	+	+(a)	+(a)		
n-C$_{11}$				+	+	+	±			±(d)	±(d)		
n-C$_{12}$						±	±			±(d)	±(d)		
Ethanol (C$_2$)	+(h)		+(c)	+	+	+	+	-	+(a,e)	+(a) / -(d)	+(a,d)	+	
Propanol (n-C$_3$)				+	+	+	+	-	+	+(a) / -(d)	+(a,d)		

Substrate				
n-Butanol (n-C₄)	+(e)			+	+	+	+	+	+	+
Isobutanol (iso-C₄)				+	+	−	+	+	+	+(a) −(d)
n-C₅			+	+	+	−	−	−	+	+(a) −(d)
n-C₆			+	+	+	−			+	+(a) +(a)
n-C₈			+	+	+	−			+	+(a) +(a)
n-C₁₀			+	+	+	−			+	+(a) +(a)
Glyceraldehyde			+	+	+	−			+	+(a) +(a)
Dihydroxyacetone			+	+	+	−			+	+(a) +(a)
Lactate	+(g)		+	+	+	−	+	+	+	+(a,d) +(a,d) −|+
Pyruvate			+	+	+	−	+	+	+	+(a) +(a,d) +

Substrate		
Glycerol	−(b)	
Glycolic acid	−(b)	−'c)
Citrate	−(b)	−'c)
Succinate	+(b,l,m)	−	+'c,g)	−(d)
Fumarate	+(b,h,m)	+'c,g)	+(d)
L-Malate	+(b,h,m)	+(c,g)	−(d)
α-Oxoglutarate	+(h)	
Isocitrate		
Glutamate	+(b)	−	+(c,g,f)
Aspartate	+(b)	−	+(c,g)
Asparagine		+(c,g)
Glycine		+(c,g)
Glycine ethyl ester		+(c)
Glutamate γ-ethyl ester		+(c)

* Key: +, growth; ±, poor growth (d); −, no growth.
† Key to references: a, Reinhardt (1950); b, Cramer and Myers (1952); c, Hutner et al. (1966); d, Provasoli (1938); e, Buetow and Padilla (1963); f, Kempner and Miller (1965b); g, Wolken (1961); h, Danforth and Wilson (1957, 1961); j, Levedahl (1965); k, Picciolo (1964); m, Wilson et al. (1959); n, Thayer (1949).

Euglena and *Astasia* species can grow on the shorter chain fatty acids including acetate (see Table IV). The net synthesis of carbohydrate from these substrates requires that the decarboxylation steps of oxidative catabolism be by-passed. Many microorganisms and certain specialized plant tissues possess two enzymes that enable this to occur. These enzymes, isocitrate lyase and malate synthase, together with citrate synthase, aconitate hydrase, and malate dehydrogenase, acting in a cyclic sequence (the glyoxylate cycle) enable the synthesis of succinate from two molecules of acetyl-CoA. Gluconeogenesis can then proceed along the pathway outlined in Fig. 3.

Isocitrate lyase and malate synthase have been shown to be present in *E. gracilis* and certain other phytoflagellates (Reeves *et al.*, 1962; Wiessner and Kuhl, 1962; Haigh and Beevers, 1964). The level of isocitrate lyase depends on the nutritional state of the cells, autotrophic cells having lower levels than heterotrophically grown cells (Haigh and Beevers, 1964).

Even-numbered fatty acids and alcohols have been shown to support the growth of *Euglena* (Table IV). These compounds could be converted to acetyl-CoA by the β-oxidative process and enter the gluconeogenic pathway via the glyoxylate cycle, but there is no information about this pathway in *Euglena*. Acetyl-CoA from odd-numbered fatty acids could also enter in this manner and the residual propionyl-CoA could enter at succinate as described earlier.

It should be emphasized that the data available for the various gluconeogenic pathways in *Euglena* is sparse and much more evidence is needed before a definitive metabolic scheme can be presented. That unknown pathways may be operative is suggested by the finding of Haigh and Beevers (1964) that isocitrate is rapidly converted to pyruvate as well as to glyoxylate.

b. Gluconeogenesis from Acetate. Danforth and co-workers have made a major contribution to the understanding of the nature of the assimilatory and oxidative metabolism of acetate in *E. gracilis* var. *bacillaris*. From respirometric studies Wilson and Danforth (1958) concluded that 42% of the acetate utilized was oxidized to CO_2. The remaining 58% was assimilated in the form of substances with the empirical formula of carbohydrate. This partition of the acetate carbon was later confirmed by independent methods (Marzullo and Danforth, 1964b). Similar figures have been reported for *Astasia* (Wilson, 1963).

Studies with acetate labeled in the carboxyl or methyl carbon atoms (Danforth, 1961) gave ^{14}C distribution patterns in carbohydrate predicted for the passage of the carbon atoms through the glyoxylate cycle (Fig. 3).

The utilization of acetate in the dark by autotrophically grown cells requires a lag period for adaptation. Complete adaptation is not attained until after four generations (Cook, 1965). This probably reflects the induction of acetate thiokinase which converts acetate → acetyl-CoA (Abraham and

Bachhawat, 1962; Ohmann, 1964) and also of isocitrate lyase and malate synthase which are known to have high activities in acetate-grown cells and low activities in cells grown on other carbon sources (Reeves *et al.*, 1962). A similar adaptation period is also required before the respiration of glucose-grown cells is stimulated by acetate (Cook and Heinrich, 1965).

Whether there is also induction of the transport system for acetate, as suggested by Danforth and Wilson (1957) on the basis of experiments with acetate- and ethanol-grown cells at pH 5.2 and 7.0, is as yet unproved. Cook (1965) was unable to distinguish between facilitation of the transport system and increase in acetate-utilizing enzymes as the mechanism of adaptation.

Cook and Heinrich (1965) compared the growth of *E. gracilis* strain Z on glucose and acetate and found that both substrates gave approximately the same growth rate, cell dry mass, and protein content during exponential growth. The acetate-grown cells had 50% more RNA than glucose-grown cells and the authors suggested that this might be a reflection of the induction of acetate-metabolizing enzymes.

c. Gluconeogenesis from Ethanol. Wilson and Danforth (1958) showed that ethanol can serve as the sole carbon source for the growth of *E. gracilis.* Approximately 71% of the total ethanol-carbon utilized by var. *bacillaris* was assimilated, with carbohydrate, and possibly lipid, as the major products (Eshleman and Danforth, 1964).

Buetow and Padilla (1963) have compared the chemical characteristics of *A. longa* grown on ethanol and acetate and sampled during the exponential growth phase. More carbohydrate, but less protein and lipid, was present in the ethanol-grown cells as compared with acetate-grown cells. In other organisms ethanol is converted to acetate by the successive action of alcohol dehydrogenase and acetaldehyde dehydrogenase, but this pathway has not been demonstrated in *Euglena*.

d. Gluconeogenesis from Succinate. Succinate appears to be transported into *Euglena* cells by a specific active process (Levedahl, 1965). Succinate would then presumably directly enter the gluconeogenic pathway via the glyoxylate cycle (see Fig. 3). Succinate proved one-third and acetate one-half as effective as ethanol in increasing the cell mass when supplied at limiting concentrations (Levedahl and Wilson, 1965).

The doubling times for carbohydrate on succinate and ethanol were 29 and 26 hours, respectively, while the cell number doubling times were 21 and 24 hours, respectively. This difference in synthetic and division rates was true of all other cell constituents investigated except DNA and is apparently responsible for the decline in dry weight per cell during exponential growth (Wilson and Levedahl, 1964; see also, Vol. I, Chapter 7).

e. Dark Fixation of Carbon Dioxide. The heterotrophic route of CO_2 fixation was first examined by Lynch and Calvin in 1953. They showed that a dark fixation of $^{14}CO_2$, which was not a postphotosynthetic event, resulted in the labeling of TCA-cycle intermediates and related amino acids, hexose- and triosephosphates, and sugar nucleotides in the 80% ethanol-soluble fraction of *E. gracilis* var. *bacillaris* cells (Table V). The rate of incorporation into these metabolites was only a fraction of the rate of incorporation in photosynthetic fixation. Qualitatively the metabolites appeared to be the same in both instances but quantitative differences are apparent from their chromatograms.

Table V

RADIOACTIVE PRODUCTS FORMED DURING A 40-MINUTE
DARK CO_2 FIXATION BY *E. gracilis*[a]

Product	80% Alcohol-soluble activity (%)[b]	
	No dark adaptation	16 hours dark adaptation in air
Fumarate	1.2	0.8
Succinate	21.3	41.2
Malate	4.8	3.4
Citrate	5.0	2.7
Glutamate	6.5	3.4
Aspartate	2.7	4.6
Alanine	2.7	10.5
Phosphopyruvate	1.1	0.3
Serine and glycine	12.4	9.6
Phosphoglycerate	4.6	6.0
Sugar monophosphates	19.8	16.0
Nucleotides	5.4	—

[a] From Lynch and Calvin (1953).
[b] Percent of total fixed activity soluble in 80% alcohol was approximately 50%.

The absence of inhibition of CO_2 incorporation by malonate and the absence of labeling on C-6 of glucose phosphates formed in dark fixation suggested that the route of dark CO_2 fixation is not the same as in photosynthesis.

The pathway of CO_2 fixation in the dark remains to be determined but it seems likely that the carboxylation of a three-carbon intermediate to give a four-carbon TCA-cycle acid as found in many other organisms would explain the results (Wood and Utter, 1965). The fragmentary labeling data for the dark synthesis of malate and glucose are consistent with such a route.

4. *Paramylon Metabolism*

a. Function of Paramylon. The disappearance of paramylon granules from *Euglena* cells under conditions of darkening or starvation and their reappearance in the light or on replenishing organic carbon sources suggested a storage role for paramylon (Zumstein, 1900; Dangeard, 1901; Bracher, 1919; Mainx, 1927; Pringsheim, 1956, 1963). Recent physiological studies support this view.

Extensive work by Danforth and Wilson (1961) showed that the respiratory quotient for endogenous respiration of *E. gracilis* var. *bacillaris* was close to 1. Von Dach (1942) obtained a similar result for *Astasia klebsii*, suggesting that carbohydrate, probably paramylon, was the major respiratory substrate. The endogenous respiratory rate is independent of the substrate on which the organism has been cultured and the medium on which the respiratory measurements are made (*A. klebsii*, von Dach, 1942; var. *bacillaris*, Danforth and Wilson, 1961; strain Z, Cook and Heinrich, 1965).

Marzullo and Danforth (1964a,b) have concluded from the kinetics of the assimilation of acetate-^{14}C that an ethanol-insoluble fraction, identified as paramylon, constitutes a major metabolic reserve (see Danforth, Chapter 2). This is supported by the observations on paramylon levels in starved cells. Blum and Buetow (1963) followed paramylon disappearance after transferring the streptomycin-bleached var. *bacillaris* from a growth medium containing acetate to one lacking a carbon source. Cell division continued for 4–5 days and in this time the paramylon content of the cells decreased by 50%. Thirteen days after the cessation of division 90–95% of cells were viable and the paramylon content had dropped by 90%. In this same period there was also a decrease in the protein and RNA content of the cells, indicating that paramylon was not contributing to the net synthesis of cell constituents under these conditions, but was probably acting as an endogenous energy source.

The reserve nature of paramylon is further indicated by the finding of Cook (1963) that paramylon accumulates in *Euglena* only when light energy is supplied in excess of its immediate needs. The utilization of paramylon for processes leading to cell division was demonstrated by Cook (1966) using the autotrophic Z strain in synchronized culture. The cells were given a 14-hour light cycle and a 10-hour dark cycle. During the light phase the cells received sufficient light energy to satisfy all requirements for basic cell growth and a sufficient excess to allow accumulation of paramylon. The light period, however, was not of sufficient duration to allow completion of protein and RNA synthesis required for cell division. In the subsequent dark period, during which cell division occurred, paramylon reserves were rapidly and almost completely depleted.

Smillie *et al.* (1963) have investigated the formation of chloroplasts when dark-grown cells are returned to the light. In the dark-grown cells paramylon constitutes 25–50% of the dry weight. It is slowly utilized in the dark, but is rapidly broken down when the cells are exposed to light. The depletion is complete within 24 hours of illumination. During this time there is a rapid increase of nonchloroplast protein followed by formation of chloroplast protein, probably at the expense of the cytoplasmic protein. Since the cells were suspended in an autotrophic medium the paramylon must have supplied the carbon for the synthesis of amino acids for cellular and chloroplast protein.

Paramylon is now firmly established as a metabolic reserve of hexose for oxidative energy production and as a source of cellular carbon.

b. Paramylon Synthesis. Lynch and Calvin (1953), in their studies on the light and dark CO_2 fixation in *E. gracilis*, noted the presence in the ethanol-soluble fraction of a compound with the chromatographic mobility of UDPG. The two enzymes needed to convert G-6-P to UDPG, namely phospho-glucomutase and UDPG-pyrophosphorylase (UTP: G-1-P uridylyl transferase) were subsequently detected in *E. gracilis* (Hurlbert and Rittenberg, 1962; Smillie, 1963). (See Smillie, Chapter 1).

The enzymic transfer of labeled glucose from UDPG (but not from ADPG, TDPG, or UDP-β-G) into a glucan with the properties of paramylon was described by Goldemberg and Maréchal (1963) and Maréchal and Goldemberg (1964). The enzyme was found in a particulate fraction from the Z strain, sedimenting between 2000 and 100,000 × g, and its charac-teristics are described elsewhere (see Smillie, Chapter 1). Attempts to demon-strate a primer for the reaction were unsuccessful, but the possibility still exists that an endogenous primer is present in close association with the enzyme protein. A very similar enzyme synthesizing the β-1,3-glucan, callose, has been described by Feingold *et al.* (1958) in seedlings of the mung bean *(Phaseolus aureus)* and in other plants.

The paramylon synthetase was activated to the extent of 20–30% by low molecular weight glucosides and oligosaccharides including laminaribiose. A similar activation has been described for the plant β-1,3-glucan synthetase although here glucose was also an activator. In neither case were the activators incorporated into the synthesized polymer. The activation may be of an allosteric nature, as suggested by Feingold *et al.* (1958), (cf. G-6-P stimulation of glycogen synthesis; Traut and Lipmann, 1963) or the activators may be intermediates in the transfer of glucose to the polymer (Leloir, 1955). An outline of the reactions leading to the synthesis of paramylon is given in Fig. 4.

In the case of the intracellular storage polysaccharides glycogen and starch, the synthetic systems are closely associated with the particles or granules

(Leloir and Goldemberg, 1960; Luck, 1961; Steiner, 1961; De Fekete *et al.*, 1960).

Sommer and Blum (1965) have presented cytochemical evidence for the presence of an acid phosphatase on the surface of paramylon granules. In addition, they have found indications of an endogenous source of phosphate on the granule surface. This could arise from the action of a surface-located UDPG-pyrophosphorylase followed by the enzymic hydrolysis of the pyrophosphate released. There is, however, no direct evidence for the association of the paramylon-synthesizing system with the granule.

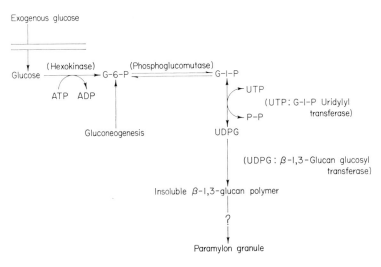

Fig. 4. Outline of the reactions leading to the synthesis of paramylon.

It has already been noted (Section II,A,1) that in autotrophic forms paramylon is often associated with the pyrenoid of the chloroplast. Gibbs (1960) considered that the pyrenoid was possibly an area of enzyme concentration containing enzymes of at least part of the pathway of paramylon synthesis. Hollande (1942) has suggested that in certain cases the pyrenoid body may become detached from the chloroplast and serve as a center of paramylon synthesis (*paramylonherde*) in the cytoplasm. Similar centers of paramylon synthesis have been referred to in descriptions of species of *Euglena* which Pringsheim (1956) classifies in the subgenus Radiatae, e.g., *E. viridis*, *E. geniculata*, and *E. stellata*. In these species there are one or two centers from which elements of the plastid radiate. The centers are often surrounded by a circle of crescent-shaped paramylon granules and have been thought of by some as pyrenoids (see Hollande, 1942; Pringsheim,

1956, for references) and by others (Mainx, 1927) as regions of differentiated cytoplasm involved in paramylon synthesis but quite distinct from the pyrenoid. There have been no reports of the examination of these structures by electron microscopy. In most species, however, the paramylon granules do not appear to be associated with any organized cytoplasmic structure and lie free in the cytoplasm.

The evidence for a membrane enclosing the granule, which might be a site of paramylon metabolizing enzymes, has been reviewed in Section II,A,4. Mention has also been made of *E. spirogyra*, a species with two prominent cytoplasmic granules (Fig. 1b). On division, one granule passes to each daughter cell and a second granule is formed *de novo* (Leedale *et al.*, 1965a). The first microscopic indication of the formation of this new granule is the appearance of a faint, translucent, ovoid image of the same dimensions as the fully formed granule (Fig. 5). The paramylon accumulates within this

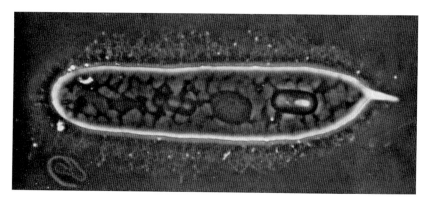

Fig. 5. Living cell of *E. spirogyra* squashed very flat to show nucleus, chloroplasts, posterior paramylon granule, and anterior paramylon "ghost." Reichert anoptral contrast. ×1250 in the original. (Photograph by courtesy of Dr. G. F. Leedale.)

structure until a granule with the optical properties of paramylon is formed (Leedale, personal communication). Such observations may be compared with those of Nath *et al.* (1960, 1961) who noted that paramylon granules in a *Khawkinea* sp. appear to arise from small lipid bodies which grow into spheres staining with neutral red. Paramylon is formed in the inner region of the lipid body, appearing as an unstained core which increases in size. The external layer stained with Sudan black B and with coupled tetrazolium, indicative of lipid and protein, respectively. The stained layer decreased in thickness until, when fully formed, the paramylon granules failed to stain for lipid or protein.

The deposition of paramylon in cells recovering from a period of carbon starvation has been followed chemically and ultrastructurally in streptomycin-bleached *E. gracilis* var. *bacillaris*. Blum and Buetow (1963) measured the paramylon levels upon returning starved cells to an acetate-supplemented medium and found that synthesis commenced within a few hours in cells that had been starved for 8 days or less, while there was an 8-hour lag in cells that had been starved for 13 days. The extreme vacuolization of the cell which occurs upon starvation was found to have disappeared within 2 hours of returning the cells to an acetate medium (Malkoff and Buetow, 1964). After 23–49 hours, paramylon granules were again evident in the cytoplasm and it was considered likely that the paramylon was secreted by the membranes of the cisternae of the endoplasmic reticulum.

   c. Depolymerization of Paramylon. The electron microscopic features of cells under conditions of carbon starvation have been examined by Malkoff and Buetow (1964) and Brandes *et al.* (1964). These authors distinguish two classes of cavities in normal cells: type A, surrounded by a poorly defined membrane and containing paramylon, and type B, showing no apparent contents and bounded by a clearly defined layer of osmiophilic material of variable thickness. During starvation the contents of the paramylon cavities became less osmiophilic until after 7-days starvation, large, empty vacuoles were observed which were believed to represent dilated paramylon "cavities." After 12-days starvation there was extreme vacuolization of the cytoplasm, possibly due to the fusion of depleted paramylon "cavities" with type B vacuoles.

   These morphological observations, together with the quantitative measurements of paramylon depletion under various physiological conditions (see Section III,B,4,*a*) make it clear that a system for the digestion of paramylon is present in the cell although the enzymic nature of this system and its control are not well understood. In other situations in which intracellular polysaccharides are depolymerized, usually more than one enzyme is involved and sometimes more than one type, e.g., both hydrolytic and phosphorolytic (Whelan, 1961). This appears to be true for *Euglena* also.

   Fellig (1960) reported the presence of soluble β-1,3-glucan hydrolases in *E. gracilis* strain Z that depolymerize laminarin (see Smillie, Chapter 1). Tocher (1962) and Meeuse (1964) have examined cell-free extracts from a range of euglenoids and have found that all preparations hydrolyze soluble laminarin but none attack native paramylon granules. Maréchal and Goldemberg (1964) found that extracts from the Z strain prepared by the method of Fellig (1960) degraded the insoluble, radioactive product of the paramylon synthase, releasing glucose-^{14}C. Under similar conditions the preparation hydrolyzed alkali-treated paramylon but not the native granules.

Barras and Stone (unpublished observations) have examined the β-1,3-glucan hydrolase system of ultraviolet-bleached *E. gracilis* var. *bacillaris*. Although crude extracts rapidly liberated glucose from insoluble laminarin, very little glucose was released from laminarin modified at both the reducing and nonreducing chain ends by oxidation with periodate and subsequent reduction with borohydride by the method of Nelson *et al.* (1963). However, small but significant amounts of reducing sugars other than glucose were released from the oxidized-reduced laminarin. The viscosity of a carboxymethyl-pachyman solution (Clarke and Stone, 1962) was reduced by the crude extract with little liberation of reducing sugar. These data suggest the presence in the extracts of both endo- and exohydrolases. Exclusion chromatography of a soluble extract confirms the multicomponent nature of the hydrolase system.

Phosphorolytic breakdown of at least the β-1,3-glucose oligosaccharides is also possible through the action of laminaribiose phosphorylase, a soluble enzyme isolated from *E. gracilis* strain Z (Maréchal and Goldemberg, 1963; Goldemberg *et al.*, 1966), *A. ocellata* (Manners and Taylor, 1965), and *Ochromonas* (Manners, quoted in Goldemberg *et al.*, 1966) (see Smillie, Chapter 1 for details of properties). This reversibly acting enzyme can depolymerize oligosaccharides in the reaction:

$$\text{Laminaritetraose} + P_i \rightleftharpoons \text{laminaritriose} + \alpha\text{-G-1-P}$$

The equilibrium constant for this reaction had an average value of 0.4 at pH 6.5 and it seems probable that the direction of its action would favor phosphorolysis since the $P_i : \text{G-1-P}$ ratio in the cell would be high (cf. glycogen phosphorylase, Stetten and Stetten, 1960). However, the possibility that localized concentrations of G-1-P might favor the reverse reaction cannot be excluded. The enzyme was unable to attack native paramylon granules, alkali-treated granules, or the product of paramylon synthase during its formation (Goldemberg and Maréchal, 1963; Goldemberg *et al.*, 1966). A tentative scheme for the multienzymic depolymerization of paramylon is outlined in Fig. 6. In addition to the combined operation of the hydrolytic

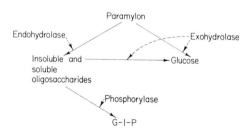

Fig. 6. Tentative scheme for the multienzymic depolymerization of paramylon.

and phosphorolytic enzymes shown, it is conceivable that a spatial separation of the pathways exists in the intact cell. Such a separation might be an important means of controlling the depolymerization of paramylon.

d. Control of Paramylon Metabolism. Data from autotrophic, hetero-trophic, and mixed autotrophic and heterotrophic incubation studies, as well as from endogenous respiration studies, indicate that the metabolism of paramylon is subject to extensive controls. In strains grown under auto-trophic conditions, paramylon accumulation is controlled by the availability of photochemically trapped energy. Cook (1963) found that unless this was in excess of the immediate energy requirements of the cell no paramylon was synthesized. Once paramylon synthesis had commenced, the synthetic rate increased with increase in light intensity until a maximum rate was observed at a light intensity which was saturating for all other aspects of growth. In further studies, using *E. gracilis* strain Z, Cook (1965) followed the percentage distribution of ^{14}C from bicarbonate-^{14}C into cell fractions of autotrophically grown cells and cells grown in the light in the presence of acetate (Table VI), and the distribution of ^{14}C from acetate-^{14}C into cell

Table VI

BICARBONATE-^{14}C INCORPORATED IN 3 HOURS IN THE LIGHT BY *E. gracilis* STRAIN $Z^{a,b}$

Fraction	Bicarbonate-^{14}C incorporated (%)	
	Autotrophically grown cells	Cells grown in the light with acetate present
Cold perchloric acid	4.9	1.0
Lipid	18.8	3.0
RNA	3.5	0.2
Paramylon	42.3	2.7
Protein	30.4	92.7

[a] Suspended in Cramer–Myers medium, pH 8.
[b] From Cook (1965).

fractions from acetate-adapted cells grown and incubated in the dark or the light (Table VII). The autotrophically derived carbon was generally distributed between paramylon, protein, and lipid, but was displaced almost exclusively toward protein synthesis in the presence of acetate. Acetate-derived carbon was directed largely into protein synthesis, with some incorporation into lipid and paramylon with cells grown in the dark. The distribution was displaced toward lipid and paramylon with cells grown in the light. These results indicate major interactions between the pathways

Table VII

ACETATE-^{14}C INCORPORATED IN 3 HOURS BY ACETATE-ADAPTED
E. gracilis STRAIN Z CELLS[a,b]

Fraction	Acetate-^{14}C incorporated (%)	
	Dark-grown and incubated cells	Light-grown and incubated cells
Cold perchloric acid	1.1	6.2
Lipid	17.6	65.2
RNA	1.9	1.3
Paramylon	11.2	21.2
Protein	68.2	6.2

[a] Suspended in Cramer–Myers medium, pH 8.0.
[b] From Cook (1965).

involved in the autotrophic and heterotrophic assimilation of carbon, although there is no indication as to possible mechanisms involved.

Marzullo and Danforth (1964a,b) examined the assimilation products in E. gracilis var. bacillaris when cells were incubated in a buffer at pH 5.5, with acetate but without a nitrogen source or a vitamin supplement. Approximately 80% of the assimilated carbon was found in paramylon, the remainder being distributed in other cell fractions (Marzullo and Danforth, 1964b) (Table VIII). The results can be compared with those of Cook (1965) (Table VII), who used the "complete" Cramer–Myers medium. The absence of an exogenous nitrogen source may be the significant factor in accounting for the diversion of the assimilatory products away from the protein toward carbohydrate under Danforth's conditions. These experiments

Table VIII

DISTRIBUTION OF ^{14}C AMONG FRACTIONS OF ACETATE-GROWN
E. gracilis VAR. bacillaris (BLEACHED STRAIN)
AFTER 6 HOURS INCUBATION WITH ACETATE-^{14}C[a,b]

Fraction	Assimilated ^{14}C (%)
Ethanol-soluble	8.0
Lipid	2.3
Protein + nucleic acid	8.8
Paramylon	81

[a] In phosphate buffer, pH 7.0.
[b] From Marzullo and Danforth (1964b).

indicate that the cell can exert a considerable control on the direction of assimilation of exogenous carbon in response to varying physiological conditions.

Thus, although there is considerable evidence for the control of the incorporation of assimilated carbon into paramylon and possibly for the selective utilization of paramylon during starvation (Blum and Buetow, 1963), very little can yet be said about the mechanisms of this control. There are indications from the work of Smillie *et al.* (1963) that in cells in which chloroplasts are developing, the increased rate of paramylon degradation is due to a synthesis of the depolymerizing enzymes. The increased rate of paramylon synthesis with increasing light intensities (Cook, 1963) may be due to synthesis of enzymes associated with paramylon formation or the activation of enzymes already present. Control of the latter type has been shown to operate for enzymes involved both in the synthesis and degradation of glycogen, by virtue of their association and dissociation from the glycogen particles. (Tata, 1964; Sie *et al.*, 1964).

IV. Concluding Remarks

Considering the extensive literature concerned with the genus *Euglena* and related organisms, surprisingly little attention has been paid to the detailed enzymology of the metabolic pathways present. Much more information on the characteristics of the individual enzyme reactions, the properties of the enzymes concerned, their kinetics, and their subcellular localization are needed for a fuller appreciation of their role in the integrated metabolism of *Euglena*. The physiological experiments outlined in this chapter make it apparent that regulatory mechanisms for the various metabolic pathways are operative. The nature of the regulatory interactions at a molecular level will be amenable to exploration by techniques such as the measurement of levels of individual enzymes and of steady-state levels of substrates only after more enzymological detail is available.

The considerable background knowledge on the nutritional physiology of *Euglena*, the availability of autotrophic and temporarily or permanently heterotrophic forms, and the ability to control growth and division, synchronously if necessary, present the biochemist with a flexible system not readily available with other tissues.

The versatility of the carbohydrate-synthesizing systems in *Euglena* as evidenced by the variety of sugars found in the mucin and glycolipids as well as the presence of paramylon, an unusual storage form of carbohydrate, commends *Euglena* to students of carbohydrate metabolism.

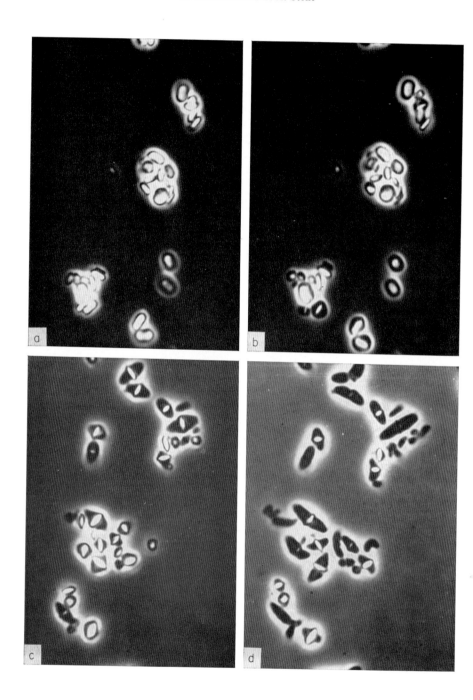

V. Addendum

A. ALKALINE SWELLING OF PARAMYLON

As noted in Section II,A,3,a paramylon granules swell when suspended in dilute alkali. The optical density of a paramylon suspension rapidly decreases at NaOH concentrations in the region of 0.25 M. At lower concentrations the change is much slower and several stages of swelling may be observed by using phase contrast microscopy. The initial change is a darkening

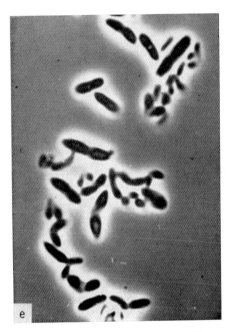

Fig. 7. Photographs of paramylon granules from *E. gracilis* taken during swelling in NaOH. A suspension of granules under a cover slip was observed using a high contrast, phase, oil-immersion lens (Nikon). A drop of NaOH (0.66 N) was allowed to diffuse under the cover slip and the changes in the paramylon granules photographed at 4 fps using a cine camera and 16 mm Agepan FF film. ×2000 in the original. (The microphotography was performed by Dr. I. K. Buckley, Pathology Department, University of Melbourne.) a, Groups of refractile granules showing normal morphology. b, Swelling of granules just commenced; some granules showing a darkened rim. c, 4 seconds later; granules showing increased areas of darkening taking the form of double cones of material extruded from the longer sides of the granules. d, 6.5 seconds after b; swelling advanced; the original refractile material of the granule reduced to a small area, extruded material pushed further from either side of the granule. e, 11 seconds after b; swelling complete; no refractile areas visible.

of the rim of the otherwise refractile granules, then rapidly from each side of the long axis of the granule cone-shaped areas with a dark image develop. Ultimately the original refractile material of the granule is reduced to a small area at the center of two "wings" of extruded material or disappears altogether (see Figs. 7a–e). The fully swollen granules are of the same width but at least twice the length of the original granule (Barras, Buckley and Stone, unpublished observations). Barber *et al.* (1967) have made similar observations in respect to the optical density changes in alkali and their electron micrographs of the material extruded from the swollen granules show long, multiple-stranded structures whose density, measured by isopycnic centrifugation, is 1.62. This is identical with the density of the intact granules and also of callose, the plant β-1,3-glucan (Frey-Wyssling *et al.* (1957)). The observation that the paramylon is organized into fibrillar threads is in accord with the evidence, reviewed in Section II,A,6 for the arrangement of paramylon with the granules.

B. Metabolism of Sugar Nucleotides

Ankel *et al.* (1967) have described the preparation of a UDP-glucuronic acid carboxylase from *E. gracilis* strain Z which converts UDP-glucuronic acid to UDP-xylose. This enzyme may be involved in the synthesis of precursors of the mucin polysaccharide which has been shown to contain xylose (see Section II,B).

C. Phosphorolysis of β-1,3-Oligoglucosides

Manners and Taylor (1967) have examined the laminaribiose phosphorylase from *Astasia ocellata*. The enzyme was less stable than its *E. gracilis* counterpart and has a different pattern of specificity for acceptor substrates.

Maréchal (1967) has reported that *E. gracilis* strain Z possesses a β-1,3-oligoglucan phosphorylase in addition to the laminaribiose phosphorylase. The two enzymes were separated chromatographically and showed an overlapping chain length specificity among the lower members of the series of β-1,3-oligoglucoside substrates. The upper chain length limit for the β-1,3-oligoglucan phosphorylase was not reported. Another distinguishing feature of this enzyme was its absolute requirement for SH-reagents.

Acknowledgments

    The authors have benefited greatly from information and comments provided by Professor D. J. Manners, Drs. W. F. Danforth, S. H. Hutner, G. F. Leedale, and R. M. Smillie. They also thank Dr. P. Plackett and Miss A. E. Moore for critically reading the manuscript.

References

Abraham, A., and Bachhawat, B. K. (1962). *Biochim. Biophys. Acta* **62**, 376.
Abraham, A., and Bachhawat, B. K. (1963). *Biochim. Biophys. Acta* **70**, 104.
Albaum, H. G., Schatz, A., Hutner, S. H., and Hirschfield, A. (1950). *Arch. Biochem. Biophys.* **29**, 210.
Ankel, H., Ankel, E., Feingold, D. S., and Schutzbach, J. S. (1967). *Biochim. Biophys. Acta* **136**, 172.
Annan, W. D., Hirst, E. L., and Manners, D. J. (1965a). *J. Chem. Soc.* p. 220.
Annan, W. D., Hirst, E. L., and Manners, D. J. (1965b). *J. Chem. Soc.* p. 885.
App, A. A., and Jagendorf, A. T. (1963). *J. Protozool.* **10**, 340.
Archibald, A. R., Manners, D. J., and Ryley, J. F. (1958). *Chem. Ind. (London)* p. 1516.
Archibald, A. R., Cunningham, W. L., Manners, D. J., Stark, J. R., and Ryley, J. F. (1963). *Biochem. J.* **88**, 444.
Arnstein, H. R. V., and White, A. M. (1962). *Biochem. J.* **83**, 264.
Baker, H., Hutner, S. H., and Sobotka, H. S. (1958). *Ann. N. Y. Acad. Sci.* **62**, 349.
Barber, A. A., Bartlett, T. W. and Levedahl, B. H. (1966). *National Cancer Inst. Monog.* **21**, 303.
Barras, D. R., and Stone, B. A. (1965). *Biochem. J.* **97**, 14P.
Barry, S. C. (1962). *J. Protozool.* **9**, 395.
Beattie, A., Hirst, E. L., and Percival, E. (1961). *Biochem. J.* **79**, 531.
Belsky, M. M. (1957). *Bacteriol. Proc.* **57** (P47), 123.
Ben-Shaul, Y., Schiff, J. A., and Epstein, H. T. (1964). *Plant Physiol.* **39**, 231.
Benson, A. A., Daniel, H., and Wiser, R. (1959). *Proc. Natl. Acad. Sci. U.S.* **45**, 1582.
Blum, J. J., and Buetow, D. E. (1963). *Exptl. Cell Res.* **29**, 407.
Blum, J. J., Sommer, J. R., and Kahn, V. (1965). *J. Protozool.* **12**, 202.
Bracher, R. (1919). *Ann. Botany (London)* **33**, 93.
Brandes, D., Buetow, D. E., Bertini, F., and Malkoff, D. B. (1964). *Exptl. Mol. Pathol.* **3**, 583.
Buetow, D. E., and Padilla, G. M. (1963). *J. Protozool.* **10**, 121.
Bütschli, O. (1906). *Arch. Protistenk.* **7**, 197.
Carter, H. E., Ohno, K., Nojima, S., Tipton, C. L., and Stanacev, N. Z. (1961). *J. Lipid Res.* **2**, 215.
Chancellor-Maddison, J., and Noll, C. R. (1963). *Science* **142**, 60.
Chapman, L. F., Cirillo, V. P., and Jahn, T. L. (1965). *J. Protozool.* **12**, 47.
Cheniae, G. M. (1963). *Biochim. Biophys. Acta* **70**, 504.
Cheniae, G. M., and Kerr, P. C. (1965). *Plant Physiol.* **40**, 452.
Cirillo, V. P. (1961). *Ann. Rev. Microbiol.* **15**, 197.
Clarke, A. E., and Stone, B. A. (1960). *Biochim. Biophys. Acta* **44**, 161.
Clarke, A. E., and Stone, B. A. (1962). *Phytochemistry* **1**, 175.
Clarke, A. E., and Stone, B. A. (1963). *Rev. Pure Appl. Chem.* **13**, 134.
Cook, J. R. (1963). *J. Protozool.* **10**, 436.
Cook, J. R. (1965). *Plant Cell Physiol. (Tokyo)* **6**, 301.
Cook, J. R. (1966). *Plant Physiol.* **41**, 821.
Cook, J. R., and Heinrich, B. (1965). *J. Protozool.* **12**, 581.
Cowling, E. B. (1963). *In* "Advances in Enzyme Hydrolysis of Cellulose and Related Materials" (E. T. Reese, ed.), p. 1. Pergamon, Oxford.
Cramer, M., and Myers, J. (1952). *Arch. Mikrobiol.* **17**, 384.
Czurda, V. (1928). *Beih. Botan. Zentr.* **45**, 97.
Danforth, W. F. (1961). *J. Protozool.* **8**, 152.

188   D. R. Barras and B. A. Stone

Danforth, W. F., and Wilson, B. W. (1957). *J. Protozool.* **4**, 52.
Danforth, W. F., and Wilson, B. W. (1961). *J. Gen. Microbiol.* **24**, 95.
Dangeard, P. (1928). *Ann. Protistol.* **1**, 69.
Dangeard, P. A. (1901). *Botaniste* **8**, 97.
Davies, W. H., Mercer, E. I., and Goodwin, T. W. (1965). *Phytochemistry* **4**, 741.
De Fekete, M. A. R., Leloir, L. F., and Cardini, C. E. (1960). *Nature* **187**, 918.
Deflandre, G. (1931). *Ann. Protistol.* **5**, 41.
Deflandre, G. (1934). *Bull. Biol. France Belg.* **68**, 382.
De Haller, G. (1958). *Proc. 4th Intern. Congr. Electronmicros.*, Berlin **2**, 517.
De Haller, G. (1959). *Arch. Sci. (Geneva)* **12**, 21.
Diskus, A. (1956). *Protoplasma* **45**, 460.
Doyle, W. L., (1943). *Biol. Rev. Cambridge Phil. Soc.* **18**, 119.
Eshleman, J. N., and Danforth, W. F. (1964). *J. Protozool.* **11**, 394.
Feingold, D. S., Neufeld, E. F., and Hassid, W. Z. (1958). *J. Biol. Chem.* **233**, 783.
Fellig, J. (1960). *Science* **131**, 832.
Frei, E., and Preston, R. D. (1964). *Proc. Roy. Soc.* **B160**, 293.
Frey-Wyssling, A., and Mühlethaler, K. (1960). *Schweiz. Z. Hydrol.* **22**, 122.
Frey-Wyssling, A., Epprecht, W. and Kessler, G. (1957). *Experientia* **13**, 22.
Gibbs, S. P. (1960). *J. Ultrastruct. Res.* **4**, 127.
Gojdics, M. (1953). "The Genus, *Euglena*." Univ. of Wisconsin Press, Madison, Wisconsin.
Goldemberg, S. H., and Maréchal, L. R. (1963). *Biochim. Biophys. Acta* **71**, 743.
Goldemberg, S. H., Maréchal, L. R., and De Souza, B. C. (1966). *J. Biol. Chem.* **241**, 45.
Gottlieb, J. (1850). *Ann. Chem. Pharm.* **75**, 50.
Günther, F. (1927). *Arch. Protistenk.* **60**, 511.
Habermann, J. (1874). *Ann. Chem.* **172**, 11.
Haigh, W. G., and Beevers, H. (1964). *Biochim. Biophys. Acta* **107**, 147.
Hall, R. P. (1939). *Quart. Rev. Biol.* **14**, 1.
Hall, R. P. (1941). *Am. Naturalist* **75**, 417.
Hamburger, C. (1911). *Sitzber. Heidelberg. Akad. Wiss. Math. Naturw. Kl. Abhandl.* 2B **4**, 1.
Handa, N., and Nisizawa, K. (1961). *Nature* **192**, 1078.
Haye, A. (1930). *Arch. Protistenk.* **70**, 17.
Heidt, K. (1937). *Arch. Protistenk.* **88**, 127.
Hers, H. G. (1962). *In* "The Enzymes" (P. D. Boyer, H. Lardy, and K. Myrbäck, eds.), 2nd ed., Vol. 6, p. 75. Academic Press, New York.
Hollande, A. (1942). *Arch. Zool. Exptl. Gen.* **83**, 1.
Horecker, B. L. (1962). *Harvey Lectures Ser.* **57**, 35.
Houwink, A. L., and Kreger, D. R. (1953). *Antonie van Leeuwenhoek J. Microbiol. Serol.* **19**, 1.
Hulanicka, D., Erwin, J., and Bloch, K. (1964). *J. Biol. Chem.* **239**, 2778.
Hurlbert, R. E., and Rittenberg, S. C. (1962). *J. Protozool.* **9**, 170.
Hutner, S. H., and Provasoli, L. (1951). *In* "Biochemistry and Physiology of Protozoa" (S. H. Hutner and A. Lwoff, eds.), Vol. I, p. 27. Academic Press, New York.
Hutner, S. H., Provasoli, L., Stokstad, E. L. R., Hoffman, C. E., Belt, M., Franklin, A. L., and Jukes, T. H. (1949). *Proc. Soc. Exptl. Biol. Med.* **70**, 118.
Hutner, S. H., Bach, M. K., and Ross, G. I. M. (1956). *J. Protozool.* **3**, 101.
Hutner, S. H., Zahalsky, A. C., Aaronson, S., Baker, H., and Frank, O. (1966). *In* "Methods in Cell Physiology" (D. W. Prescott, ed.), Vol. 2, p. 217. Academic Press, New York.
Jahn, T. L., (1946). *Quart. Rev. Biol.* **21**, 246.
James, A. T., and Nichols, B. W. (1966). *Nature* **210**, 372.

Jarosch, R. (1962). *In* "Physiology and Biochemistry of Algae" (R. A. Lewin, ed.), p. 573. Academic Press, New York.

Kamptner, E. (1952). *Oesterr. Botan. Z.* **99**, 556.

Kempner, E. S., and Miller, J. H. (1965a). *Biochim. Biophys. Acta* **104**, 11.

Kempner, E. S., and Miller, J. H. (1965b). *Biochemistry* **4**, 2735.

Kidder, G. W. (1951). *Ann. Rev. Microbiol.* **5**, 139.

King, K. W. (1965). *J. Ferment. Technol.* **43**, 79.

Kitahara, M., and Takeuchi, Y. (1959). *Gifu Daigaku Nogakubu Kenkyu Hokoku* (*Res. Bull. Fac. Agr. Gifu Univ.*) **11**, 127.

Klebs, G. (1883). *Untersuch. Botan. Inst. Tübingen* **1**, 233.

Klebs, G. (1886). *Untersuch. Botan. Inst. Tübingen* **2**, 333.

Kreger, D. R., and Meeuse, B. J. D. (1952). *Biochim. Biophys. Acta* **9**, 699.

Kutscher, F. (1898). *Z. Physiol. Chem.* **24**, 360.

Landau, B. R., and Katz, J. (1965). *In* "Handbook of Physiology," Sect. 5: Adipose Tissue (A. E. Renold and G. F. Cahill, Sect. eds.), p. 253. *Am. Physiol. Soc.*, Washington, D. C.

Leedale, G. F. (1964). *Brit. Phycol. Bull.* **2**, 291.

Leedale, G. F. (1966). *Advan. Sci.* **23**, (107), 22.

Leedale, G. F., Meeuse, B. J. D., and Pringsheim, E. G. (1965a). *Arch. Mikrobiol.* **50**, 68.

Leedale, G. F., Meeuse, B. J. D., and Pringsheim, E. G. (1965b). *Arch. Mikrobiol.* **50**. 133.

Lefort, M. (1963). *Compt. Rend. Acad. Sci.* **256**, 5190.

Leloir, L. F. (1955). *Proc. 3rd. Intern. Congr. Biochem.*, *Brussels* p. 154, Academic Press, New York.

Leloir, L. F., and Goldemberg, S. H. (1960). *J. Biol. Chem.* **235**, 919.

Levedahl, B. H. (1965). *Exptl. Cell Res.* **39**, 233.

Levedahl, B. H., and Wilson, B. W. (1965). *Exptl. Cell Res.* **39**, 242.

Lloyd, D., and Cially, A. G. (1965). *Biochem. J.* **97**, 176.

Luck, D. J. L. (1961). *J. Biophys. Biochem. Cytol.* **10**, 195.

Lwoff, A. (1932). "Recherches biochimiques sur la nutrition des protozoaires. Le pouvoir de synthèse" (Monographies de l'Institut Pasteur). Masson, Paris.

Lwoff, A. (1938). *Ann. Inst. Pasteur* **61**, 580.

Lwoff, A., and Dusi, H. (1934). *Ann. Inst. Pasteur* **53**, 641.

Lynch, V. H., and Calvin, M. (1953). *Ann. N. Y. Acad. Sci.* **56**, 890.

Mainx, F. (1927). *Arch. Protistenk.* **60**, 355.

Malkoff, D. B., and Buetow, D. E. (1964). *Exptl. Cell Res.* **35**, 58.

Manners, D. J., and Taylor, D. C. (1965). *Biochem. J.* **94**, 17P.

Manners, D. J. and Taylor, D. C. (1967). *Arch. Biochem. Biophys.* **121**, 443.

Manners, D. J., Ryley, J. F., and Stark, J. R. (1966). *Biochem. J.* **101**, 323.

Maréchal, L. R. (1967a). *Biochim. Biophys. Acta* **146**, 417.

Maréchal, L. R. (1967b). *Biochim. Biophys. Acta* **146**, 431.

Maréchal, L. R., and Goldemberg, S. H. (1963). *Biochem. Biophys. Res. Commun.* **13**, 106.

Maréchal, L. R., and Goldemberg, S. H. (1964). *J. Biol. Chem.* **239**, 3163.

Marzullo, G., and Danforth, W. F. (1964a). *J. Gen. Microbiol.* **34**, 9.

Marzullo, G., and Danforth, W. F. (1964b). *J. Gen. Microbiol.* **34**, 21.

Meeuse, B. J. D. (1964). *Basteria* **28**, 67.

Mignot, J. P. (1965). *Protistologica* **1**, 5.

Mollenhauer, H. H., and Morré, D. J. (1966). *Ann. Rev. Plant Physiol.* **17**, 27.

Müller, O. F. (1786). *In* "Animalcula Infusoria, Fluviatilia et Marina," (O. Fabricus, ed.), Sect. 135. N. Möller, Royal Printery, Copenhagen.

Murakami, S., Norimura, Y., and Takamiya, A. (1963). *In* "Studies on Microalgae and

Photosynthetic Bacteria" (Japan. Soc. of Plant Physiologists, eds.), p. 65. Univ. of Tokyo Press, Tokyo.

Nath. V., Dutta, G. P., and Dhillon, B. (1960). *Res. Bull. Panjab. Univ.* **11**, Parts III-IV, 159.

Nath, V., Dutta, G. P., and Dhillon, B. (1961). *Res. Bull. Panjab. Univ.* **12**, Parts III-IV, 237.

Nelson, T. E., Scalletti, J. V., Smith, F., and Kirkwood, S. (1963). *Can. J. Chem.* **41**, 1671.

Neufeld, E. F., and Hall, C. W. (1964). *Biochim. Biophys. Res. Commun.* **14**, 503.

O'Colla, P. S. (1962). *In* "Physiology and Biochemistry of Algae" (R. A. Lewin, ed.), p. 337. Academic Press, New York.

Ohmann, E. (1963). *Naturwissenschaften* **50**, 552.

Ohmann, E. (1964). *Biochim. Biophys. Acta* **82**, 325.

Picciolo, G. L. A. W. (1964). Ph. D. Thesis, Dept. of Zoology, Univ. of Maryland, College Park, Maryland.

Pochmann, A. (1953). *Planta* **42**, 478.

Pochmann, A. (1956). *Oesterr. Botan. Z.* **103**, 110.

Pochmann, A. (1958). *Oesterr. Botan. Z.* **104**, 321.

Pringsheim, E. G. (1942). *New Phytologist* **41**, 171.

Pringsheim, E. G. (1954a). *Nature* **173**, 775.

Pringsheim, E. G. (1954b). *Naturwissenschaften* **41**, 380.

Pringsheim, E. G. (1955). *Arch. Mikrobiol.* **21**, 414.

Pringsheim, E. G. (1956). *Nova Acta Leopoldina* **18**, 1.

Pringsheim, E. G. (1963). "Farblose Algen." Fischer, Stuttgart.

Provasoli, L. (1938). *Boll. Zool. Agrar. Bachicolt. Univ. Studi Milano* **8**, 1.

Provasoli, L., Hutner, S. H., and Schatz, A. (1948). *Proc. Soc. Exptl. Biol. Med.* **69**, 279.

Reeves, H. C., Kadis, S., and Ajl, S. (1962). *Biochim. Biophys. Acta* **57**, 403.

Reger, J. F., and Beams, H. W. (1954). *Proc. Iowa Acad. Sci.* **61**, 593.

Reinhardt, K. (1950). *Arch. Mikrobiol.* **15**, 270.

Ringo, D. L., (1963). *J. Protozool.* **10**, 167.

Rosenberg, A. (1963). *Biochemistry* **2**, 1148.

Rosenberg, A., and Pecker, M. (1964). *Biochemistry* **3**, 254.

Schiller, J. (1952). *Oesterr. Botan. Z.* **99**, 413.

Selby, K., and Maitland, C. C. (1965). *Biochem. J.* **94**, 578.

Sher, S., and Aaronson, S. (1959). *Brookhaven Symp. Biol.* **11**, 343.

Shibuya, I., Yagi, T., and Benson, A. A. (1963). *In* "Studies on Microalgae and Photosynthetic Bacteria" (Japan. Soc. of Plant Physiologists, eds.), p. 627. Univ. of Tokyo Press, Tokyo.

Sie, H. G., Hablanian, A., and Fishman, W. H. (1964). *Nature* **201**, 393.

Siegesmund, K. A., Rosen, W. G., and Gawlik, S. R. (1962). *Am. J. Botany* **49**, 137.

Singh, K. P. (1956). *Am. J. Botany* **43**, 274.

Smillie, R. M. (1960). *Nature* **187**, 1024.

Smillie, R. M. (1963). *U. S . At. Energy Comm.* **BNL-6945.**

Smillie, R. M. (1964). *In* "Fructose-1,6,diphosphatase and Its Role in Gluconeogenesis" (R. M. McGilvery and B. M. Pogell, eds.), p. 31. The American Institute of Biological Sciences, Baltimore, Maryland.

Smillie, R. M., Evans, W. R., and Lyman, H. (1963). *Brookhaven Symp. Biol.* **16**, 89.

Sommer, J. R. (1965). *J. Cell Biol.* **24**, 253.

Sommer, J. R., and Blum, J. J. (1965). *J. Cell Biol.* **24**, 235.

Spicer, S. S. (1960). *J. Histochem. Cytochem.* **8**, 18.

Steiner, D. F. (1961). *Biochim. Biophys. Acta* **54**, 206.

Stetten, O., and Stetten, M. R. (1960). *Physiol. Rev.* **40**, 505.

Tata, J. R. (1964). *Biochem. J.* **90**, 284.
Taylor, F. J. (1960a). *Proc. Roy. Soc.* **B151**, 400.
Taylor, F. J. (1960b). *Proc. Roy. Soc.* **B151**, 483.
Thayer, P. S. (1949). M. A. Thesis, Biology Department, Amherst College, Amherst, Massachusetts.
Tocher, R. D. (1962). Cited by Meeuse (1964).
Traut, R. R., and Lipmann, F. (1963). *J. Biol. Chem.* **238**, 1213.
Ueda, K. (1958). *Cytologia (Tokyo)* **23**, 56.
Ueda, K. (1960). *Cytologia (Tokyo)* **25**, 8.
von Brand, T. (1935). *Ergeb. Biol.* **12**, 161.
von Dach, H. (1942). *Biol. Bull.* **82**, 356.
Warsi, S., and Whelan, W. J. (1957). *Chem. Ind. (London)* p. 1573.
Whelan, W. J. (1961). *Nature* **190**, 954.
Wiessner, W., and Kuhl, A. (1962). *Vortr. Gesamtgebiet Botan. Deut. Botan. Ges.* **1**, 102.
Wilson, B. W. (1963). *J. Cellular Comp. Physiol.* **62**, 49.
Wilson, B. W., and Danforth, W. F. (1958). *J. Gen. Microbiol.* **18**, 535.
Wilson, B. W., and Levedahl, B. H. (1964). *Exptl. Cell Res.* **35**, 69.
Wilson, B. W., Buetow, D. E., Jahn, T. L., and Levedahl, B. H. (1959). *Exptl. Cell Res.* **18**, 454.
Wolken, J. J. (1956). *J. Protozool.* **3**, 211.
Wolken, J. J. (1961). "*Euglena.* An Experimental Organism for Biochemical and Biophysical Studies." Rutgers Univ. Press, New Brunswick, New Jersey.
Wood, H. G., and Utter, M. F. (1965). *In* "Essays in Biochemistry" (P. N. Campbell and G. D. Greville, eds.), Vol. I, p. 1. Academic Press, New York.
Yaden, S. (1965). Ph. D. Thesis, Univ. of Minnesota, Minneapolis, Minnesota.
Zumstein, M. (1900). *Jahrb. Wiss. Botan.* **34**, 149.

CHAPTER 8

INHIBITORS OF GROWTH AND METABOLISM

S. H. Hutner, A. C. Zahalsky, and S. Aaronson

I. Permeability as a Phyletic Constraint on Susceptibility of *Euglena* to Metabolic Inhibitors

A. INTRODUCTION

Metabolic inhibitors, thanks to their successes as probes in molecular biology, as antiviral and antitumor agents, and as agents for correcting metabolic imbalances expressed in diseases as diverse as gout and psychoses, are reviewed incessantly. To avoid rehashing old material, we assume that the reader's acquaintance with inhibitors is that obtainable from a broad-spectrum textbook of biochemistry, e.g., Mahler and Cordes's (1966), supplemented with a comprehensive pharmacology text, e.g., Goodman and Gilman (1965) or DiPalma (1965). The pre-1963 literature on metabolic inhibitors was covered by the two volumes edited by Hochster and Quastel (1963). Webb's volumes stand out, especially II and III (1966); publication of the volumes in preparation should round out this exhaustive, tour-de-force treatment of the most used inhibitors.

   Euglena gracilis with its limited permeability is ill suited for discerning the mode of action of many, probably most, metabolic inhibitors, aside from those affecting photosynthesis (see Chapter 12). Aside from photo-synthesis and behavior (e.g., motility, phototaxis), the indispensability of *Euglena* for inquiry into animal origins justifies the otherwise biochemically repetitious. Papers on *Euglena* chemistry often remark—a near traditional rite—that *Euglena* combines plant and animal characters, notably in having different chloroplast and mitochondrial pathways for making long-chain fatty acids. The following taxonomic paragraphs, while old hat to proto-zoologists, are aimed at people who, delighting in *Euglena* as a tool, are curious about the terms *plant* and *animal* as viewed from a *Euglena* eyespot. Pringsheim's (1963) magisterial treatise is a starting point for aligning macro-morphological and molecular data in reconstructing plant → animal evolu-tionary lines; he spotlights the connections between photosynthetic and nonphotosynthetic algal species. As noted (Hutner and Provasoli, 1965), a decently comparative biochemical zoology is emerging. Developments in nutrition make it worthwhile to view *Euglena* in this context:

   (1) An animal, i.e., a phagotrophic euglenoid, *Peranema*, is in pure culture (Allen *et al.*, 1966).

   (2) Animal, yet photosynthetic, members of a very different group of flagellates—chrysomonads—are receiving much attention, notably *Ochromonas danica* and *Ochromonas malhamensis*, along with nonphago-trophic chrysomonads, e.g., *Prymnesium parvum* and some coccolithophorids.

   (3) Defined media are available (a) for the phagotrophic dinoflagellate *Oxyrrhis marina* (Droop and Doyle, 1966); (b) *Cryptothecodinium (Gyro-dinium) cohnii*, a colorless osmotrophic dinoflagellate (Gold and Baren, 1966); (c) a host of photosynthetic dinoflagellates, especially marine forms (Provasoli, 1963), opening the way to making the spectacular *Noctiluca* a more accessible biochemical tool. A phagotrophic cryptomonad, *Cyathomonas*, is available, unfortunately not yet axenically.

   These salients have flank support from electron microscopy: one can tell which organelles are grossly altered by a given inhibitor, and when

coordinated with advances in molecular biology, especially of the control
of ribosomal, mitochondrial, and chloroplast function, surmises can be
made as to why. New antibiotics may save work: it may become practical
to so combine antibacterial and antifungal agents as to eliminate autoclave-
or filter-sterilization of experimental culture media, thus facilitating use of
unstable compounds, especially those active metabolically and detectable
by counteracting inhibitors. Antibiotic combinations should also facilitate
axenizing other phagotrophs. Should common but biochemically untouched
euglenoid phagotrophs, e.g., *Entosiphon*, prove to have complex food
requirements, antibiotic-killed food organisms may ease the surmounting
of the initial obstacles to axenic culture. Tracer methods should speed
identification food organisms, as with foraminifera (Lee *et al.*, 1966).

Interest in *Euglena* as a signpost in a plant → animal series also comes
from the new emphasis on membrane biology. The cardinal attribute of
animals is phagotrophy (ingestion of particulate food), which implies that
animals are the experts in improvising food vacuoles, i.e., digestive membranes
(Hutner, 1961). Lysosomes are stockpiles of building materials and enzymes
for these membranes; lysosomes are targets for many drugs (McLean
et al., 1965; Duncan, 1966). Adding to this enhanced vulnerability to drugs,
the evolution of animals must have meant expansion of pre-existing transport
systems and invention of new ones to exploit better the foodstuffs made
accessible by phagotrophy.

A common reason for drug resistance is impairment of transport (Moyed,
1964). Transport specificity limits the permissible variations in a particular
class of inhibitor. Since antibiotics and chemotherapeutic agents exploit
deep-seated metabolic differences among organisms, they are phyletic tools
(Aaronson and Hutner, 1966). Comparative drug sensitivities are thus
relevant in speculations as to how protozoa evolved and where metazoa
came from.

B. EUGLENOID EVOLUTION*

The treatment of euglenoids by Mackinnon and Hawes (1961, pp. 73-87)
and Fott (1959, pp. 329-346) gives a fair if brief notion of morphological
affinities between the plant and animal euglenoids. *Euglena* is obviously
related to the voracious peranemids, and perhaps also to a host of colorless
flagellates, some tiny, e.g., *Bodo*. Pringsheim (1963) emphasizes that the
bodonids are polyphyletic. The intergrading of euglenoids and bodonids in
gross morphology suggests a euglenoid ancestry for at least some bodonids.
The suborder Bodonina shares with the trypanosomatid flagellates a kineto-

---

* *Editor's Note:* This topic is further covered in Vol. I, Chapter 1.

plast at the base of the flagella (Honigberg *et al.*, 1964); this acriflavine-sensitive organelle appears to control mitochondrial differentiation.

Gross morphological resemblances can inspire over-hasty conclusions about euglenoid–trypanosomatid affinities, Leishmanias and trypanosomes may have evolved from insect trypanosomatids like *Crithidia* with its reservoirlike anterior depression; *Crithidia* probably has, as do trypanosomes, a small lateral cytostome, however, quite unlike the feeding apparatus of *Peranema*. One might happily conclude that euglenoids, via bodonids, gave rise to the trypanosomatids, and that the vast efforts on chemotherapy of trypanosomatid diseases bear a special relevance to *Euglena*, or at least to the phagotrophic euglenoids.

On the other—the plant side—many euglenoids, including many species of *Euglena* available in pure culture, are obligate photoautotrophs—they cannot be grown in the dark—presumably because external metabolites for lack of kinases cannot be drawn enough into the stream of metabolism to replace photosynthesis. It is traditional to call photoautotrophs more "plantlike." The extreme photoautotroph *E. mutabilis* (*E. klebsii*) in our laboratory has failed to detect anything that, added to an adequate inorganic medium, stimulates growth in light or prolongs survival in darkness. Unfortunately, the responses to inhibitors of these euglenas are completely unknown, as are those of other euglenoid photoautotrophs less obviously specialized than *E. mutabilis*, e.g., *E. pisciformis* and *E. anaebaena*. *Euglena viridis* has a strategic position: it can be grown in the dark (Pringsheim, 1963, p. 195); in our unpublished experiments it grew slowly in the dark on a malate–glutamate medium.

A relationship of euglenoids to volvocines is plausible: twist a *Chlamydomonas* into a helix, push in the area between the contractile vacuoles to form a reservoir, reduce one flagellum to a stump, and *voilà* a *Euglena*—superficially at least (euglenoid chromosomes are, however, quite distinctive, likewise their Michelin tire man-like corrugated pellicle). The green euglenoid *Eutreptia* has two functional flagella—presumably a primitive feature. Mindful that the higher plants undoubtedly have chlorophycean ancestors, *Euglena*, in keeping with its presumed *Chlamydomonas*-like ancestry, should have a metabolism essentially like higher plants. Unlike higher plants, saprolegniales, and bacteria, however, which use the diaminopimelic acid pathway for synthesis of lysine, *Euglena* uses the α-aminoadipic acid pathway, as do chytrids, mucorales, ascomycetes, and basidiomycetes (Vogel, 1965). Indeed it may be safter to extrapolate to *Euglena* information on fungicides than on herbicides, except for those herbicides such as 3-(3,4-dichlorophenyl)-1,1-dimethyl urea (DCMU) which inactivate the Hill reaction of photosynthesis or, like 3-amino-1,2,4-triazole, paralyze synthesis of the photosynthetic apparatus, including that of *E. gracilis* (Aaronson, 1960), by interfering with purine precursors in histidine synthesis (Siegel and Gentile, 1966). One may expect that *Euglena* will find wide use in screening for herbicides affecting photosynthesis, as begun by Hoffmann and McGahen (1964). Such enterprises may tell whether or not *Euglena* is as closely related to higher plants as its photosynthetic pigments suggest, but so far *Euglena* shows no clear response to any of the metaphytan-active antihormones. If one nevertheless thinks that Chlorophyceae are closer than fungi to *Euglena*—suggested by its metaphytanlike carotenoids [if one ignores its antheraxanthin, etc. (Goodwin, 1965)]—and regards the term *Chlorella* as merely a convenient tag for chlamydomonadines whose zoospores lost motility and, retained in the mother cell, became autospores, then the permeability pattern of *Euglena*, reflected in its drug sensitivities, should resemble that of *Chlorella* (assuming that the drug responses by *Chlorella* are uniform). In a survey of antimetabolites and *Chlorella* (Tamiya *et al.*, 1962), its generally low sensitivity to purine and pyrimidine analogs emerged. One might construe this as evidence of affinity—it seems close to the *E. gracilis* pattern—but this also seems to be the yeast pattern. To complicate matters, *Crithidia fasciculata*, from its morphological resemblances to *Euglena*, ought to have the aminoadipic pathway for lysine synthesis; it uses the diaminopimelic pathway (Gutteridge, 1966; Guttman, 1967) which, as noted, characterizes bacteria and higher plants and not chytrids and higher fungi. This temporary confusion nonetheless is encouraging, for until recently these questions were unthinkable for want of pure cultures and biochemical insight. Such metabolic divergences must have originated far back in geological time: they are conservative. Many such characters must be extant, e.g., the main amino acid sequences of key enzymes of metabolism. The euglenoids are good sites for a biochemical archeology aimed at elucidating plant and animal origins; metabolic inhibitors make excellent excavation tools—as seen by the way in which penicillin and other "cell wall" antibiotics dramatized how wide a gap separates procaryotes from eucaryotes, and how closely related blue-green algae are to bacteria (Aaronson and Hutner, 1966).

C. METABOLIC INHIBITORS AND TRANSPORT MECHANISMS

Green and Tzagoloff (1966) and Van Deenan (1966) assert that membranes carry hallmarks of individuality as much as chromosomes do. Present models of plasma membranes (Maddy, 1966) hardly attempt to explain how membranes deploy their various transport mechanisms; an exception is a model for β-galactoside transport in *Escherichia coli* (Kennedy *et al.*, 1966); a beginning has been made for drug transport (van Os *et al.*, 1964). For perspective one needs the backdrop of information on plant plasma membranes. Some relations between antimetabolite action and membranes may be postulated:

(1) Antimetabolites, except for those directly injuring the cell membrane, must penetrate in order to act. Penetration is via transport mechanisms pre-existing for transport of metabolites, hence sensitivity to an antimetabolite points to a transport mechanism for a normal metabolite. These considerations may not apply sharply to small, lipid-soluble, highly diffusible molecules that may penetrate appreciably without specific transport.

(2) Heterotrophic members of a plant → animal series have more variety in transport mechanism, higher transport capacity, or both, as compared with the photoautotrophs. (The direction of the arrow in *plant → animal* is another postulate.) Corollaries:

(a) In a plant → animal series, the plant members may be less sensitive to a given antimetabolite and perhaps sensitive to fewer antimetabolites;

(b) A great variety in effective antimetabolites denotes a corresponding variety in assimilable nutrients, especially in phagotrophs.

For many antibiotics the protective metabolites have not been clearly identified. For some antibiotics such metabolites are complex cell wall constituents, e.g., the phospholipid–sterol cell membrane complexes which are the target of the polyene antibiotics (Lampen, 1966); in bacteria, direct annulment of penicillin action by cell wall constituents has not been seriously studied despite being obvious, and suggested, moreover, by protoplast studies. The distinction *antibiotic* and *antimetabolite* often reflects differences in application, not in principle. A metabolic inhibitor may have multiple targets perhaps as illustrated by streptomycin: its uptake may be mediated by the transport mechanism for inorganic cations, perhaps with assistance from a transport mechanism for strongly basic cations, e.g., arginine, histidine, and polyamines such as spermine or spermidine. How this uptake precedes action against inner targets—its attachment to, and penetration of ribosomes in bacteria or, in *Euglena*, to the organelle ("protoplastid"?) controlling chloroplast synthesis (see Chapter 10 and 11)—is a major mystery. Brock (1966) has reviewed subtilties in streptomycin action, including perplexities in deciding whether or not effects on permeability subtend protein miscoding. The protection against streptomycin antibiotics afforded bacteria by anaerobiosis (Stern *et al.*, 1966) may prompt similar experiments on *Euglena* bleaching. (Incidentally, the term "*albinization*" used by Greenblatt *et al.* (1966) seems better than "bleaching" and will be used later.)

Inhibitors may uncover otherwise overlooked nutrients—a lesson learned from the way in which *p*-aminobenzoic acid was revealed by its annulling sulfanilamide action. Such new nutrients may speed the growth of *E. gracilis*, as well as the growth in light of the "obligately" photosynthetic species, and so show how to coax them to grow in the dark.

No euglenoids that are both photosynthetic and phagotrophic are known, unlike the situation in regard to chrysomonads, dinoflagellates, and perhaps cryptomonads.

Aside from some dinoflagellates and chrysomonads, euglenoids are the richest presently available material for exploring relationships between permeability and pellicular differentiation. The roster of euglenoids maintained by George (1966) documents this availability. Blocks to dark growth of algae have been reviewed (Danforth, 1962).

II. Considerations of Maintenance and Culture Media–Antimetabolite Relations in the Use of *Euglena* as a Biochemical Tool

A. GENETIC MARKERS AND DRUG RESISTANCE

Organisms aspiring to eminence as biochemical research tools must become genetic banks. Drug resistance provides markers for chromosome mapping—the ultimate way to prove that *Euglena* has a sexual or parasexual genetic recombination (a desideratum inspiring torrents of talk and small accomplishment). The limited maneuverability in exploiting every antimetabolite-uncovered transport mechanism is hinted at by the scarcity of different nutritional mutants in the small angiosperm *Arabidopsis thaliana* in which only biotin and thiamine-less mutants were obtained (Feenstra, 1964; Langridge, 1965), along with the *Neurospora*-(Wagner and Mitchell, 1964, pp. 286-324) and yeast–reminiscent (Mortimer and Hawthorne, 1966) array of uracil, histidine, tryptophan, methionine, *p*-aminobenzoic acid, inositol, and nicotinic acid mutants (Jacobs, 1965). The array for *Chlamydomonas reinhardi* is remarkably similar: "acetate," thiamine, *p*-aminobenzoate, nicotinamide, arginine and, significantly, cycloheximide resistance (Sager, 1964). The ability of *E. gracilis* Z to take up biotin (Guttman *et al.*, 1964) should make *Euglena* eligible for inhibition by biotin antagonists. Could a means be established in *Euglena* for distinguishing between Mendelian and non-Mendelian inheritance, *Euglena* might be the best protistan alternative to maize for mapping the genetic determinants of the chloroplast (reviewed by Kirk, 1966a)—assuming that in the meantime there had been no progress in demonstrating sexuality, transformation, or transduction in photosynthetic bacteria.

Aside from studies with trypanosomes and malarial parasites, little use with algae and protozoa has yet been made of the powerful technique of cross-resistance to judge whether an agent is novel or, at least, how it enters.

To decide whether or not an antibiotic in fermentation beers is novel, it is applied to a "spectrum" of organisms resistant to known antibiotics. This fingerprinting can require 50 or more induced resistant strains alongside the wild-type sensitive. This poses no great difficulty with bacteria: reference resistant strains are readily stored lyophilized or frozen at liquid-nitrogen temperatures. However, no method is known for freeze-preservation of *E. gracilis:* it dies out in a month or even in a week at ordinary refrigerator temperatures (ca. 6°C). Cultures do keep a year or longer in dilute peptone agar dimly illuminated at ca. 10–20°C. Maintenance is thus a sorely neglected aspect of *Euglena* research.

B. Choice of Media for Drug Studies; pH

As the existence of this volume implies, *E. gracilis* is hardy. Culture media for it cover a wide pH range, 3.1–8.0 (Hutner *et al.*, 1966). Since pH by governing ionization affects lipid solubility and, therefore penetration of ionizable drugs (Ariëns *et al.*, 1964; Sexton, 1963; van Os *et al.*, 1964; Albert, 1965), this wide pH range facilitates handling pH-sensitive drugs—an important consideration when supply of a drug is limited and it must be used to best advantage. This may require balancing the pH favoring penetration against the pH for maximal stability. This dilemma arises with many complex antibiotics, e.g., streptomycin: bleaching effectiveness increases with pH (Mego and Buetow, 1966), as does its familiar antibiotic action (optimum ∼7.9), but a higher pH inactivation presumably overshadows penetration. The high-pH medium, constructed around amino acid esters to prevent runaway alkalinization when aliphatic fatty acids serve as substrate (Hutner *et al.*, 1966), originally developed for work with antihistamines, has been used in studies of bleaching by macrolide antibiotics (Ebringer, 1966; Celmer and Ebringer, 1967).

Euglena gracilis, an "acetate flagellate" (not strictly so: it uses glucose), grows in light and darkness vigorously on acetate (or ethanol) (see Vol. I, Chapter 6). As expected, *E. gracilis* is rich in acetate kinases (see Chapter 1). Hence, *E. gracilis* cells might be expected to be more susceptible to inhibitors of acetate metabolism than would be an organism unable to use acetate as sole substrate.

Kaplan (1965) emphasizes that it is generally more feasible to characterize enzymes by their catalytic behavior, especially in the presence of inhibitors, than by elucidating their amino acid sequences. Inhibition of lactic acid, ethanol, and malic uptake by *Euglena* would complement studies of inhibitions of the isolated dehydrogenases; isoenzymes are receiving intense attention as models for tracing protein evolution. *Euglena* transport systems for substrates are largely unexplored; presumably the diffusion gradients are maintained by dehydrogenase-mediated removal of the substrates near the cell membrane, followed by removal by mitochondrial enzymes. To assess the relationships of the dehydrogenases concerned in uptake of a particular substrate by the cell membrane, chloroplast, mitochondria, and endoplasmic reticulum, requires cells in quantity. Inhibitor studies may, as a by-product, uncover hitherto nutritionally unexploited transport mechanisms to be used to improve media, the assumption being that fastest growth and highest yield will be attained when *every* transport mechanism is saturated so that synthases originating from photosynthetically fixed CO_2 are bypassed to the utmost by fixed carbon. If no inescapable limit is imposed by accumulation of a toxic metabolic product, growth rates will be higher, populations reached sooner, and drug studies correspondingly speeded. Present high-yield media exploit the exceptional capacity of *Euglena* to utilize some Krebs-cycle intermediates or closely related compounds, e.g., malic acid, glutamic acids, and aspartic acids, with a concomitant, poorly understood utilization of glucose and glycine. This permeability pattern would probably have been recognized independently had metabolic inhibitors received an attention matching that accorded nutrition. Unlike *Euglena*, yeast are specialists in use of carbohydrates, with the Krebs cycle serving mainly to supply intermediates for biosynthesis; Kornberg (1966) terms such biosynthesis-supporting metabolic routes *anaplerotic*. The transport mechanisms of *Euglena* and yeast, while different in capacity, may well be qualitatively similar. Even hexokinase being adaptive in *Euglena* (see Chapter 1) may not spell a difference from yeast, for normal *Saccharomyces* can be grown on lactate, and restoration to carbohydrate perhaps involves adaptation. No serious effort has been made to grow *Euglena* under conditions favoring glycolysis, i.e., anaerobically or near anaerobically—aside from the observation that anaerobic growth of *Euglena* was favored by CO_2 (Bergmann, 1955). It would be apropos to try inhibitors of glucose metabolism, e.g., 2-deoxy-D-glucose and pentoses (Hochster, 1963). In selecting media for drug studies, other nutritional peculiarities of *Euglena* should be taken into account. For example, for malonate experiments a non-Krebs–cycle medium might serve, containing for example, acetate as sole substrate, and, as shown by Danforth (1953), a low-pH medium should be used with such inhibitors as malonate to favor penetration. For work with antipurines, antipyrimidines, or antivitamins, a highly heterotrophic medium might suffice.

In applying scarce inhibitors to intact cells, especially in growth systems, defined media are better than complex media (e.g., those containing "peptone" or yeast extracts and the like); defined media lack the protectants—generally target metabolites—in natural materials. This poses little difficulty with *Euglena* with its few absolute requirements and limited stimulation by nonsubstrate metabolites in substrate-rich media. To illustrate: actinomycin D inhibited growth much more in a synthetic than in a peptone medium (Pogo and Pogo, 1964). Counteractors of actinomycin toxicity (reviewed by Modest *et al.* 1963) include, beside 2-deoxyguanosine, polypeptides plus at least several unidentified compounds. Procedures have been detailed for dissecting out such protectants from complex mixtures, and for determining whether or not they are biochemically known (Aaronson *et al.*, 1965, Aaronson and Bensky, 1965). Limitations in present methodology are uncertainties in handling lipids, thermolabile compounds, and autoxidizable compounds. Such pigeon-holing procedures are essentially no different from those aimed at identifying nutritional mutants. A survey of the toxicity of antioxidants, measured by cytotoxicity to *Tetrahymena* and inhibition of the oxygen-dependent photodynamic test for polybenzenoid carcinogens, revealed that many antioxidants were quite toxic (Epstein *et al.*, 1967). These data agreed in the main with the limited data on *Peranema* viability prolongation (Allen *et al.*, 1966). It will be interesting to re-examine *Peranema* and extend antioxidant studies to *Euglena* to see whether or not antioxidants prolong survival of *Euglena* at refrigerator temperatures, and whether or not *Peranema*, obeying the hypothesis aired earlier, is more sensitive to their toxicity. In any case, these agents may be poisoning lipidic sites, as do the agents discussed in the next section.

III. Specific Inhibitors

A. Steroids and Inhibitors of Lipid Metabolism

Many microbiologists have yearned for an antisterol that will specifically inhibit sterol transformation, and not merely the low-turnover positioning of unaltered sterol in the cell membrane or some interior membrane. The will-o-the-wisp-ish spur is that this antisterol will uncover the primary dynamic function in metazoa of hormonal steroids. *Euglena* growth was stimulated under some conditions by steroids but, as reviewed by Buetow and Levedahl (1964), these may be superficial membrane effects. Another approach is to apply steroid analogs and other inhibitors of sterol synthesis in metazoa, notably those acting as hypocholesteremics. Instead of uncovering connections between the sterols and the hormonal steroids, such agents, to which *E. gracilis* Z was rather insensitive as compared with *Ochromonas danica* and *Tetrahymena pyriformis*, uncovered a miscellany of unexplained annulments (Aaronson and Bensky, 1965):

(1) Vanadyl sulfate inhibition of multiplication was annulled by a shotgun mixture of water-soluble metabolites but not by oleate or sterols.

(2) Nicotinic acid was reported to inhibit completely multiplication of *E. gracilis* at 0.01%; cholesterol annulled the 50% inhibition produced by 0.025% nicotinic acid (Miller and Hamilton, 1964). Aaronson and Bensky (1965) confirmed the inhibition of multiplication by nicotinic acid but not the annulment by cholesterol.

(3) The nicotinic acid analog, pyridylacetamide, also inhibited multiplication; this inhibition was not annulled by the standard metabolite mixtures ("complete supplement").

(4) Inhibition of multiplication by L-thyroxine was annulled by L-cystine. In unpublished experiments by Aaronson and Bensky, this inhibition turned out to be a nonspecific effect of the iodine in the thyroxine molecule.

B. CARCINOGENS AND ALBINIZATION; NITROQUINOLINE *N*-OXIDE; ACRIFLAVINE

The celebrated permanent albinization of *Euglena* is treated elsewhere in this volume (see Chapter 12). Nevertheless for completeness, and because albinization by carcinogens opens new vistas and much of the pertinent literature is too recent to have been previously reviewed, we will touch on some aspects of this topic. Albinizing agents are not necessarily carcinogens, as obvious from the activity of heat, macrolide antibiotics, certain anti-histamines, and nitrofurans. However, our impression is: if a compound is a proximate or near-proximate, i.e., a direct-acting carcinogen—one not requiring metabolic transformation to be carcinogenic—it may albinize. Hence a negative result might rule out direct carcinogenicity; a positive test does not necessarily mean carcinogenicity but arouses suspicion. The problem is to predict which carcinogens albinize, and which albinizers are carcinogens. There is circumstantial evidence encouraging pursuit of this idea:

(1) The powerful mutagen *N*-methyl-*N'*-nitrosoguanidine albinized *Euglena:* however other mutagens did not (propiolactone, nitrogen mustard, dimethylsulfate, methyl methanesulfonate, butadiene diepoxide, mitamycin C, triethylene melamine, proflavine, acriflavine, hydroxylamine, and nitrous acid (McCalla, 1965, 1966a).

(2) The powerful carcinogen aflatoxin, produced by *Aspergillus flavus* and some other fungi, albinizes cress (*Lepidium sativum*) seedlings (Schoental and White, 1965). This may have been foreshadowed by the report (Anonymous, 1935) that some maize seedlings infected with *A. flavus* had no chlorophyll.

(3) The carcinogen 4-nitroquinoline *N*-oxide (NQO) (Fig. 1) albinizes. The narrow margin between albinizing and toxic concentrations (Zahalsky *et al.*, 1963) can be widened by washing out the NQO before exposing cells to light, as NQO is very active in the photodynamic test for carcinogens (S. S. Epstein and C. Nagata, personal communication).

It was first thought possible to bring out the distinctiveness of NQO as a carcinogen by testing its cross-resistance with the ostensibly very different carcinogen, ethionine. Even though NQO apparently penetrated via tryptophan transport, as shown by competitive annulment of NQO-induced growth inhibition by tryptophan, and enthionine via methionine transport, strains of *E. gracilis* Z made 50-fold resistant to NQO and 350-fold for L-ethionine were virtually completely cross-resistant (Hutner *et al.*, 1967). Whether or not this cross resistance extends to a *Euglena* rendered resistant to nitrosoguanidine in respect both to growth inhibition and albinizing effects (McCalla, 1966b) is an interesting point. Other compounds annulling the toxicity of NQO to *Euglena* were riboflavin, nicotinic acid, L-tyrosine, thymine, and menadione as well as several other naphthoquinones; much the same held for *O. danica*, *Rhodopseudomonas palustris*, and *Corynebacterium bovis* (Zahalsky *et al.*, 1963). A complication: naphthoquinones,

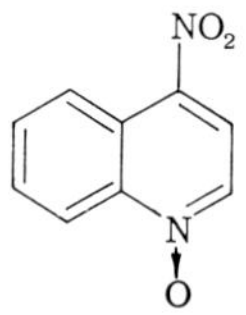

Fig. 1. 4-Nitroquinoline *N*-oxide.

e.g., menadione (vitamin K_3), are themselves toxic; this toxicity was annulled noncompetitively, for *Euglena* by nicotinic acid (Schopfer and Keller, 1951). The stupendous literature on inhibition by quinones has been summarized by Webb (1966, Vol. III); at this time one must endorse this remark, "the quinones are possibly the most difficult inhibitors to discuss because of...multiplicity of actions."

NQO is a strong inhibitor of photosynthesis. As shown by studies led by R. M. Smillie, this inhibition appeared to result from NQO short-circuiting the electron flow between the photoreductant produced in photosystem II and cytochrome 552 (Hutner *et al.*, 1967). Presumably NQO interferes with a corresponding site in the mitochondrial electron chain, much as the 2-alkyl-4-hydroxyquinoline *N*-oxides do. NQO—a quinoid, flat, highly charged molecule—could bind to so many intracellular structures, and might block so many different reaction sequences as to preclude conclusions as to primary attachment and action as metabolic inhibitor and carcinogen. To illustrate: by reduction of the N → O group, the hydroxyamino (NOH) group readily yields the free-radical nitroso (NO·) derivative (Nagata *et al.*, 1966), which aligns NQO with free-radical compounds of the nitroso type that are mutagenic, carcinogenic, and radiomimetic. Its conversion to a hydroxylamine derivative relates it to the aryl hydroxylamines which appear to be the proximate carcinogens in the amino-azo, naphthylamine, and aminofluorene series. Finally, as a quinonelike ("quinoid") molecule, it would be expected to be an antagonist of the monocyclic ubiquinones in the mitochondrion and plastoquinones in the chloroplast, and even the bicyclic vitamin K naphthoquinones—as indeed shown by the aforementioned protection by naphthoquinones. Still another possibility is suggested by the reductase in spinach chloroplasts for organic nitro compounds (Wessels, 1965); this enzyme, if more active than a counterpart in mitochondria, could explain the margin between albinization by NQO and Killing.

The logical target for a carcinogen is DNA. NQO in thin-layer chromatography, did not migrate in the presence of total DNA extracted from *Euglena*, thymus, or *E. coli* (Malkin and Zahalsky, 1966). There was some binding by poly-dAT (alternating deoxyadenylate-thymidylate copolymer) and poly-A (homopolymer of adenylate), but not by heat-denatured single-stranded DNA, soluble RNA's from *E. coli*, and yeast, or by the polymeric pyrophosphates of other purines and pyrimidines, nor did actinomycin D interfere with the interaction of NQO with DNA, suggesting that the guanine residues that bind actinomycin (Reich, 1966) do not bind NQO.

Since, obviously, speculation here can easily outrun the data, only a few points need be mentioned. Aflatoxin inhibits DNA-dependent RNA polymerase (Gelboin *et al.*, 1966), which raises questions: do carcinogens bind specifically to DNA ? To return to the ease of albinizing *Euglena*, is the DNA in the *Euglena* chloroplast especially prone to bind NQO because of a high A–T content ? Aside from its intrinsic susceptibility as shown by albinization by ultraviolet, has *Euglena* exceptionally efficient transport systems for albinizers or is the explanation lack of the barrier to penetration of such agents ? Perhaps significantly, *Euglena* chloroplast DNA runs to 70–76% A + T compared with 45–52% for the main band, i.e., nuclear DNA (reviewed by Schiff and Epstein, 1965).

Acriflavine induces petites in yeast, akinetoplasty in trypanosomatids, and cures bacteria of episomal factors including the sex factor; hence it must have been tried in many laboratories as an albinizer. Presumably the lack of reports indicates universally negative results. In our experiments, killing intervened before any albinization was manifested. Some findings from the literature on acriflavine-induced akinetoplasty may be kept in mind for future experiments: akinetoplastidic *Crithidia fasciculata* (Cosgrove, 1966) or *Leishmania tarentolae* (Trager and Rudzinska, 1964) defy cultivation. A nutrient permitting cultivation might also permit cultivation of acriflavine-albinized euglenas. Optimism is fostered by the fact that akinetoplastic strains of *Trypanosoma evansi* occur in the blood of camels and cattle (Hawking, 1963, p. 165).

Riboflavin flickers in and out of experiments with planar, polycyclic inhibitors. As a quinone, [e.g., it forms a semiquinone (Hemmerich *et al.*, 1965)], its activity as an annulling agent for NQO was not surprising and reveals a transport system that might effect the entrance of other large ring compounds and account for the ready entrance of acridine dyes into cells generally. Riboflavin opposed the action of acriflavine on *L. tarentolae* (Trager and Rudzinska, 1964).

Binding of acriflavine to DNA is being studied in several laboratories. Since acriflavine is not carcinogenic yet is in a way mutagenic, acriflavine-type binding must be of a kind not connected with carcinogenicity. One may expect that galleries of DNA models for the different kinds of binding will illustrate future discussions of carcinogenesis and, as McCalla (1966a) puts it, ". . . the extreme selectivity of bleaching agents . . ."

C. ANTIBIOTICS

1. Chloramphenicol, Cycloheximide, and Puromycin

Chloramphenicol, a broad-spectrum antibiotic, has been used on virtually every kind of organism and cell-free preparation to see whether or not a phenomenon depends on protein synthesis, as does, e.g., rubidium uptake in *Euglena* (Brenner and Maynard, 1966); applied to growing *E. gracilis* Z, it slightly increased the proportion of bleached cells and, as with actinomycin D noted earlier, higher concentrations (1–2 mg/ml) were required to inhibit growth in a peptone media (Loefer, 1951; Pogo and Pogo, 1965). Presumably much less chloramphenicol would have been required in a defined medium— perhaps in such a medium *Euglena* would have approached the sensitivity of yeast in which 1.0 μg/ml inhibited protein synthesis by 50% and the cells were 10 to 20 times more sensitive in the absence of casein hydrolysate (de Kloet, 1966).

Cycloheximide, an antibiotic toxic to all eucaryotes, especially yeast, is an inhibitor of protein synthesis (Umezawa, 1964, pp. 40-43). Sensitivity of *Euglena* is on the order of that of *Chlorella* (Morimura and Tamiya, 1964; Schrift, 1966); *Chlamydomonas reinhardi* (Jacobson *et al.*, 1964); and lucerne seedlings as compared with *Euglena* by Kirk (1966b).

Puromycin, like chloramphenicol, is widely used as an inhibitor of protein synthesis, probably by acting as an analog of the amino-acyl groups in transfer RNA (review: Goldberg, 1965). In a preliminary report, *Euglena* greening was not differentially inhibited in a neutral medium (Selsky, 1964).

2. Miscellaneous Cytotoxic Compounds and Antibiotics

Euglena has been used in screening programs for cytotoxic compounds of potential interest as antitumor agents. In control experiments with known cytotoxic compounds, it showed no clear advantage over *O. malhamensis* and *T. pyriformis* (Johnson *et al.*, 1962). In a pH 3.5 defined medium, it was sensitive to amethopterin, azaserine, 6-mercaptopurine, amphotericin B, and 6-diazo-5-oxo-L-norleucine, but not to 8-azaguanine. It resembled the aforementioned organisms in lack of inhibition by myleran, colchicine, and cortisone. 5-Fluoronicotinamide was toxic; 20 μg was reversed by 10 μg nicotinic acid or nicotinamide or 2.5 μg NAD or NADP.

Inhibition by the antitumor agent hadacidin (*N*-formylhydroxyaminoacetic acid) was counteracted by adenine and aspartate, as observed in suspensions of greening cells (Mego, 1964).

The insensitivity of *Euglena* to penicillin became known at the same time as bleaching by streptomycin (Jírovec, 1949a,b, 1951). Tyrothricin and patulin were rather toxic when tested in a peptone–acetate medium.

The antitumor agent anthramycin, obtained from a thermophilic *Streptomcyes*, albinizes (Guttman and Tendler, 1966). It is extremely labile and contains a novel, strained, tricyclic nucleus (Anonymous, 1966).

Primycin (composition unknown), active against *Mycobacterium tuberculosis* and gram-positive bacteria, reacts *in vitro* with RNA and DNA. Accordingly, *E. gracilis* and *Astasia longa* were protected by RNA and DNA as well as by deoxyadenine–thymidine pyrophosphate copolymer; purine and pyrimidine bases and nucleosides were inactive (Blum, 1965). *Astasia longa* was adapted to live in 12 μg/ml primycin, which killed unadapted cells.

Data on toxicity of antibiotics to *Chlorella* and *Scenedesmus* have been compiled (Krauss, 1962). There is no present reason to think that the *E. gracilis* responses differ from theirs, aside from its proneness to albinization by streptomycin- and macrolide-family antibiotics. Since most of the antibiotics listed have been discussed earlier in this chapter and elsewhere in this volume (see Chapter 12), it seems enough to say that bacitracin and gramicidin were not toxic to *Chlorella:* polymyxin B was fairly toxic; tetracycline moderately toxic; and thiolutin and puromycin very toxic.

Another antitumor agent, hydroxyurea, at concentrations of 0.02–0.035 *M* inhibited chlorophyll synthesis by 50% and also inhibited cell division of the Z strain in light or darkness; DNA synthesis was more sensitive than RNA or protein synthesis (Buetow and Mego, 1967).

D. PURINE AND PYRIMIDINE ANALOGS

1. *Uptake of Purines and Pyrimidines*

The sensitivities of *E. gracilis* seem, as mentioned, much like those of other algae, higher plants, and fungi, and require little discussion. Sensitivity to purine and pyrimidine analogs was foreshadowed by the appearance of various nutritional mutants in algae and fungi for adenine and uracil.

Euglena takes up thymine and thymidine but not uridine and cytidine; green euglenas take up thymidine much more than do colorless ones (Sagan, 1965). This may be construed as evidence for a transport system for nucleosides as well as for free bases. As background to studies of purine analogs, one notes that *Euglena* takes up guanine and adenine (Brawerman and Chargaff, 1959; Bolton *et al.*, 1963; Sagan, 1965).

2. 5-*Fluorouracil;* 8-*Azaguanine;* Caffeine

Effective pyrimidine analogs include 5-fluorouracil; its inhibition of greening of Z-strain cells was reversed by uracil (Evans and Smillie, 1962). An uptake of bromouracil led to plastid mutations (Scher and Collinge, 1965).

The most detailed work has been done with 8-azaguanine, which inhibits division of synchronized *A. longa:* *E. gracilis* var. *bacillaris* was insensitive (Kahn and Blum, 1965). Both *Euglena* and *Astasia* cells converted adenine, guanine, hypoxanthine, and 8-azaguanine to the nucleotides; both incorporated the same amount of 8-azaguanine into their nucleic acids (corresponding to 0.2% of the guanine in the RNA). Kahn and Blum conclude that it is unlikely that a disturbed RNA metabolism underlies the inhibition. The insensitivity of *Euglena* to 8-azaguanine could not be accounted for by lack of guanine pyrophosphorylase, decreased permeability, or degradation of 8-azaguanine. The growth inhibition of *Astasia* was released by high levels of hypoxanthine or of adenine plus guanine.

In *Chlorella*, 8-azaguanine retarded cell devision but hardly affected increase in cell mass (Tamiya *et al.*, 1962). Schrift (1966) on the other hand found that 8-azaguanine inhibited both uptake and incorporation of L-methionine-^{35}S into *Chlorella*. Since the variation from *Chlorella* to *Chlorella* may be of the same order as that from *Euglena* to *Astasia*, it may be hard to pinpoint the site of action of azaguanine as indeed may often be the case with anti-purines: a multiplicity of metabolic branch points are eligible targets (Hitchings and Elion, 1963).

Euglena and *Chlamydomonas* are so resistant to caffeine (0.01–0.03 M) that it is recommended as a means of ridding cultures of fungi imperfecti and nonphotosynthetic protozoa (Bowne, 1964).

3. 6-*Mercaptopurine and Vitamin* B_{12}*; Benzimidazoles*

Several benzimidazoles and 6-mercaptopurine competed with B_{12} in *Euglena* grown with minimal B_{12} (some 300 compounds were screened (Epstein and Timmis, 1963)), adding a complication to those enumerated by Hitchings and Elion (1963) for purine analogs: whether in *Euglena* these analogs compete for the dimethylbenzimidazole or deoxyadenosine moieties of coenzyme B_{12}, and whether the antivitamin-B_{12} effect compounds action against other coenzymes and nucleic acid purine. The peculiar vulnerability of the target in *Euglena* represented by its B_{12} requirement extends to benzimidazole itself (Funk and Nathan, 1958). In a preliminary note Reinisch and Funk (1966) reported that a mutant of the Z strain lacking chlorophyll, which was obtained with benzimidazole, had β-carotene in contrast to the parent's 3,3'-dihydroxy-5,6-epoxy-β-carotene and, unlike the parent, grew without thiamine or vitamin B_{12}.

E. 2,4-DINITROPHENOL; ARSENITE; FLUORIDE

2,4-Dinitrophenol (DNP), from a superficial examination of the vast literature on its use to inhibit oxidative phosphorylation, might be thought to be essentially a reagent for making ATP ineffective, and so a means of demonstrating factors supporting ATP synthesis and function. Indeed, ethionine acts precisely in that way: by sequestering adenine as S-adenosylethionine instead of the normal adenosylmethionine, the liver becomes depleted of ATP; exogenous adenine opposes ethionine (Shull *et al.*, 1966). In the presence of excess phosphate, in a low-pH medium, inhibition of growth by DNP was reversed competitively by glutamic acid—which would make DNP approach the activity of such inhibitors of L-glutamic acid dehydrogenase as 5-bromo- or 5-nitrofuroic acid (Hutner *et al.*, 1958). There is as yet no coherent picture of the intermediary metabolism of *Euglena*. A few topics have been treated in some detail: utilization of acetate and ethanol, repression by glucose and other substrates of chloroplast synthesis and, as for other organisms utilizing two-carbon compounds as sole substrates, demonstration of key enzymes of the glyoxylic acid cycle. This topic is developed elsewhere in this book (see Vol I, Chapter 6; Chapter 2), and so only snippets of information gained from application of some of the classic metabolic inhibitors will be mentioned.

Arsenite and inorganic phosphate were competitive for *E. gracilis* var. *bacillaris* grown on acetate; respiration of acetate was inhibited by 0.001 *M* thiophosphate (an uncoupler of oxidative phosphorylation) (Danforth and Kaplan, 1964).

Fluoride-poisoned *Euglena*, like *Chlorella*, accumulates γ-aminobutyric acid in the medium (Vishniac and Fuller, 1958). The same acid was then independently identified as a normal excretion product (McCalla, 1963).

F. HEAVY WATER

Euglena gracilis Z after adaptation in a simple glucose medium could be grown in 99.4% D_2O; it then required an aqueous extract from fully deuterated

Scenedesmus (Katz, 1965). Similar conditions induced a thiamine requirement in *Candida* (*Torula*) *utilis*, and pyridoxine and inositol as well as
thiamine for *Saccharomyces cerevisiae*. Whether any of these spare or
replace the *Scenedesmus* extract was not stated. Deuterated *Euglena* was
shorter and broader than normal *Euglena* and had fewer chloroplasts
(Mandeville *et al.*, 1964). Deuterium is thought to act like a hydrophilic
solvent in slowing protonation of an active site in the respiratory chain
(Tyler and Estabrook, 1966); unfortunately, effects of solvents on *Euglena*
are unexplored except for casual descriptions of its tolerance to ethanol in
connection with studies of ethanol as a substrate.

G. ANTIHISTAMINES

The toxicity of the albinizing antihistamines may not necessarily be connected with albinization. Some lines of pyribenzamine-albinized *E. gracilis*
var. *bacillaris* grown in a peptone–yeast extract medium had diminished
viability (Tong *et al.*, 1965). In experiments in defined media, strains bleached
by the antihistamines tripelennamine and pyrilamine had no obviously
impaired vigor (Zahalsky *et al.*, 1962). No effort was made to see whether
or not histidine, which rather than histamine opposed the toxicity of antihistamines to *O. malhamensis* and *O. pyriformis*, (Sanders and Nathan, 1959),
acted likewise on *Euglena*.

H. TARTRATE; CHLORPROMAZINE; AMINO ACID ESTERS; SULFANILAMIDE

An acid phosphatase inhibited by (+)-tartrate is thought to be associated
with "animal" organisms. With *p*-nitrophenylphosphate as substrate, acted
on at pH 5.0 by aqueous extracts, *Euglena, Astasia, Tetrahymena, Physarum,*
and fungi imperfecti were positive; *Chlamydomonas, Rhizopus, Mucor,*
Saccharomyces Agaricus, and bacteria were negative (Kilsheimer and
Axelrod, 1958). The possibility of paralleling the phyletic occurrence of
lysine pathways suggests that a follow-up of this preliminary work might
be worthwhile.

Since *Euglena* is widely used to assay vitamin B_{12} in body fluids, especially
blood, information accrues from patients given drugs. Thus it was early
discovered that there could be enough sulfa drugs in blood to interfere with
the assay; it became routine practice to include *p*-aminobenzoic acid in the
basal medium (Hutner *et al.*, 1956). A recrudescence of this situation is the
claim (Herbert *et al.*, 1965) that the high incidence of vitamin B_{12} deficiencies
in mental patients was an artifact resulting from many of the patients receiving
chlorpromazine—metabolites of chlorpromazine toxic to *Euglena* could be
present in the serum. There was inhibition on adding 1.0 μg of chlorpromazine

to 5 pg of vitamin; however, chlorpromazine in serum is stated to seldom exceed 4 μg/ml. By radioisotope assay the sera had normal B_{12}. Unfortunately, the spate of polemic comment this stimulated from various laboratories has not presented clear information as to the toxicity of chlorpromazine or its known metabolic products to *Euglena*, with or without serum or other natural materials in the medium.

As mentioned earlier, a medium developed for drug work at near-neutrality (pH 6.8) contains glycine ethyl ester and L-glutamic acid γ-ethyl ester (Hutner *et al.*, 1966). A survey of amino acid esters carried out with *Astasia* and *Euglena* (Owens and Blum, 1966) confirmed the relatively low toxicity of the glutamic acid γ-ester. These esters showed little inhibition below pH 5.0, and maximum inhibition above pH 6.0.

References

Aaronson, S. (1960). *J. Protozool.* **7**, 289–294.
Aaronson, S., and Bensky, B. (1965). *J. Protozool.* **12**, 236–240.
Aaronson, S., and Hutner, S. H. (1966). *Quart. Rev. Biol.* **41**, 13–46.
Aaronson, S., Baker, H., Bensky, B., Frank, O., and Zahalsky, A. C. (1965). *Develop. Ind. Microbiol.* **6**, 48–58.
Albert, A. (1965). "Selective Toxicity," 3rd ed. Methuen, London; Wiley, New York.
Allen, J. R., Lee, J. J., Hutner, S. H., and Storm, J. (1966). *J. Protozool.* **13**, 103–108.
Anonymous (1935). *47th Ann. Rept. Illinois Agr. Expt. Sta.* 53–54.
Anonymous (1966). *Chem. Eng. News* **44**, (45), 42–43.
Ariëns, E. J., Simonis, A. M., and van Rossum, J. M. (1964). *In* "Molecular Pharmacology" (E. J. Ariëns, ed.), Vol. I, pp. 287–393. Academic Press, New York.
Bergmann, L. (1955). *Flora* **142**, 493–539.
Blum, J. J. (1965). *Arch. Biochem. Biophys.* **111**, 635–645.
Bolton, E. T., Britten, R. J., Byers, T. J., Cowie, D. B., Hoyer, B., McCarthy, B. J., McQuillen, K., and Roberts, R. B. (1963). *Carnegie Inst. Wash. Ybook* **1962–1963**, 324–326.
Bowne, S. W., Jr. (1964). *Nature* **204**, 801.
Brawerman, G., and Chargaff, E. (1959). *Biochim. Biophys. Acta* **31**, 172–174.
Brenner, M. L., and Maynard, D. N. (1966). *Plant Physiol.* **41**, 1285–1288.
Brock, T. D. (1966). *Symp. Soc. Gen. Microbiol.* **16**, 131–168.
Buetow, D. E., and Levedahl, B. H. (1964). *Ann. Rev. Microbiol.* **18**, 167–194.
Buetow, D. E., and Mego, J. L. (1967). *Biochim. Biophys. Acta* **134**, 395–401.
Celmer, W. D., and Ebringer, L. (1967). *J. Protozool.* **14**, 263–267.
Cosgrove, W. B. (1966). *Acta Protozool.* **4**, 155–160.
Danforth, W. F. (1953). *Arch. Biochem. Biophys.* **46**, 164–173.
Danforth, W. F. (1962). *In* "Physiology and Biochemistry of Algae" (R. A. Lewin, ed.), pp. 99–123. Academic Press, New York.
Danforth, W. F., and Kaplan, J. H. (1964). *J. Protozool.* **11** (Suppl.), 26.
De Kloet, S. R. (1966). *Biochem. J.* **99**, 566–581.
DiPalma, J. R., ed. (1965). "Drill's Pharmacology in Medicine," 3rd ed. McGraw-Hill, New York.
Droop, M., and Doyle, J. (1966). *Nature* **212**, 1474–1475.

Duncan, C. J. (1966). *Nature* **210**, 1229–1230.

Ebringer, L. (1966). *Folia Microbiol.* **11**, 379–386.

Epstein, S. S., and Timmis, G. M. (1963). *J. Protozool.* **10**, 63–73.

Epstein, S. S., Saporoschetz, I. B., and Hutner, S. H. (1967). *J. Protozool.* **14**, 238–244.

Evans, W. R., and Smillie, R. M. (1962). *Plant Physiol.* **37** (Suppl.), 38.

Feenstra, W. J. (1964). *Genetica* **35**, 259–269.

Fott, B. (1959). "Algenkunde." Fischer, Jena.

Funk, H. B., and Nathan, H. A. (1958). *Proc. Soc. Exptl. Biol. Med.* **93**, 394–397.

Gelboin, H. V., Wortham, J. S., and Wilson, R. G. (1966). *Science* **154**, 1205–1206

George, E. A. (1966). "Culture Collection of Algae and Protozoa." Botany School, Univ. of Cambridge, Cambridge.

Gold, K., and Baren, C. F. (1966). *J. Protozool.* **13**, 252–257.

Goldberg, I. H. (1965). *Am. J. Med.* **39**, 722–752.

Goodman, L. S., and Gilman, A., eds. (1965). "The Pharmacological Basis of Therapeutics," 3rd ed. Macmillan, New York.

Goodwin, T. W., ed. (1965). *In* "Chemistry and Biochemistry of Plant Pigments," pp. 127–173. Academic Press, New York.

Green, D. E., and Tzagoloff, A. (1966). *J. Lipid Res.* **7**, 587–602.

Greenblatt, C. L., Park, H. D., Mattern, C., and Merril, C. R. (1966). *Abstr. 6th Ann. Meeting Am. Soc. Cell Biol. Houston, Texas.* p. 42A.

Gutteridge, W. E. (1966). *J. Gen. Microbiol.* **44** (Proc.), 4.

Guttman, H. N. (1967). *J. Protozool.* **14**, 267–271.

Guttman, H. N., and Tendler, M. D. (1966). *Proc. Soc. Exptl. Biol. Med.* **121**, 1140–1141.

Guttman, H. N., Funk, H. B., and Krulwich, T. A. (1964). *Abst. 6th Int. Cong. Biochem. New York,* p. 720. Secretariat, 6th Int. Congr. Biochem., Washington, D.C.

Hawking, F. (1963). *In* "Experimental Chemotherapy" (R. J. Schnitzer and F. Hawking, eds.), Vol. I, pp. 129–256. Academic Press, New York.

Hemmerich, P., Müller, F., and Ehrenberg, A. (1965). *In* "Oxidases and Related Redox Systems" (T. E. King, H. S. Mason, and M. Morrison, eds.), Vol. I, pp. 157–203. Wiley, New York.

Herbert, J., Gottlieb, C. W., and Altschule, M. D. (1965). *Lancet* II, 1052–1053.

Hitchings, G. H., and Elion, G. B. (1963). *In* "Metabolic Inhibitors" (R. M. Hochster and J. H. Quastel, eds.), Vol. I, pp. 215–237. Academic Press, New York.

Hochster, R. M. (1963). *In* "Metabolic Inhibitors" (R. M. Hochster and J. H. Quastel, eds.), Vol. I, pp. 131–152. Academic Press, New York.

Hochster, R. M., and Quastel, J. H., eds. (1963). "Metabolic Inhibitors," Vols I and II. Academic Press, New York.

Hoffman, C. E., and McGahen, J. W. (1964). *Nature* **202**, 577–578.

Honigberg, B. M., Balamuth, W., Bovee, E. C., Corliss, J. O., Gojdics, M., Hall, R. P., Kudo, R. R., Levine, N. D., Loeblich, A. R., Jr., Weiser, J., and Wenrich, D. H. (Committee on Taxonomy and Taxonomic Problems, Soc. Protozool.). (1964). *J. Protozool.* **11**, 7–20.

Hutner, S. H. (1961). *Symp. Soc. Gen. Microbiol.* **11**, 1–18.

Hutner, S. H. (1966). *In* "Methods in Cell Physiology" (D. M. Prescott, ed.), Vol. II, pp. 217–228. Academic Press, New York.

Hutner, S. H., and Provasoli, L. (1965). *Ann. Rev. Physiol.* **27**, 19–50.

Hutner, S. H., Bach, M. K., and Ross, G. I. M. (1956). *J. Protozool.* **3**, 101–112.

Hutner, S. H. Nathan, H. A., Aaronson, S., Baker, H., and Scher, S. (1958). *Ann. N. Y. Acad. Sci.* **76**, 457–468.

Hutner, S. H., Zahalsky, A. C., Aaronson, S., and Smillie, R. M. (1967). *In* "Biochemistry of Chloroplasts" (T. W. Goodwin, ed.), Vol. II, pp. 703–720. Academic Press, New York.

Jacobs, M. (1965). *In* "Arabidopsis Research" Report Intern. Symp. Univ. of Göttingen (G. Röbbelen, ed.), pp. 106–109. Univ. of Göttingen, West Germany.

Jacobson, B. S., Solmon, R. J., and Lansky, L. L. (1964). *Exptl. Cell Res.* **36**, 1–13.

Jírovec, O. (1949a). *Vestn. Cesk. Zool. Spolecnosti* **13**, 216–237. (English summary pp. 236–237.)

Jírovec, O. (1949b). *Experientia* **5**, 74–77.

Jírovec, O. (1951). *Schweiz. Z. Allgem. Pathol. Bakteriol.* **14**, 653 666.

Johnson, I. S., Simpson, P. J., and Cline, J. C. (1962). *Cancer Res.* **22**, 617–626.

Kahn, V., and Blum, J. J. (1965). *J. Biol. Chem.* **240**, 4435–4443.

Kaplan, N. O. (1965). *In* "Evolving Genes and Proteins" (V. Bryson and H. J. Vogel, eds.), pp. 243–277. Academic Press, New York.

Katz, J. J. (1965). *39th Ann. Priestley Lectures Ser., Phi Lambda Upsilon.* Penn. State Univ., University Park, Pennsylvania.

Kennedy, E. P., Fox, C. F., and Carter, J. R. (1966). *In* "Macromolecular Metabolism" (J. Hurwitz, ed.), pp. 347–354. Little, Brown, Boston, Massachusetts.

Kilsheimer, G. S., and Axelbrod, B. (1958). *Nature* **182**, 1735–1736.

Kirk, J. T. O. (1966a). *In* "Biochemistry of Chloroplasts" (T. W. Goodwin, ed.), Vol. I, 319–40. Academic Press, New York.

Kirk, J. T. O. (1966b). *Biochem. J.* (Proc.), (in press).

Kornberg, H. L. (1966). *In* "Essays in Biochemistry" (P. N. Campbell and G. D. Greville, eds.), Vol. II, pp. 1–31. Academic Press, New York.

Krauss, R. W. (1962). *In* "Physiology and Biochemistry of Algae" (R. A. Lewin, ed.), pp. 673–685. Academic Press, New York.

Lampen, J. O. (1966). *Symp. Soc. Gen. Microbiol.* **16**, 111–130.

Langridge, J. (1965). *Australian J. Biol. Sci.* **18**, 311–321.

Lee, J. J., McEvery, M., Pierce, S., Freudenthal, H. D., and Muller, W. A. (1966). *J. Protozool.* **13**, 659–670.

Loeffer, J. P. (1951). *Physiol. Zool.* **24**, 155–163.

McCalla, D. R. (1963). *J. Protozool.* **10**, 491–495.

McCalla, D. R. (1965). *Science* **148**, 497–499.

McCalla, D. R. (1966a). *J. Protozool.* **13**, 472–474.

McCalla, D. R. (1966b). *Plant Physiol.* (Proc.), **41**, 10.

Mackinnon, D. L., and Hawes, R. S. J. (1961). "An Introduction to the Study of Protozoa," Oxford Univ. Press, London and New York.

McLean, A. E. M., McLean, E., and Judah, J. D. 1965. *Intern. Rev. Exptl. Pathol.* **4**, 127–157.

Maddy, A. H. (1966). *Intern. Rev. Cytol.* **20**, 1–65.

Mahler, H. R., and Cordes, E. H. (1966). "Biological Chemistry." Harper, New York.

Malkin, M. F., and Zahalsky, A. C. (1966). *Science* **154**, 1665–1667.

Mandeville, S. E., Crespi, H. L., and Katz, J. J. (1964). *Science* **146**, 769–770.

Mego, J. L. (1964). *Biochim. Biophys. Acta* **79**, 221–225.

Mego, J. L., and Buetow, D. E. (1966). *J. Protozool.* **13**, 20–23.

Miller, O. N., and Hamilton, J. G. (1964). *In* "Lipid Pharmacology" (R. Paoletti, ed.), pp. 275–323. Academic Press, New York.

Modest, E. J., Foley, G. E., and Farber, S. (1963). *In* "Metabolic Inhibitors" (R. M. Hochster and J. H. Quastel, eds.), Vol. I, pp. 75–129. Academic Press, New York.

Morimura, Y., and Tamiya, H. (1964). *J. Indian Botan. Soc.* **42A**, 22–29.

Mortimer, R. K., and Hawthorne, D. C. (1966). *Ann. Rev. Microbiol.* **20**, 151–168.

Moyed, H. S. (1964). *Ann. Rev. Microbiol.* **18**, 347–366.

Nagata, C., Kataoka, N., Imamura, A., Kawazoe, Y., and Chihara, G. (1966). *Gann* **57**, 323–325.

Owens, I. S., and Blum, J. J. (1966). *Abstr. 6th Ann. Meeting, Am. Soc. Cell Biol. Houston, Texas.* p. 83A.

Pogo, B., and Pogo, A. O. (1964). *J. Cell Biol.* **22**, 296–301.

Pogo, B., and Pogo, A. O. (1965). *J. Protozool.* **12**, 96–100.

Pringsheim, E. G. (1963). "Farblose Algen. Ein Beitrag zur Evolutionsforschung." Fischer, Stuttgart.

Provasoli, L. (1963). *In* "The Sea" (M.N. Hill, ed.), Vol. II, pp. 165–219. Wiley (Interscience), New York.

Reich, E. (1966). *Symp. Soc. Gen. Microbiol.* **16**, 266–280.

Reinisch, C. C., and Funk, H. B. (1966). *J. Protozool.* **13** (Suppl.), 7.

Sagan, L. (1965). *J. Protozool.* **12**, 105–109.

Sager, R. (1964). *In* "Biochemistry and Physiology of Protozoa" (S. H. Hutner, ed.), Vol. III, pp. 297–318. Academic Press, New York.

Sanders, M., and Nathan, H. A. (1959). *J. Gen. Microbiol.* **21**, 264–270.

Scher, S., and Collinge, J. C. (1965). *Nature* **205**, 828–830.

Schiff, J. A., and Epstein, H. T. (1965). *In* "Reproduction: Molecular, Subcellular and Cellular" (M. Locke, ed.), pp. 131–189. Academic Press, New York.

Schoental, R., and White, A. F. (1965). *Nature* **205**, 57–58.

Schopfer, W. H., and Keller, V. (1951). *Bull. Soc. Chim. Biol.* **33**, 1253–1260.

Schrift, A. (1966). *Plant Physiol.* **41**, 405–410.

Selsky, M. I. (1964). *J. Protozool.* **11** (Suppl.), 26.

Sexton, W. A. (1963). "Chemical Constitution and Biological Activity," 3rd ed. Spon, London.

Shull, K. H., McConomy, J., Vogt, M., Castillo, A., and Farber, E. (1966). *J. Biol. Chem.* **241**, 5060–5070.

Siegel, J. N., and Gentile, A. C. (1966). *Plant Physiol.* **41**, 670–672.

Stern, J. L., Barner, H. D., and Cohen, S. S. (1966). *J. Mol. Biol.* **17**, 188–217.

Tamiya, H., Morimura, Y., and Yokota, M. (1962). *Arch. Mikrobiol* **42**, 4–16.

Tong, N. C. H. L., Gross, J. A., and Jahn, T. L. (1965). *J. Protozool.* **12**, 153–160.

Trager, W., and Rudzinska, M. A. (1964). *J. Protozool.* **11**, 133–143.

Tyler, D. D., and Estabrook, R. W. (1966). *J. Biol. Chem.* **241**, 1672–1680.

Umezawa, H. (1964). "Recent Advances in Chemistry and Biochemistry of Antibiotics." Microbiol. Chem. Res. Found., Tokyo.

Van Deenen, L. L. M. (1966). *Progr. Chem. Fats Lipids* **8**, Part 1, 1–127.

van Os, G. A. J., Ariëns, E. J., and Simonis, A. M. (1964). *In* "Molecular Pharmacology" (E. J. Ariëns, ed.), Vol. I, pp. 7–52. Academic Press, New York.

Vishniac, W., and Fuller, R. C. (1958). *Federation Proc.* **17**, 328.

Vogel, H. J. (1965). *In* "Evolving Genes and Evolution" (V. Bryson and H. J. Vogel, eds.), pp. 25–40. Academic Press, New York.

Wagner, R. P., and Mitchell, H. K. (1964). "Genetics and Metabolism." Wiley, New York.

Webb, J. L. (1966). "Enzyme and Metabolic Inhibitors," Vols. II and III. Academic Press, New York.

Wessels, J. S. C. (1965). *Biochim. Biophys. Acta* **109**, 357–371.

Zahalsky, A. C., Hutner, S. H., Keane, M., and Burger, R. M. (1962). *Arch. Mikrobiol.* **4**, 36–55.

Zahalsky, A. C., Keane, M. M., Hutner, S. H., Lubart, K. J., and Amsterdam, D. (1963). *J. Protozool.* **10**, 421–428.

CHLOROPHYLL STUDIES*

Marcia Brody

* Preparation of this chapter was supported, in part, by a grant from Hunter College.

I. Introduction

Despite the richness of the literature in the area of photosynthesis, the conversion of electromagnetic energy to chemical energy *in vivo* is a process not well understood. In view of the fact that chlorophyll a is ubiquitous to all photosynthetic organisms above the level of bacteria, and since photosynthesis cannot occur in its absence, chlorophyll a is believed to be the photochemically reactive pigment.

While carotenoids are also always associated with photosynthetic organisms, it is the widely held opinion that they function as accessory pigments by transferring absorbed energy to chlorophyll (Warburg and Negelein, 1923; Emerson and Lewis, 1942, 1943; Dutton and Manning, 1941; Dutton *et al.*, 1943; Tanada, 1951; Duysens, 1951, 1952) and also as protective agents against chlorophyll photo-oxidation (Sistrom *et al.*, 1956; Cohen-Bazire and Stanier, 1958; Chance and Sager, 1957; see also Chapter 6).

It is therefore reasonable that information on the states of chlorophyll a *in vivo* should aid both in understanding the primary photochemical and photophysical reactions occurring in the living organism, and in the construction of model systems.

Recent evidence indicates that only a small and special portion of chlorophyll a functions in a photocatalytic fashion; the bulk may be considered "accessory" or "antennae" pigment, acting in absorption and energy transfer to the special photoreactive chlorophyll a in a fashion similar to the other accessory pigments (which may include, in addition to the carotenoids, the phycobilins and other chlorophylls).

Although the experiments that led to these conclusions are more fully reviewed in Chapter 2, some of them will be summarized here as an adjunct to understanding the significance of certain of the chlorophyll studies to be presented in the following discussion.

That photosynthesis involves two chlorophyll a–containing systems grew out of earlier work on the requirement for quanta of two different energies. The latter requirement was in a large part based on the observations of Emerson *et al.* (1956), Emerson (1958), and M. Brody and Emerson (1959b) that at long wavelengths (but still within the red absorption band of "chlorophyll" *in vivo*) the quantum yield of photosynthesis drops. Since the effect of shorter wavelength light was to increase the yield at the longer wavelengths ("enhancement effect"), it was concluded that pigments absorbing at shorter wavelengths performed one photochemical function and pigments at longer wavelengths another.

While Emerson *et al.* (1957) suggested that the pigments responsible for enhancement were accessory pigments other than chlorophyll a (which they held to be responsible for absorption at longer wavelengths) other workers suggested that efficient photosynthesis requires the excitation of two different kinds of chlorophyll a. Even earlier, Franck (1955) had postulated that two different excited states of chlorophyll a give rise to the red absorption band of chlorophyll a *in vivo*. His ideas were expanded (1958) to explain the two-quantum requirement (see also Franck and Rosenberg, 1964). S. Brody (1958) and S. Brody and M. Brody (1961a) suggested that chlorophyll a exists as monomeric and aggregated species *in vivo*, that both are found under the red absorption envelope (also see Section IV,A,2), and that excitation of both is necessary for photosynthesis.

In 1952, Duysens had made extensive action spectra measurements which showed that energy absorbed by the accessory pigments gave rise primarily to fluorescence at 685 nm while energy absorbed by chlorophyll a gave rise primarily to fluorescence at 720 nm. In 1961, Duysens (see also Duysens and Amesz, 1962) incorporated these earlier observations in an elaboration of the two-pigment requirement theory; he called the long-wavelength pigment system "system I," the short-wavelength pigment system "system II"—energy from chlorophyll b and phycobilins going preferentially to chlorophyll a of system II, energy from carotenoids going preferentially to chlorophyll a of system I. His nomenclature will be used in this work.

As a result of the flashing-light experiments of Emerson and Arnold (1932) on the efficiency of photosynthesis, the concept evolved (for a review of this concept, see Rabinowitch, 1956; M. Brody and S. Brody, 1962) that energy absorbed anywhere in a "photosynthetic unit," consisting of several hundred chlorophyll molecules, was transferred to a special reaction center within the unit. Such a special "reaction center chlorophyll a" was found in the anticipated small amounts; it was bleached (oxidized) by light absorbed by system I and restored (reduced) by system II. Kok, who discovered this pigment and found it to absorb maximally at 705 nm, (Kok, 1959; Kok and Gott, 1960; Kok and Hoch, 1961) named it P700 and suggested it was the energy trap for system I. (In this case, the prefix "P" stands for pigment, however, see Section IV,A,1 for other designations.)

Various schemes have been presented (Clayton, 1965) that incorporate pigment systems I (including P700) and II into electron-transport pathways coupled to photophosphorylations. Some of the features common to these schemes, and pertinent to the present topic, are given below.

System II: Energy absorbed at short (<670 nm) wavelengths, directly by the antennae chlorophyll a of this system, or transferred to it from accessory pigments (including chlorophyll b), mediates the splitting of water, the liberation of oxygen, and the reduction of certain intermediates, the terminal one of which is oxidized P700.

System I: Energy absorbed at long (>680 nm) wavelengths, directly by antennae chlorophyll a of this system and/or P700, or transferred to it from system II, mediates the oxidation of reduced P700 and the reduction of TPN. [The proposed mechanisms for transfer of energy from system II to system I, which is energetically possible because of the "downhill" flow of energy, cannot be considered here; the reader is referred to Myers (1963) and Clayton (1965).]

The present chapter is devoted to recent studies made with *Euglena* on the chlorophylls and related derivatives; however, emphasis is placed on the effect of light on formation of chlorophyll, and particularly on the states in which chlorophyll a is found *in vivo*.

II. Structure of the Chlorophylls and Related Compounds

The proposed structure of the chlorophyll a chromophore (Fischer, 1940) has been firmly established by recent synthesis (Woodward *et al.*, 1960; Strell and Kalojanoff, 1962). As can be seen from Fig. 1c, chlorophyll a is a substituted porphyrin (see Fig. 1a for basic unsaturated porphyrin skeleton, porphin) having a fifth cyclopentanone ring in addition to the four pyrroles; note particularly its long phytol "tail." Chlorophyll b differs from chlorophyll a in that the methyl group of carbon atom 3 (see Fig. 1c) is replaced by a formyl group. Since in the case of protochlorophyll, the hydrogen atoms at carbons 7 and 8 are lacking, a double bond is introduced in this position. The following derivatives, or "degradation products" should also be noted for later discussion. Pheophytins are chlorophylls in which magnesium has been replaced by two hydrogens. Phyllides, on the other

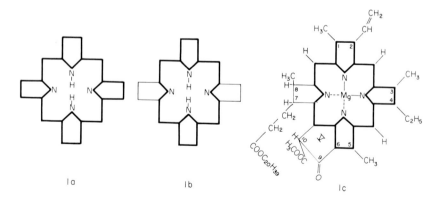

Fig. 1. Molecular structures: 1a, porphin; 1b, tetrahydroporphin; 1c, chlorophyll a. The line thickness of the conjugated ring system has been increased.

hand, retain their magnesium, but have had their phytol removed, by virtue of which they are monobasic acids, the esters of which are chlorophyllides. For this reason chlorophyll may be referred to as the phytyl ester of the acid, or phytyl chlorophyllide. Phorbides are formed by removal of phytol from pheophytins. For information on the structure, distribution, preparation, physical properties, quantitative tests, tests for purity, etc. of the chlorophylls and their derivatives, the reader is referred to Smith and Benitez (1955), Bruinsma (1963), Holt (1965), and Holden (1965).

Because several excellent reviews have recently been written on the biosynthetic pathways of chlorophylls a and b (Bogorad, 1960, 1962, 1965; Godnev *et al.*, 1963; Granick and Mauzerall, 1961; Smith and French, 1963; Shlyk *et al.*, 1963) and because little of this work has been done with *Euglena*, the topic will not be covered in the present chapter. Note however, Chapter 1 for references to *Euglena* in this area.

III. The Effect of Light on the Formation of Chlorophyll

In the present work, the term chlorophyll "content" will be used for studies in which the quantity of chlorophyll is expressed in reference to the number of cells; the term chlorophyll "concentration" will be reserved for those studies in which the quantity of chlorophyll has been related to the chlorophyll-bearing structures—the chloroplasts or their components.

It has been shown by numerous workers (specific references to their works will be made in the following discussion), that when dark-grown cells of *Euglena* are illuminated, chlorophyll formation as a function of time in light exhibits a dependence similar to that given in the composite illustration of Fig. 2.* In Sections III,A, B, C, and D, reference will be made to segments AB, BC, CD, and DE in Fig. 2, respectively.

A. TRANSFORMATION OF CHLOROPHYLL PRECURSOR TO CHLOROPHYLL AND ACTION SPECTRUM FOR CHLOROPHYLL FORMATION IN DARK-GROWN CELLS

Because *Euglena* loses its chlorophyll after many generations of growth in the dark, and reforms it upon exposure to light, studies have been made

---

* Rosenberg and Pecker (1964) report a slightly different dependence; after a short lag period, etiolated cells of *E. gracilis* produced chlorophyll in three successive stages in light of 90 ft-c. During stage I, which lasts about 15 hours, chlorophyll was found to be produced at a slow rate with an eventual levelling off of production. During stage II, a renewed synthesis of chlorophyll occurred at a linear rate, lasting some 25 hours. Stage III followed with further increase in chlorophyll synthesis until maximum greening occurred. In this work, Rosenberg and Pecker followed lipid changes during light adaptation and their chlorophyll studies consisted of optical density determinations, at 668 nm, with solvents used for total lipid extraction.

with it in an effort to identify the precursor of chlorophyll. Determinations of the action spectrum for this process have resulted in the suggestion that protochlorophyll is the precursor (Wolken *et al.*, 1955; Wolken and Mellon, 1956; Wolken, 1961; Nishimura and Huzisige, 1959). As Schiff and Epstein (1965) point out, however, it has not really been determined with *Euglena* whether protochlorophyll or protochlorophyllide is the actual precursor reduced by light.

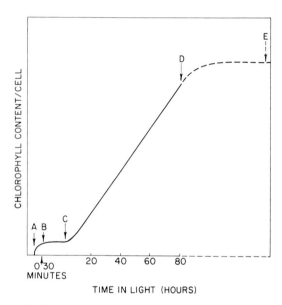

Fig. 2. Composite illustration; chlorophyll formation in dark-grown *Euglena* as a function of length of illumination period. Segments AB, BC, CD, and DE of the curve are discussed in the text (Section III).

These workers introduced temporarily, the compound term protochloro-phyll(ide) for this precursor. In higher plants it is thought that phytylization occurs immediately after the photoconversion of protochlorophyllide to chlorophyllide a (Wolff and Price, 1957; see also Smith and French, 1963). The photoconversion is thought to occur in about 10^{-3} seconds (Madsen, 1963).

Stern *et al.* (1964a) demonstrated that dark-grown cells of *E. gracilis* var. *bacillaris* contain a much smaller amount of protochlorophyll(ide), 3×10^{-3} pg per cell (equal to about 18×10^8 molecules per cell) than would be expected from an intermediate accumulating behind a dark block. On this basis and also on the basis of unpublished experiments from their laboratory, Schiff and Epstein (1965) suggested that the formation of protochlorophyll(ide) in dark-grown cells is under a feedback control in which protochlorophyll(ide) acts in inhibiting the first enzyme in its biosynthesis (δ-aminolevulinic synthetase); light conversion of protochlorophyll(ide) to chlorophyll(ide) acts in unblocking the first step in the synthesis.

In a study designed to separate the effect of ultraviolet light on chloroplast development from its effect on chloroplast replication in *E. gracilis* var. *bacillaris*, Schiff *et al.* (1961) observed that the conversion of protochlorophyll(ide) to chlorophyll in dark-grown cells was unaffected by ultraviolet light doses sufficient to yield 100% albino colonies.

In 1966, Butler and Briggs undertook an investigation of the influence of structure on spectral changes that occur during greening in etiolated leaves and in *E. gracilis* var. *bacillaris*. For the most part, they used low-temperature (77°K) absorption spectroscopy to follow these pigment changes. Shibata, using higher plants had shown, in 1957, that light transforms protochlorophyllide a absorbing at 650 nm to a form of chlorophyll a absorbing at 684 nm; in a subsequent, light-independent step, this—is converted into a form of chlorophyll a absorbing at shorter wavelengths—at 673 nm.

In their studies, Butler and Briggs used either freezing to 77°K and thawing, or grinding with sand and buffer, to bring about structural changes in proplastids. They concluded that in leaves these structural changes were causing deaggregation of protochlorophyllide a 650 to protochlorophyllide a 635 (treatment given in the dark), and deaggregation of chlorophyllide a 684 to chlorophyll(ide) a 673 (treatment given immediately after the photoconversion step). No spectral changes were brought about when treatment was given after the normal conversion to chlorophyll(ide) a 673 had occurred (this process takes about 20 minutes). Butler and Briggs suggested that normal greening in leaves consists of transformation of aggregated protochlorophyllide a 650 into aggregated chlorophyllide a 684 by light, followed by a light-independent deaggregation to monomeric chlorophyll(ide) a 673. The interpretation of these spectral changes in terms of aggregation is related to earlier theories of aggregation discussed in Sections IV, introduction; IV,A; and especially IV,A,2,*a*. Although Butler and Briggs noted fluorescence-yield changes consistent with deaggregation, they also mention the possibility that the spectral changes they observed may arise from different chromophore–protein interactions.

These workers found, in the case of *Euglena* [which does not have prolamellar bodies in its proplastids, according to Epstein and Schiff (1961)] that the absorption maximum of protochlorophyll(ide) a is at 630 nm; immediately after photoconversion the chlorophyll(ide)-a absorption band is found at about 667 nm. (No dark reaction analogous to that which occurs in leaves, i.e., 684 → 673, was observed.) Freezing and thawing did not change the position of these absorption maxima. Their observations would seem to suggest that in *Euglena* the first-formed chlorophyll is monomeric and is formed from monomeric chlorophyll(ide). Subsequent formation of aggregated chlorophyll will be discussed in Sections III,C; IV, A,2,*a* and V,B.

B. THE LAG PHASE

After the initial conversion of the small amount of protochlorophyll(ide) to chlorophyll there follows a lag phase during which little or no chlorophyll is formed. [This lag phase is similar to that originally reported for higher plants by Liro (1909).] Lag phases of 5–15 hours have been reported for *E. gracilis* strain Z by Brawerman and Chargaff (1959) and for *E. gracilis* var. *bacillaris* by Nishimura and Huzisige (1959). Stern *et al.* (1964a), working with dark-grown var. *bacillaris*, point out that the amount of chlorophyll formed after 2 hours of light exposure is not stoichiometric with the protochlorophyll(ide) content of dark-grown cells since the chlorophyll content noted at 2 hours represents a 10-fold increase. They therefore suggested that the initial synthesis of chlorophyll is followed by resynthesis of more protochlorophyll(ide) and conversion to chlorophyll; chlorophyll synthesis then proceeds slowly (if at all)* until about 10 hours, when they found further significant synthesis began. M. Brody *et al.* (1965), in a similar study with strain Z also noted a marked increase in chlorophyll concentration at 10 hours; however, they often observed lag periods as short as 2 hours (Fig. 23). For purposes of comparison they measured the lag phase in var. *bacillaris* and found it to be much longer, sometimes lasting 25 hours. They proposed that these differences may reflect the existence of greater physiological distinctions than morphological ones between the two organisms. They also referred to observations by Virgin *et al.* (1963) with leaves, however, in which it was found that the length of the lag phase appeared to be a function of several factors, including nutritional state. Although the latter workers suggested that there is probably no relation between the lag period and phytolation (which presumably takes about 1 hour—see Wolff and Price, 1957; Virgin, 1960), M. Brody *et al.* (1965) noted that the lag value for strain Z corresponds closely to that required for the process.

C. CONCLUSION OF LAG PHASE FOLLOWED BY PERIOD OF RAPID CHLOROPHYLL SYNTHESIS[†]

The conclusion of the lag phase is heralded by a dramatic increase in chlorophyll a formation. According to Stern *et al.* (1964a), who followed

---

* There is too much scatter in the data of Stern *et al.* (1964a) to be sure of the pigment changes during these early hours.

[†] *Editor's Note:* This topic is further covered in Chapter 10.

the kinetics of the appearance and development of chlorophyll, carotenoids, and photosynthesis (the last measured both as O_2 evolution and $^{14}CO_2$ incorporation), these phenomena show an essentially linear rate until about 80 hours, at which time a steady state is reached (Fig. 3). At the end of the lag phase, taken to be at about 10 hours of illumination, at 100–150 ft-c, the dark-grown cells have their first lamellae; further rate of lamellae formation parallels the above cited phenomena, so that at 80 hours the full complement is present (Ben-Shaul et al., 1964; Stern et al., 1964a,b). Oxygen

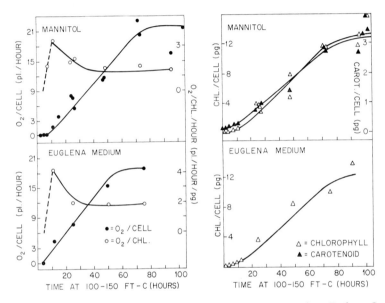

Fig. 3. Photosynthetic capacity and pigment content of greening *Euglena*. Lower curves, *Euglena* medium (in which cells undergo divisions); upper curves, mannitol (a resting medium). Adapted from Stern et al. (1964a).

evolution was measurable at 10 hours and it was suggested that photosynthesis probably starts before this time (see also Schiff, 1963). Oxygen evolution was found to be high on a chlorophyll basis, initially, and then to decline to a steady-state value. It was also noted that the kinetics of pigment formation and oxygen evolution were unaffected by the presence or absence of division. Photosynthetic carbon dioxide fixation was found to become apparent at about 6 hours of development. Since M. Brody et al. (1965), working with strain Z, also found evidence of photosynthetic oxygen evolution at about 10 hours, it can probably be assumed that dark-grown cells of *E. gracilis* develop a functional photosynthetic apparatus after about 5–10 hours of illumination at 100–150 ft-c.

Because such cells contain chlorophyll even before this time, several workers have attempted to answer the question why they are not capable of photosynthesis at an earlier period. The parallel formation of chlorophyll and carotenoids during the linear period of development was already noted (Stern et al., 1964a); dark-grown cells also contain appreciable carotenoids (Krinsky and Goldsmith, 1960; Lewis, 1963; Stern et al., 1964a). [Lewis (1963) showed that energy transfer from carotenoids to chlorophyll occurs as early as 2 hours.] At about 4 hours of development, however, neoxanthin appears for the first time and subsequently continues to increase (Krinsky et al., 1964). The latter authors suggested the necessity of this pigment for photosynthesis, but it is possible that this carotenoid plays an indirect role related to photosynthesis—a role similar to that described above (see Section I).

Although M. Brody et al. (1965) confirmed the findings of Stern et al. (1964a,b) about the essentially linear kinetics of the phenomena mentioned above (including chlorophyll formation) they additionally noted that at about 10 hours there is readily observed at 77°K a sharp, steplike increase in long-wavelength fluorescence (at ∼720 nm) relative to that at short wavelengths (at 685 nm). See Figs. 21 and 22. Since they consider the 720-nm fluorescence to originate in an aggregated species of chlorophyll (F_A), while attributing the 685-nm fluorescence (F_M) to a monomeric species, they concluded that in *Euglena* there is very little aggregate present in cells that have "greened" for less than about 10 hours, and recalled their earlier contentions (S. Brody, 1958; S. Brody and M. Brody, 1961a) that the presence of aggregated chlorophyll is a necessary condition for photosynthesis. (See also Sections IV, introduction; and IVA, 2, a.) In this regard, it is of interest to note that in 1961, Goedheer, on the basis of studies with greening bean leaves, also concluded that the development of photosynthetic capacity is more closely related to the presence of the form of chlorophyll a giving rise to long-wavelength emission (from the aggregate) than it is to total chlorophyll a content. Butler (1965) came to essentially the same conclusion, using the techniques of low-temperature fluorescence action spectroscopy on greening bean leaves.

D. THE STEADY STATE

Stern et al. (1964a) and M. Brody et al. (1965) seem to agree fairly well on the essentially linear kinetics of chlorophyll formation and photosynthetic activity that follow the lag phase. However, the latter workers did not note attainment of the steady state for chlorophyll content within the 80-hour period, although both groups used light intensities of about 100–150 ft-c for the "greening" process. Stern et al. (1964a) stated that after 80 hours of illumination, dark-grown *E. gracilis* var. *bacillaris* contain (as do light-grown cells) 12–14 pg chlorophyll per cell (or 7.2–8.4 × 10⁹ chlorophyll molecules per cell). In the same paper they calculate a theoretical value based on number of lamellae of 16 pg per cell (9.6 × 10⁹ molecules per cell). M. Brody *et al.* found that 80-hour *E. gracilis* strain Z contain 1.06 × 10⁹ chlorophyll molecules per cell, in contrast to light-grown cells which have 2.5 × 10⁹ chlorophyll molecules per cell. In his book, Wolken (1961) gives 5.1 × 10⁹ chlorophyll molecules per cell for light-grown var. *bacillaris*.

The following comparisons can be made of data on total amount of chlorophyll per cell, in light-grown versus dark-grown cells. M. Brody *et al.* noted with strain Z more than an 800-fold difference between the chlorophyll content found after 10 minutes exposure of dark-grown cells to light (less than 10⁶ molecules) and the situation encountered in light-grown cells. They also found an increase in chlorophyll content of more than 300-fold between the lag phase and 70-hour cells. Stern *et al.* (1964a) found with var. *bacillaris* a 400-fold increase between the lag phase (taken by these authors to be 3 hours) and 80-hour cells.

E. INFLUENCE OF LIGHT INTENSITY DURING DEVELOPMENT ON TOTAL CHLOROPHYLL CONTENT*

Stern *et al.* (1964b) used nondividing cells of dark-grown *E. gracilis* var. *bacillaris* in a study of the influence of light intensity and duration on total chlorophyll content (a plus b) and related phenomena. They found with cells light-adapted for 95 hours, that photosynthesis (measured as oxygen evolution or carbon dioxide fixation) and pigment formation both reach maximum values at light intensities of about 100 ft-c. Higher or lower intensities resulted in lower rates and pigment content (Fig. 4). In respect to pigment content, *Euglena* seems to differ from the red alga *Porphyridium cruentum* grown under similar conditions of illumination (M. Brody and Emerson, 1959a). In the latter organism (which has no chlorophyll b), while diminished pigment content *is* noted at the higher intensities, maximal pigment development occurs at the lower light intensities—the anticipated dropoff in pigment content not having been reached within the range of low light intensities used by M. Brody and Emerson.

Stern *et al.* (1964b) found that with cells light-adapted at an intensity of 7 ft-c, rate of oxygen evolution and total chlorophyll content reached only 50% of maximum, even after 10 days (Fig. 4), although oxygen evolution on a chlorophyll basis was equivalent to that in cells developing at optimal intensity (Fig. 4). The *kinetics* of development of pigments and photosynthetic

---

* *Editor's Note:* This topic is further covered in Chapter 10 and in Vol. I, Chapter 6.

capacity indicate that cells light-adapted at low intensities (4 or 7 ft-c) do not reach maximal levels (Fig. 5). Cells allowed to green at 440 or 700 ft-c show initial rates comparable to those at 100 ft-c, but by 60 hours the rates diminish and the levels eventually fall to yield the inhibition noted in Fig. 4. Stern *et al.* (1964b) noted that the chlorophyll/carotenoid ratio (on a mole/mole basis) in cells developing at high light intensities never reaches the optimal value of 2.5 (Figs. 4 and 5)—this greater inhibition of chlorophyll formation (or greater rate of chlorophyll destruction) being in agreement with the findings of M. Brody and Emerson on *Porphyridium.*

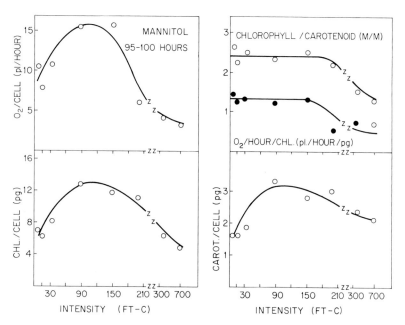

Fig. 4. Photosynthetic oxygen evolution and chlorophyll and carotenoid content of dark-grown *Euglena*, exposed for 95–100 hours to light of various intensities. Also shown are oxygen evolution per hour on a chlorophyll basis and the chlorophyll to carotenoid ratios (mole/mole). Photosynthetic oxygen evolution measured at saturating light intensity (2500 ft-c). Adapted from Stern *et al.* (1964b).

Stern *et al.* (1964b) reported, additionally, that when cells that have developed at 7 ft-c for 87 hours are allowed to continue their development at 100 ft-c, they attain normal levels for oxygen evolution and pigment content by 40 hours. After this time, they continue to develop, so that by 80 hours they have exceeded the normal levels of these parameters and have become "hyperdeveloped," for example, at 80 hours, they have 18 pg chlorophyll per cell (10.8×10^9 chlorophyll molecules per cell) compared to 13 pg chlorophyll per cell (7.8×10^9 chlorophyll molecules per cell) under normal conditions.

In this same paper, these workers point out a correlation between chlorophyll/carotenoid ratio (on a mole/mole basis) and ability of cells to evolve oxygen photosynthetically. (They used data from various experiments in which cells were allowed to green or light-adapt under dividing and non-dividing conditions, for different lengths of time, and at different light intensities.) They observed that only when the pigment ratio is greater than one, can a "significant" amount of oxygen evolution be detected. In regard

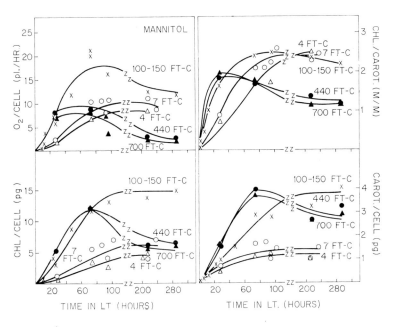

Fig. 5. Kinetics of photosynthetic oxygen evolution and chlorophyll and carotenoid content of dark-grown *Euglena* exposed to the indicated light intensities at zero time. Oxygen evolution measured at saturating light intensity (2500 ft-c). Also shown are the chlorophyll to carotenoid ratios (mole/mole). Adapted from Stern *et al.* (1964b).

to this observation (similar to those of workers with other organisms) the reader is again referred to Section I of this chapter for a possible indirect role of carotenoids in photosynthesis.

F. INFLUENCE OF LIGHT INTENSITY ON CHLOROPHYLL a AND b CONTENT

Euglena has often been considered an extreme type of sun plant because of its low proportion of chlorophyll b to a (S. Brody and M. Brody, 1963).

Wolken (1961), using *E. gracilis* var. *bacillaris* cells (which he reported as showing little evidence for the presence of pheophytin, see Sections III, G and IV, A, 1), estimated that chlorophyll b ranged from 15 to 20% of the total amount of chlorophyll; the percentage decreasing with age of the culture. As might be anticipated, however, the proportions of chlorophylls vary with the light intensities used for growth.

Brown (1960) and Brown and French (1961) cultured (light-grown?) cells of *E. gracilis* "T" (Chick, Emerson, Starr Collection #752) at four different intensities of light. Since the average intensity of light incident on the individual cells decreased during the growth of the culture (due to mutual shading) these workers report having harvested cells before the culture density became so great as to markedly influence the amount of light received by each cell. From Table I several features of these cells may be noted. Whereas high light intensities resulted in reduced chlorophyll a content [as Stern *et al.* (1964b) also showed later for total chlorophyll content], lowering the intensity to 50 ft-c resulted in increased chlorophyll a content [in contrast to the findings of Stern *et al.* (1964b) who noted that intensities of less than about 90 ft-c gave reduced amounts of total chlorophyll]. In this respect, the data of Brown and French (1961) on *Euglena* are similar to those obtained with *Porphyridium* by M. Brody and Emerson (1959a).

Brown (1960) and Brown and French (1961) reported that chlorophyll b is stable and does not vary in amount with light intensity as does chlorophyll a. It may be seen from Table I that the ratio chlorophyll a/chlorophyll b changes from about 4, under high light intensity, to about 7, under low light intensity. Stern *et al.* (1964b) were led, on the basis of computations from their own data, to conclude that although chlorophyll a and b are both affected by high light intensity, the effect on b is minute.

Table I

THE INFLUENCE OF LIGHT INTENSITY ON CHLOROPHYLL a AND b CONTENT OF *Euglena*[a]

	Intensity during growth (ft-c)			
	1200	700	200	50
Age of culture (days)	2	3	4	2
Chl a + b (mg/ml culture)	1.0×10^{-2}	4.6×10^{-2}	8.5×10^{-2}	0.2×10^{-2}
Cell volume (ml/ml culture)	3×10^{-3}	6×10^{-3}	9×10^{-3}	—
Cells (number/ml culture)	980×10^{3}	2152×10^{3}	3720×10^{3}	86×10^{3}
Chl a (mg/cell)	0.86×10^{-8}	1.8×10^{-8}	2.0×10^{-8}	2.4×10^{-8}
Chl a/chl b	4.1	5.1	6.5	7.2

[a] From Brown (1960).

Brown (1960) and Brown and French (1961) pointed out that their results with *Euglena* were different from those given for *Chlorella* by Myers (1946) who observed that the amount of chlorophyll per cell does not vary with growth at different light intensities. In the case of *Chlorella* grown at low light intensity there is more chlorophyll per unit dry weight than at high light intensity, but there is not more chlorophyll per cell, due to the small size of cells grown at low light intensity.

G. Dark Adaptation: Chlorophyll Loss and Degradation

In addition to ascribing the loss of chlorophyll from *E. gracilis* transferred to darkness, to a simple dilution process resulting from cell division and growth, Wolken (1961) noted the presence of chlorophyll degradation. The spectral characteristics of extracts of such "dark-adapted" cells led him to suggest that pheophytin might be formed within a short (but variable) period of time after cells were placed in the dark. Because of similar spectral changes, he concluded that other environmental conditions (such as poor nutrition, age, specific drug action, temperature above 40°C) are also able to induce this shift from chlorophyll to pheophytin. Earlier, Greenblatt and Schiff (1959) had dark-adapted cells of *E. gracilis* var. *bacillaris* without aeration for periods of about 24 hours. With these cells they observed a shift in absorption maximum; there was also a slight increase at 535 nm as well. They made further experiments on extracts, which when purified, yielded absorption spectra similar to pheophytin a. Unfortunately, the absorption spectrum of pheophorbide a corresponds almost identically to that of pheophytin a and to that of several other related compounds. Greenblatt and Schiff concluded, however, on the basis of further chemical identification, cochromatography with crystalline pheophytin a, and the position of the fluorescence peak of the *Euglena* pigment (between 670 and 675 nm), that the compound formed in dark-adapted *Euglena* is probably pheophytin a. These workers also found the following: when cells are grown and dark-adapted in high pH media (pH 8) no pheophytin-like pigment is detected; aeration slows down the process of pheophytinization; increase in temperature and also decrease in pH during dark adaptation promote pheophytinization.

Ben-Shaul *et al.* (1965) also studied dark adaptation in var. *bacillaris*. They used cells that had been illuminated for 96 hours at 100 ft-c, in which chloroplast development was complete. These cells were then either repeatedly transferred to fresh growing medium in the dark to keep them in the logarithmic phase of growth, or they were inoculated into resting medium and shaken for about 50 hours (until cell division ceased) and then placed in the dark. The kinetics of pigment loss are given in Fig. 6. From this figure it may be seen that, in the case of dividing cells, the loss of chlorophyll a is initially at the rate of 50% per generation, that is, loss is by simple dilution among chloroplasts of progeny cells, in accordance with the suggestion of Wolken (1961). After about three generations the rate becomes comparable to the loss of structure (as determined with the electron microscope)—about 37% per generation. Ben-Shaul et al. (1965) interpreted these observations as indicating that when light is turned off, chlorophyll synthesis stops immediately [in agreement with the known light requirement for the proto-chlorophyll(ide) to chlorophyll(ide) step], but some discs and lamellae continue to be produced at a low rate. The data for chlorophyll a loss are complicated because, upon dark adaptation, there is some conversion to pheophytin a. With dividing cells, about 18% of the initial loss of chlorophyll is due to this conversion; thereafter both chlorophyll a and pheophytin a are lost at comparable rates. Chlorophyll b also progressively diminishes in amount during dark adaptation, but its estimation, as well as that of pheophytin a, is hampered because of low concentration and because of uncertainties in extinction coefficients at several wavelengths.

Ben-Shaul et al. (1965) found very different results with cells dark-adapted

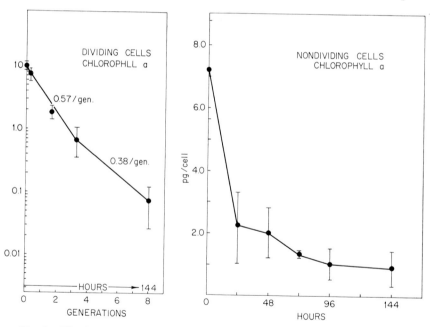

Fig. 6. Kinetics of loss of chlorophyll a during dark adaptation of cells under conditions of division (left) and nondivision (right). Adapted from Ben-Shaul et al. (1965). Reproduced by permission of the National Research Council of Canada from the Can. J. Botany 43, 129 (1965).

under nondividing conditions; in this case, much less loss of structure results than with dividing cells which return to the proplastid condition after 144 hours or in about 8 generations. With nondividing cells there is extensive loss of chlorophyll a during the first 24 hours (Fig. 6), but the rate of loss subsequently decreases. After the 24-hour period, about 50% of the chlorophyll a appears as pheophytin a; thereafter there is no significant increase in the amount of pheophytin a. Chlorophyll b (as well as could be estimated) seemed to drop below the limit of detection by 24 hours. Because of their observations with nondividing cells (that lamellar structure undergoes little change, while about 88% of the chlorophyll a is lost either by conversion to pheophytin a or by degradation), Ben-Shaul et al. (1965) concluded, in agreement with von Wettstein (1961) (whose experiments were with higher plants) that chlorophyll a, per se, is not a determinant of lamellar structure. These workers offer no explanation as to the difference in kinetics of chlorophyll disappearance under dividing and nondividing conditions.

IV. Different Forms of Chlorophyll a

Long before the photosynthetic requirement for two chlorophyll a systems was recognized, the existence of more than one type had been suggested. Since the main red absorption band of all chloroplast-containing systems is quite certainly due to chlorophyll a, and since it is much broader *in vivo* than *in vitro*—the shape as well as the maximum varying (from about 670 to 680 nm) with different organisms—its nature soon became suspect. None of the components responsible for the appearance of the band *in vivo* survive extraction, however, and all appear in the form of monomeric chlorophyll a, the red absorption maximum of which is at wavelengths 10–20 nm shorter in organic solvents (for example, at 662 nm in ether) than *in vivo*. (It is impractical to work with absorption bands other than the red because of interference by other pigments, particularly carotenoids. Chlorophyll b, which has an *in vitro* absorption at 644 nm in ether, is usually recognizable as a shoulder at approximately 650 nm on the short-wavelength side of the chlorophyll a band *in vivo*.)

Because space does not permit, it will not be possible to list here all the workers who contributed to this area of investigation and, therefore, the reader is referred to three of the many sources that review the pertinent literature (Rabinowitch, 1951; Smith and French, 1963; S. Brody and M. Brody, 1963).

Section IV of this chapter will present a review of the work on the different forms of chlorophyll a found in *Euglena*. In the paragraph immediately below are cited three of the interpretations that have been advanced to account for the nature of the different forms of chlorophyll a *in vivo*; addition-al interpretations have been made (see, for example, Kamen, 1963 and Clayton, 1965), however, those set forth below are among the ones most frequently cited and commented upon in the literature, and hold the added advantage, for us, of having been made on the basis of experiments with *Euglena* as well as other photosynthetic organisms.

Although it is widely accepted that the chlorophyll a chromophore is attached to protein, the three major interpretations are based additionally on the concept that the different forms of chlorophyll a *in vivo* arise because of (1) various states of aggregation of the chlorophyll a chromophore, (2) binding of the chlorophyll a to specific protein sites in the chloroplast and, (3) crystalline orientation of chlorophyll a,—all of which may affect not only spectral properties but chemical ones as well.

Interpretation (2) is preferred by Brown and French (1961) (see also Myers and French, 1960) who have largely used absorption techniques for their studies; these are described in Section A,1. M. Brody and S. Brody have favored interpretation (1) and have primarily used fluorescence tech-niques in their studies, which are presented in Section A,2. Data that have been interpreted in accordance with (3) come largely from the work of Goedheer and that of Olson and colleagues; these are presented in Section A,3.

A. Methods of Detection

1. *Absorption Measurements*

That chlorophyll a exists in two or more forms in the green plant was proposed by Albers and Knorr (1937) who resolved two absorption maxima, at about 670 and 680 nm, by photographic densitometry of single chloro-plasts. The most recent research has probably been stimulated by several Russian workers, particularly those in Krasnovsky's laboratory. In 1952, he and his colleagues (Krasnovsky *et al.*, 1952) duplicated some of the infrared bands of bacteriochlorophyll by drying solutions of the pure pigment on glass slides; they attributed the longer wavelength absorption bands to polymerization of chlorophyll molecules. In the same year, Krasnovsky and Kosobutskaja noted in greening leaves that chlorophyll a absorbing at 673 nm was soon replaced by a form absorbing at 678 nm; they attributed this shift to aggregation. Later, in 1955, Krasnovsky and Kosobutskaja found that environmental conditions affected the ratio of the 670- and 680-nm-absorbing forms (which together yielded the 678-nm form in higher plants) by observing the differential photobleaching of the two forms. They attributed the 670-nm peak to monomeric chlorophyll a and the longer wavelength peak at 680 nm to a polymeric form.

Absorption studies with bacteriochlorophyll, which more readily lend themselves to the interpretation favored by French and Brown (namely, that the different forms of chlorophyll a arise because of binding of the chromophore to specific protein sites) were made in 1959 by Newton and Levine. These workers observed that treatment with the enzyme trypsin progressively causes loss of the three bacteriochlorophyll absorption peaks, beginning with the longest wavelength component.

Attention will now be turned to the studies of French and Brown on various forms of chlorophyll; their efforts in this area have spanned several years and have been both very extensive in surveying many organisms and very intensive with respect to *Euglena*.

It has been only very recently that accurate absorption spectra of even the "conventional" variety have been obtained with living organisms, and these with great difficulty, by using integrating spheres or special optical techniques, including the placement of the sample cuvette close to the detector to capture scattered light. In 1954, in an attempt to reduce the amount of light lost by scattering, Shibata *et al.* introduced the technique of interposing a sheet of light-diffusing material (such as opal or milk glass, or oiled filter paper) between the sample and the light-sensing element of the spectrophotometer, as close to the sample as possible, a similar plate being placed in a comparable position with respect to the blank control. It was with such techniques that Shibata *et al.* (1954), Greenblatt and Schiff (1959),

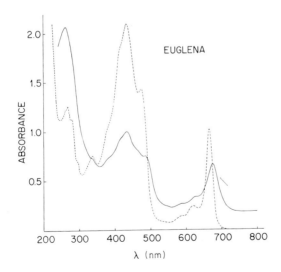

Fig. 7. Absorption spectra of *Euglena* suspension (unbroken line) and alcoholic extract (broken line). Adapted from Shibata *et al.* (1954). Reproduced from *Biochim. Biophys. Acta* **15**, 465 (1954).

and Wolken (1961) obtained their absorption spectra of *Euglena*; see Fig. 7. (The much later use, by Butler and Norris in 1960, of a large area phototube behind the sample, led to results to be discussed in Section IV,A,2,*a*.)

A year after the publication of Shibata *et al.* (1954) an instrument to plot directly the first derivative or slope of absorption as a function of wavelength was built by French (1956, 1957; see also French and Harper, 1957); such an instrument facilitates the location of absorption peaks. In conventional or integral plots the wavelengths of maximum and minimum absorbance appear as positive and negative peaks, respectively. In a derivative plot these positions correspond to places where the curve crosses the zero line; thus differences in positions of these peaks become readily apparent. Also, variations in the slope of the integral curve are converted into bands in the derivative curve, making discernible small amounts of pigments whose presence might ordinarily be masked.

In the case of *Euglena* (probably *E. gracilis* #752), French and Elliot (1958) found not only the expected two bands for chlorophyll a at 673 and 683 nm but a new band at 695 nm which appeared in old but not in young cultures (Fig. 8). When this band is present, the derivative absorption spectrum has a peak at 703 nm; without this component, the negative peak is at

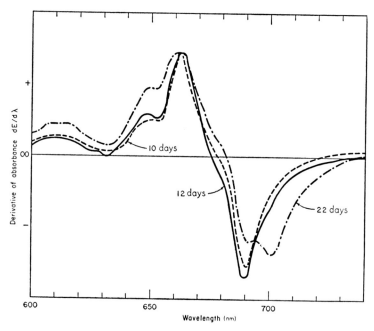

Fig. 8. Derivative absorption spectra of *Euglena* cultures at various ages. Adapted from French and Elliot (1958).

about 690 nm. Since extraction with acetone revealed the presence of no chlorophyllous pigment other than a and b (the small amount of absorption due to the latter may be seen as an inflection at about 650 nm in Fig. 8), it was concluded that the extra pigment was also a form of chlorophyll a. Figure 9 shows two integral curves for young and old cells (obtained from their respective derivative curves) and the difference between them; a band with maximum at 695 nm, is clearly discernible in the difference curve. In Fig. 10 are plotted fluorescence spectra for the cells for which derivative spectra were given in Fig. 8. From such data French and Elliot, (1958)

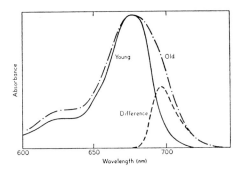

Fig. 9. Absorption spectra of 9-day and 36-day *Euglena* cultures adjusted to the same height. The curves were integrated from the measured derivative spectra. Adapted from French and Elliot (1958).

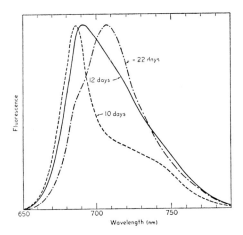

Fig. 10. Fluorescence spectra of *Euglena* cultures of different ages. The same cultures were used as in Fig. 8. Adapted from French and Elliot (1958).

concluded that as *Euglena* ages the fluorescence at 710 nm increases relative to that of "ordinary chlorophyll" at about 685 nm (see also French, 1958a,b). In 1959 and 1961, Brown, and Brown and French, respectively, undertook a series of studies to determine the conditions that make the 695-nm component appear or disappear in *Euglena*. (While not specifically cited, it is assumed that they used *E. gracilis* #752 in all their works, since, when references are made, they are to this organism.) These workers found that C_a 695* forms as well in synthetic media with CO_2 as carbon source, as in completely organic media; it can be detected when the chlorophyll content reaches about 0.03 mg/ml culture. The most significant factor in its formation seemed to be the light intensity during growth. At less than 300 ft-c (which they call low light intensity) it appears within 2 days and continues to increase during the succeeding 2 weeks. However, at about 600 ft-c, no C_a695 formed, even though growth and chlorophyll formation otherwise appeared normal. It was also reported that if a culture grown under low light intensity is placed in high light intensity, C_a695 disappears; this led Brown and French (1961) to suspect that at high light intensities C_a695 either does not form or it becomes bleached.

In preparation for studies with red light, *Euglena* cells were ruptured either by extrusion through a needle valve under pressure, or by grinding with sand. When fragments from cells not containing C_a695 were bleached, the results were very similar to those obtained with *Chlorella*, i.e., the shoulder near the peak position shifted slightly toward longer wavelengths. With fragments from cells containing C_a695, breakage and bleaching caused a considerable loss of this component.

In these studies, a fourth absorption band was reported in *Euglena* at 707 nm. Cells containing this pigment appeared brownish-green and were nonmotile and rounded rather than elongated. Because this pigment seemed to come only from cells that had previously accumulated an appreciable amount of C_a695, Brown and French (1961) undertook a study of the development of C_a695 as a function of light intensity. The results of this study may be seen in relation to Table I (Section III,F) which comes from their work. The largest amount of C_a695 is found in cells grown at 50 ft-c;

---

* To distinguish the various *in vivo* pigments (all of which contribute to the red chlorophyll absorption band) an abbreviation is used in which the capital "C" for chlorophyll (Duysens, 1952) is followed by the subscript "a" or "b" for the two main chlorophyll forms and then by a number which labels the wavelength of the absorption maximum in nanometers (Allen *et al.*, 1960). Likewise, the letter "P" is used to designate protochlorophyll (French, 1960a) or (unfortunately) pheophytin (Brown, 1960). By an extension of this suggestion, "F" has been used for fluorescence emission peaks (as in F698, F_M, or F685, etc.), and in the present work "A" will be used to designate fluorescence action (excitation) maxima.

in cells grown at 1200 ft-c (in which there is three times less chlorophyll a), C_a695 is not measurable.

Since in this same study they found that cells with the 707-nm band contain a proportionate amount of pheophytin-like pigment, detectable in alcoholic extracts, they inferred that the 707-nm absorption *in vivo* arises from a complex of pheophytin a (see Section III,G). Therefore, attempts were made to produce absorption at 707 nm by acid treatment of intact or disintegrated cells. These experiments were made as part of a longer series designed to determine the influence of diversified treatments on the formation and stability of the various forms of chlorophyll and pheophytin in *Euglena*; the data are given in Table II. They concluded from these studies that heating cells to 45°C for 15 minutes greatly reduces the amount of C_a695 and slightly increases absorption at 673 nm, indicating that C_a695 is more heat labile than the other forms of chlorophyll a and that it may be converted in part to 673-nm absorption. Acidification of cells or cell components (such as chloroplasts or chloroplast fragments) was carried out using *Euglena* of high C_a695 content. Spectral changes were very different from those brought about by heating or partial bleaching with red light. In the acid-treated material the major absorption components appeared at about 695 and 673 nm while C_a683 appeared to be lacking. Thus, acid treatment was seen to have little effect on C_a695 (which is particularly susceptible to bleaching and to heating); chlorophyll b, which resists bleaching and heating very well, was almost completely removed. Brown and French (1961) noted, however, that the P_a710 component (previously called P_a707) did not appear as a result of acid treatment. Therefore, they concluded that while it seemed to be a bound form of pheophytin a, P_a710 cannot be produced in appreciable quantities by acid treatment (in contrast to the findings of Greenblatt and Schiff, 1959; see also Section III,G). Brown and French (1961) observed, however, that once formed, P_a710 is resistant to drastic treatment.

Table II

RELATIVE STABILITY OF CHLOROPHYLL FORMS[a]

Treatment	C_b650	C_a673	C_a683	C_a695	P_a707
Bright light	Stable	Slightly bleached	Partially bleached	Bleached	Slightly bleached
Heat 45°C (15 minutes)	Stable	Stable	Stable	Bleached	Stable
Acid, pH 2	Bleached	Slightly bleached	Bleached	Slightly bleached	Stable

[a] From Brown (1960).

In their 1961 paper, these workers additionally reported that when cells are cultured at a light intensity of approximately 250 ft-c C_a695 forms in amounts equal to 20% of the total chlorophyll absorbing in the red region. They also confirmed their earlier finding that the appearance of P_a710 coincides with decrease in absorption at 695 nm and increase in amount of extractable pheophytin a. Moreover, they noted that although C_a695 is observed with several varieties of *E. gracilis* it is not observed in *E. mutabilis*.

In 1960 and 1962, Frei applied the technique of derivative absorption spectroscopy to cells that had been cooled to $-180°C$ by liquid nitrogen in glycerine–sorbitol–borate solutions to give a clear glass. It proved to be a useful tool in helping to determine the number of components and the peak position of pigments in various organisms. Although no additional absorption bands were revealed in *Euglena*, there was considerable sharpening of the derivative spectrum.

To learn more about C_a695, Brown (1961, 1963b) prepared a partially purified aqueous colloidal extract which contained C_a695 in the same proportion to the rest of the chlorophylls as in whole cells. The method she used is shown in a detailed flow diagram in her 1961 paper, but it can be summarized as follows. Cells that had been growing autotrophically for 3 weeks at low light intensity were chilled overnight in a 5°C cold room. During the subsequent repeated process of breakage and differential centrifugation, cell materials were suspended in a special pH 9.5 buffer. The final sediment, obtained by centrifugation for 90 minutes at 144,700 g, could be lyophilized and stored in the cold for long periods of time without undergoing spectral changes.

With such colloidal extracts it was found that oxidizing or reducing agents (potassium ferri- and ferrocyanide, borohydride, and ascorbate) have no affect on C_a695 absorption. Neither petroleum ether or carbon tetrachloride, shaken in equal volume amounts with the aqueous suspension, appeared to affect this pigment. However, Brown (1961) found that C_a695 is destroyed fairly rapidly and irreversibly below pH 5 and above pH 11 by treatment with aqueous acetone above 20% and by being shaken with the detergent Triton X-100. At pH 4, C_a695 was found to completely disappear in 1 minute.

Not only did Brown report that it was not possible to separate cleanly the chlorophyll complexes from each other by breakage and differential centrifugation, but also by ammonium sulfate fractionation or by chromatography on DEAE or Sephadex (G-75) columns. Attempts to alter the proportionate amounts of chlorophylls in *Euglena* by growing cultures in alternating light and dark periods was also unsuccessful.

When Brown used cells containing a large proportion of P_a710 for the same extraction procedure described above, part of the brownish color remained in the supernatant of the final centrifugation. Because the main absorption bands in the sediment were found to be derived from C_a673 and C_a695 while the main one in the supernatant was from C_a683, Brown concluded that C_a673 and 695 are tied together on a separate particle heavier than C_a683 (however, see below).

In 1962, Brown reported that in cells aged to about $4\frac{1}{2}$ weeks, the brownish-green P_a710 is mostly in the cytoplasm and can be readily separated from the other green chloroplast pigments by centrifugation of ruptured cells. Ether extraction and ascending paper chromatography, carried out in collaboration with Dr. J.H.C. Smith, strongly indicated that the pigment absorbing at 710 nm is pheophorbide a or a closely related compound. In this work, they posed the still unanswered question as to whether the organism first forms pheophytin a in the chloroplasts and then excretes it into the cytoplasm as a pheophorbide complex, or forms the pheophorbide directly from C_a695.

Some of the 1960 and 1961 experiments referred to above were further expanded and described by Brown in 1963(b); in this later paper, Brown again suggests that chlorophyll a 673 and 695 are more closely allied to each other than to C_a683—the first two chlorophylls being bound to one lipoprotein molecule and C_a683 to another. In this disposition, she proposed that C_a673 and C_a695 together mediate one light reaction and C_a683 another (see also Brown, 1963a).

Brown (1963c) further described absorption changes that occur during "aging." She made comparative studies on light-grown cells containing C_a673, C_a683, and C_a695 and on similar cells that had been aged 2 weeks in darkness so that P_a710 had become apparent. She found that at 4°C, the absorption band at 710 nm becomes evident after 1 week in the dark and continues to increase for 3–4 weeks; at room temperature in the dark it forms more rapidly In contrast to the findings of Greenblatt and Schiff (1959, see also Section III,G) on pheophytin, she found that bubbling the aging cultures with nitrogen did not seem to increase the rate of formation of P_a710. During aging, the number of motile, green cells was found to decrease and the proportion of nonmotile, brownish cells to increase. She again noted a change in the shape of cells, from long cylindrical ones with one end more pointed than the other, to ellipsoidal ones with both ends symmetrically rounded. She pointed out that when the change has occurred in half the population, it is relatively easy to separate the two types of cells by allowing a mixed culture to sit in room light for one-half hour. The green motile cells settle to the bottom and the brown cells remain suspended. P_a710 is found only in nonmotile round cells. The older the cells at the beginning of the dark aging period, the faster P_a710 becomes apparent. Brown points out in this work that Greenblatt and Schiff (1959) had not noted the 710-nm band *in vivo* in their study, and she suggests that growing and aging cells in a neutral medium is favorable for the formation of P_a710 since acidifying the green cells, or an aqueous extract from them, forms pheophytin readily—but not P_a710.

In an earlier work, Brown and French (1961) had reported that *Euglena* grown at low light intensity and subsequently aged lost C_a695 as P_a710 formed, and had suggested a conversion of one form to the other. In their 1963 work (see Brown, 1963c), however, Brown observed that in the dark, under nitrogen, P_a710 is formed in cells grown at high light intensity but under such conditions they contain no detectable C_a695. Since from her previous experiments she had learned that C_a695 is more photosensitive that the other chlorophyll forms, she proposed that when cells are grown in bright light C_a695 is bleached, but when cells are removed from the light C_a695 is directly metabolized to P_a710. She also proposed an alternative suggestion, that P_a710 is formed directly from C_a673, and that the presence or breakdown of C_a695 is coincidental. Brown (1963c) also reports that the ratio of pheophytin a to pheophorbide a in the cytoplasmic fraction varies with different aged *Euglena* preparations. Apparently, the older the culture, the lower this ratio, indicating that pheophorbide is a step further than pheophytin in the degradation process.

It is of interest to note that Brown (1963a) states that the amount of chlorophyll b present in *Euglena* that has formed C_a695 is very low. She points out that after the aging to form P_a710, no chlorophyll b is visible, but adds that the careful chromatography needed to detect small amounts of chlorophyll b has not been done. (See Section III,F.)

In another study in 1963, Brown (1963d) concentrated her efforts on C_a 683, interpreting it, on the basis of her experiments, either as a discrete particle similar to C_a673 (but with a different lipoprotein composition), or as a particular structural arrangement of the chlorophyll–lipoprotein complex.

Continuing attempts to fractionate chloroplasts into fragments with different pigment composition met with some success when detergents were utilized. In 1964, Brown, and Brown and Duranton (1964) described the partial separation of C_a673 from C_a683 by means of the action of the anionic detergent sodium dodecyl sulfate (SDS) on chloroplast particles from spinach or tobacco. They noted that more chlorophyll b was associated with C_a673 than with C_a683. Brown and Duranton considered their experiments an indication that the double absorption bands observed in all plants are due to the single pigment chlorophyll a but that the pigment is attached to two different types of protein material.

In 1965, Bril used techniques of repeated freezing and thawing of chloroplasts in tris buffer in an effort to achieve fractionation of chlorophyll forms. Although these techniques worked with other organisms, they did not with *Euglena*; in addition, C_a695 was destroyed.

Probably because of the above-cited partial success in separating C_a673 from C_a683 in spinach and tobacco chloroplasts and the even better separation achieved by Boardman and Anderson (1964), Brown and Bril (1965) studied the effects of a number of detergents (sodium deoxycholate, digitonin, sodium dodecyl sulfate, Triton-X) on nine different kinds of plants including *Euglena*. In this study they pointed out that attempts to fractionate the various forms of chlorophyll a without detergents are rarely successful. (See Section IV,A,2,*b*.) With these detergents they obtained a good separation of pigment material only with the *Euglena* chloroplast fragments, and even in this case, only sodium deoxycholate and digitonin* were useful; with the other two detergents Brown *et al.* (1965a,b) reported rapid destruction of the chlorophyll complexes. As an outcome of the successful treatment, the supernatant fraction was found to contain mainly C_a673 (which constitutes about one-fifth of the total chlorophyll) and the sediment was found to be enriched (relative to untreated material) in C_a683, C_a695, and chlorophyll b. These results were achieved when roughly equal weights of detergent and chlorophyll were used. Increased detergent concentration induces time-dependent spectral changes in the fragments—the longest wavelength forms of chlorophyll a being destroyed first.

These results, as well as those on light-induced absorbance changes (Brown *et al.*, 1965a) are described in greater detail in another paper (Brown *et al.*, 1965b). In these studies, it is pointed out that the results of pigment separation achieved with detergents differ from those encountered in earlier experiments (which involved chloroplast rupture followed by differential centrifugation; see above). In the later detergent experiments (in which better separation was also achieved), it was observed that C_a683 and 695 are closely allied and that C_a673 is on a separate particle. These workers also suggested that the detergent experiments could be interpreted as an indication that P_a710 is not related to C_a695.

Boardman and Anderson had earlier (1964) succeeded in separating the two different systems involved in photosynthesis by treatment of spinach fragments with 0.5% digitonin. Particles left suspended after differential centrifugation at $10,000\,g$ seemed to contain only pigment system I,

* Wolken had earlier reported the isolation of chloroplastin, a pigment–protein complex obtained from frozen and thawed cells of *E. gracilis* var. *bacillaris* by grinding and extracting with 1–2% digitonin or other detergents. However, if separation of pigment forms was achieved, it was not noted. For more information on this complex of chlorophyll, carotenoids, and protein, as well as on its photo- and biochemical activities, the reader is referred to the following papers: Wolken (1956a,b, 1958, 1959, 1961, 1963).

because they were capable of NADP reduction (with ascorbate plus TCIP as electron donor) but not oxygen evolution.

Although the experiments of Brown *et al.* were not as successful as those of Boardman and Anderson (both fractions were found to exhibit some common activity, perhaps in part due to incomplete separation of the complexes), enough difference in response between the fractions was detected to indicate that different parts of the electron-transport system of photosynthesis are attached to each.

2. Fluorescence Measurements

That energy could be transferred from pigment to pigment in photosynthetic organisms was first shown by Dutton and Manning (1941) with the diatom *Nitzschia*; implication of such energy transfer to a photoreactive center was already present in the flashing-light experiments of Emerson and Arnold (1932). The former workers took advantage of the phenomenon of "sensitized fluorescence" to demonstrate energy transfer; chlorophyll fluorescence was seen to be emitted as a result of carotenoid excitation. Presumably a small amount (now known to be about 2–3%) of the energy of excited chlorophyll *in vivo* is lost through fluorescence—the rest being used for photosynthesis. Because of this relationship*, and because fluorescence measurements are more easily and rapidly made than photosynthesis measurements, the former have been used to follow the latter, yielding information about the pigments involved in photosynthesis and about the role they play in this process.

To this end, not only are fluorescence emission spectra determined, but also fluorescence "excitation" (or action) spectra. Using the above-mentioned system of Dutton and Manning, an example of the second-mentioned spectrum can be given. If a determination of the spectral efficiency for exciting chlorophyll fluorescence were made, the participation of the carotenoids would have been evident as a band (in the region of carotenoid absorption) in the action or excitation spectrum.

With these relationships in mind, we may now proceed to what has been learned from fluorescence studies about states of chlorophyll *in vivo* and other related phenomena.

a. Whole Cells and Chlorophyll a in Vitro. It may be recalled from Section IV,A,1 that French and Elliot (1958), French (1958a,b), and Brown and French (1961) had observed that as cultures of *Euglena* age, fluorescence at 710 nm (described variously between 705 and 710 nm) increases relative

---

* The yields of photosynthesis and fluorescence are parallel during steady-state conditions at moderate light intensities; at very high light intensities (above saturation for photosynthesis), and during the so-called "induction period" (which occurs when the light is first turned on) they exhibit complex dependencies on each other.

to that of "ordinary" chlorophyll a *in vivo*, at about 685 nm. (Chlorophyll b does not ordinarily fluoresce *in vivo*, probably as a result of strong spectral overlap with chlorophyll a assuring approximately 100% efficient energy transfer.) When comparisons were made with derivative absorption spectra of these cells, increasing absorption at 695 nm was noted and, therefore, the fluorescence band at 710 nm was attributed to C_a695.

In this same section, it was mentioned that Krasnovsky and co-workers (1952, 1955) had attributed the broad bacteriochlorophyll and chlorophyll a bands *in vivo* to the existence of polymerized states of these pigments. Probably the most convincing proof for the existence of aggregated chlorophyll a comes from the work of S. Brody. In 1958, he reported a new fluorescence band at $77°K$ ($-193°C$) (the temperature of liquid nitrogen) with a maximum at about 715 nm, from a concentrated solution of chlorophyll ($10^{-2}M$). This new band was observed in addition to the "ordinary" band with a maximum at 685 nm (also found in dilute solutions). S. Brody (1958) attributed this new fluorescence to a dimer or to higher aggregates of chlorophyll a. Since he also noted the presence of two fluorescence bands (at 685 and 720 nm) with *Chlorella* and *Porphyridium* cooled to $77°K$, he suggested that chlorophyll a *in vivo* also exists in monomeric and aggregated forms. He further suggested that the 720-nm fluorescence band is correlated with Kok's difference absorption band at 705 nm (which later became known as P700).

Brown (1960) and Brown and French (1961) were interested in seeing whether or not the 700-nm absorption changes described by Kok were related to C_a695. In collaboration with him, they studied light-induced absorption changes in *Euglena* grown at high or low light intensities. In both types of cells, the spectrum of the bleached pigment had an absorption peak at about 680 nm, but the cells grown at low light intensity, containing a large amount of C_a695, evidenced another higher absorption peak at about 700 nm. There was very little reversibly bleached pigment at this wavelength in the high light intensity cells which had little C_a695. Brown and French (1961) interpreted this data as favoring the possibility that C_a695 and the 700-nm pigment observed by Kok are the same. They suggested that while most actively photosynthetic green plants have about 2–4% of their chlorophyll a in a similar form absorbing at 695–700 nm, for some reason, as yet unknown, *Euglena* can accumulate 15–20% of its total chlorophyll a in this form when the light intensity is kept low.

S. Brody and M. Brody (1961a,c) made determinations of action spectra for exciting fluorescence from the two bands observed at $77°K$ *in vivo* and *in vitro*. The results for the 720-nm band *in vivo* were in good qualitative agreement with those for the aggregate *in vitro* (and also with the absorption spectra they gave for the aggregate in solution). The difference in shape of the action spectra for the two fluorescence bands, and the observation that accessory pigments transferred their energy to them in a preferential fashion, lent support to their view that there is more than one form of chlorophyll a *in vivo*. It was at this time that they suggested that the excitation of two different forms of chlorophyll a is necessary for photosynthesis (see introduction above).

M. Brody and Linschitz (1961) further extended the study of fluorescence emission to various higher plants and algae, including *E. gracilis*. In contrast to the bacteria (which exhibited only one emission band) the other photosynthetic organisms (which liberate oxygen) all exhibited at least two bands at 77°K. These workers noted that as dark-grown cells of *Euglena* begin to green (light-adapt), the shorter wavelength band (from the "monomer," in accordance with the interpretation of S. Brody and M. Brody, 1961a) becomes difficult to detect because of the great height and breadth of the long-wavelength band (from the "aggregates"). In the case of *Euglena*, in which fluorescence was measured at several intervals during the greening process, they confirmed the findings of French and co-workers (French and Elliot, 1958; French, 1958a,b; Brown and French, 1961) that, with aging, the room-temperature emission spectra show increased broadening, shifts in peak location, and the appearance of a shoulder at longer wavelengths. Brody and Linschitz (1961) found that at low temperature, emission from the aggregate (720 nm) far exceeds that from the monomer (685 nm) not only in *Euglena* but also in *Porphyridium*; because of the high intensity of fluorescence of the long-wavelength band, it is not surprising that in these species emission can be observed even at room temperature. In addition, a fluorescence band was noted near 515 nm in *Euglena* and was attributed to antheraxanthin.

These fluorescence studies on *E. gracilis* strain Z and other photosynthetic organisms were described in greater detail later in 1961 (M. Brody and S. Brody, 1961), at which time data were also presented to show that in addition to the two major bands readily observed at 77°K, a third minor fluorescence band was seen to appear at 697–699 nm in *Chlorella* and (erratically) in other organisms including *Euglena*.

A little later in the same year, Goedheer (1961) determined low-temperature fluorescence spectra of greening bean leaves and also measured, concurrently, photosynthetic capacity. He reported that protochlorophyll a is transformed into a chlorophyll a that has its fluorescence maximum at 694 nm. The shape of the fluorescence spectrum of this form does not change upon cooling. After 15 minutes of illumination the fluorescence maximum shifts from 694 to 683 nm, in agreement with Shibata (1957), but cooling again does not result in a change of shape of fluorescence spectrum (see also Butler and Briggs, 1966 and Section III,A). Thus, neither the 694- or 683-nm forms resulting from protochlorophyll transformation give rise to 720-nm fluorescence. Goedheer (1961) observed formation of new protochlorophyll to begin after 2.5 hours of illumination; no oxygen is produced before this time. Between 2.5 and 3.5 hours the chlorophyll content of the leaves double. The 3.5-hour leaf shows marked 720-nm fluorescence and only after 3.5 hours can photosynthesis be measured (as oxygen evolution with the mass spectro-

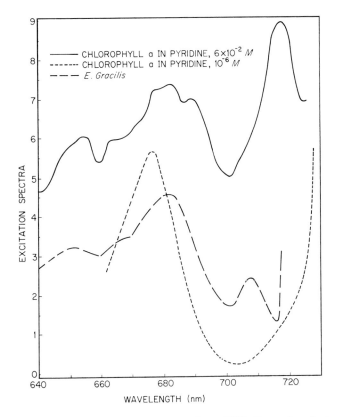

Fig. 11. Fluorescence excitation spectra; samples at 77°K. Curve given by long dashes is for emission at 730 nm from dark-grown cells of *Euglena* exposed to light for 80 hours; curve given by solid line is for emission at 736 nm from chlorophyll a in pyridine ($10^{-6}M$). Adapted from S. Brody and M. Brody (1963).

meter). During further greening, more chlorophyll develops, accompanied by an increase of both oxygen production and height of 720-nm fluorescence. Goedheer (1961) interpreted his observations as supporting the contention of S. Brody and M. Brody (1961a) that the chlorophyll a type responsible for 720-nm fluorescence is essential for photosynthesis.

Butler (1961, 1962) confirmed the suggestion first made by S. Brody (1958) that the 720-nm fluorescence band is correlated with an absorption band close to the position given by Kok for light-induced changes in absorption (at 705 nm, pigment referred to as P700). Butler (1961, 1962) detected this pigment at 705 nm in bean leaves and other green tissues using low-temperature absorption spectroscopy, and also noted a band with this maximum in the action (excitation) spectrum for exciting fluorescence at 720 nm. He, however, regarded this pigment, which serves as an energy sink for system I, as being a chlorophyll–cytochrome complex rather than an aggregate (however, see below, this Section). In 1963, S. Brody and M. Brody determined the low-temperature excitation spectrum for emission at 730 nm from *E. gracilis* strain Z, light-adapted for 80 hours. This spectrum contained a band with maximum at 708 nm, and exhibited features similar to those found in the low-temperature action spectrum for emission at 736 nm from a concentrated ($10^{-2}M$) solution of chlorophyll a in pyridine. These workers suggested that the excitation band with maximum at 718 nm, which they found *in vitro*, corresponds to the 708-nm band *in vivo*. Similar experiments with dilute solutions of chlorophyll yielded excitation spectra (for emission at 726 nm) that did not contain the band at 718 nm (see Fig. 11). With *Euglena* light-adapted for only a few hours, the band at 708 nm was found to be much smaller. It was also observed that the magnitude of the absorption band at 708 nm *in vivo* and the intensity of the emission band between 720 and 730 nm increased in parallel fashion. On this basis, S. Brody and M. Brody (1963) concluded that the 708-nm excitation band in *Euglena* corresponds to an aggregate. In a later paper (S. Brody and M. Brody, 1965), they compared the excitation spectra for the aggregate in *Euglena* with that of the aggregate in ethanol and found a closer correspondence than with pyridine.

In the 1963 paper, S. Brody and M. Brody cited previous experimental findings (both theirs and those of other workers) which had been (or could have been) interpreted as evidence for the existence of aggregated forms of chlorophyll a in solution and *in vivo*. They suggested that the pigment system alone (that is, interactions between chromophores) can give rise to the different spectral properties seen in nature. As a result of this survey, and on the basis of new data, they attributed the numerous peaks in the red end of the chlorophyll a absorption spectrum to (a) transitional distributions of chlorophyll aggregates during formation of the pigment system (in growth or greening) and (b) distributions of chlorophyll aggregates characteristic of the various species of photosynthetic organisms in the "steady" or "mature" state. For much of this work they used both light- and dark-grown *E. gracilis* strain Z. Fluorescence measurements were made at room temperature and at the temperature of liquid nitrogen. They observed that the quality of light used for exciting fluorescence affects the shape of the emission spectrum. Figure 12 shows room-temperature fluorescence emission spectra of light-grown 1.5-day-old cells, excited with 405, 436, or 545-nm lines. To S. Brody and M. Brody (1963) these data suggested that even at room temperature there exist at least two different fluorescent species of chlorophyll in *Euglena*—species having different absorption spectra and giving rise to the 685- and 720-nm emission bands.

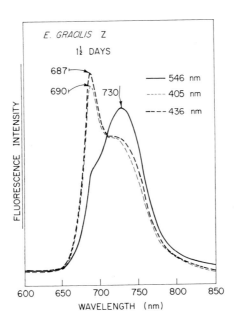

Fig. 12. Fluorescence emission spectra of 1.5-day cells excited with wavelengths indicated; excitation at room temperature. Adapted from S. Brody and M. Brody (1963).

For experiments with greening *Euglena*, S. Brody and M. Brody (1963) used cells cultured in the dark on organic media and then placed these log-phase cells in light for specified periods of time—referred to as "age" of cells. Figures 13, 14, and 15 show emission spectra for such 1-, 2-, and 3-day "old" cells, excited with the 436-nm mercury line. Cells light-adapted for 1 day exhibit little fluorescence at room temperature; at liquid nitrogen, emission from the aggregate (at 715 nm) is less than that from the monomer (at 685 nm). As the cells age, emission from the monomer increases, however, the increment of aggregate emission is far greater, so that at about 48 hours (the time depending upon density of culture, intensity of light, etc.), the monomer band becomes just an inflection on the short-wavelength side of

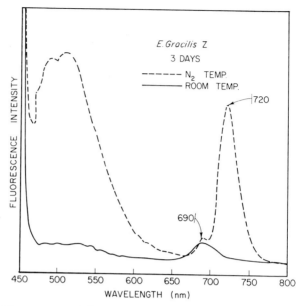

Fig. 13. Fluorescence emission spectra of *Euglena*, light-adapted for 1 day; excitation at 436 nm and 77°K. Adapted from S. Brody and M. Brody (1963).

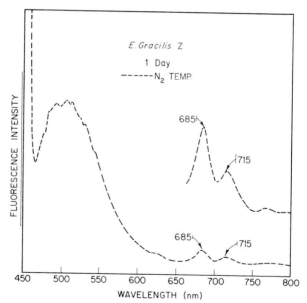

Fig. 14. Fluorescence emission spectra of *Euglena* light-adapted for 2 days. Excitation at 436 nm; room temperature given by unbroken line; 77°K given by broken line. Adapted from S. Brody and M. Brody (1963).

the aggregate band—and is soon all but completely masked. Consequently, in *Euglena*, aggregate fluorescence far exceeds monomer fluorescence during the major portion of the organism's life. As cells continue to green, the position of the monomer band moves from 685 to 687 nm, but the long-wavelength band (due to aggregation) shifts much more toward the red end of the spectrum, so that by 80 hours it reaches 732 nm. The position of this long-wavelength fluorescence maximum as a function of time in light is shown in Table III; the shift was attributed by S. Brody and M. Brody (1963) to a change in the population of different size aggregates with age.

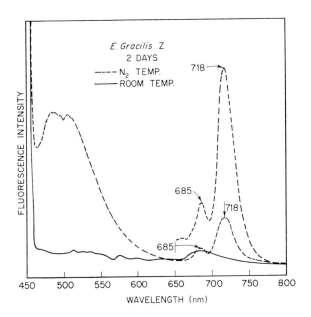

Fig. 15. Fluorescence emission spectra of *Euglena* light-adapted for 3 days. Excitation at 436 nm; room temperature given by unbroken line; 77°K given by broken line. Adapted from S. Brody and M. Brody (1963).

Using a mathematical expression derived by McRae and Kasha (1958), S. Brody and M. Brody (1963) estimated the number of molecules in the average-sized aggregate giving rise to the red absorption band. This number changes, of course during greening, as does the peak position of the red band. They used their data on fluorescence emission to make this estimate, assuming that the same wave number difference exists between the absorption and emission maxima of the aggregate and that of the monomer. In this work it was presupposed that the observed changes in spectroscopic properties that accompany greening arise solely from changes in size of aggregate.*

It was further assumed that the long-wavelength emission maximum (719 nm) observed at low temperature with *Euglena* exposed to light for only a few hours, arises from the smallest possible aggregate—namely a dimer (Table III). The longest wavelength for the emission maximum observed in these experiments (for cells kept up to 80 hours in light) is 732 nm, which yields an effective size for the aggregate of 3.77 chlorophyll molecules. The position of the long-wavelength absorption maximum for the various aggregates was calculated from emission maxima, using 676 nm as the value of the monomer maximum giving rise to fluorescence at 687 nm (Table III). [In a later paper by S. Brody (1964a) the monomer absorption maximum of *Euglena* was chosen at 673 nm to correspond with the short-wavelength absorption maximum given by French *et al.* (1959) and French (1960b) and Krasnovsky and Kosobutskaja (1952) from numerous photosynthetic organisms; the numbers from this later paper are given in parentheses in Table III.] S. Brody and M. Brody (1963) suggested that the spectral transformations they observed in *Euglena* represent changes in populations of monomers, dimers, tetramers, etc., and that these populations undergo considerable modification between the time of initial formation of chlorophyll and the attainment of a "steady state." It had also earlier been seen (M. Brody and Linschitz, 1961) that the steady-state population seems to depend on the particular organism. If these two situations do indeed exist, they would explain in large part the diversity of the reported maxima for the various forms of chlorophyll a *in vivo*.

In Table III, by letting N (the number of molecules in the aggregate) go to infinity, S. Brody and M. Brody (1963) were able to calculate a limiting value of 750 nm for the emission maximum of an infinitely large aggregate; the accompanying calculated absorption maximum turns out to be at 736 nm, which compares favorably with the absorption maximum of large microcrystals of ethyl chlorophyllide a—at 740 nm (Jacobs *et al.*, 1957).

It is of interest to note that the 705-nm absorption maximum, which S. Brody and M. Brody (1963) calculated (on the basis of their fluorescence emission data) for dimeric chlorophyll *in vivo*, corresponds so closely with the wavelengths reported for Kok's light-induced absorption changes (P700) in irradiated organisms (Section I), with French and Brown's C_a695, located through derivative absorption spectroscopy (Section IV,A,1) and

---

* One must also take into account the possibility that geometry, rather than size of aggregate, changes. Such an analysis for the shift in emission maximum in *Euglena* as a function of greening (with the dimer taken as a model for the aggregate) was reported in 1964 by S. Brody (1964b).

Table III

ABSORPTION MAXIMA AND EFFECTIVE SIZE OF AGGREGATE AS CALCULATED
FROM EMISSION MAXIMA OBSERVED AT 77°K IN GREENING *Euglena*[a]

Observed emission maximum		Calculated effective size of aggregate	Calculated absorption maximum	
$\nu(cm^{-1})$	$\lambda(nm)$	N	$\nu(cm^{-1})$	$\lambda(nm)$
14,556	687	1	14,793 (14,859)	676 (673)
13,947	719 (717)	2	14,184 (14,245)	705 (702)
13,661	732	3.77	13,898 (13,966)	719 (716)
13,338 (13,333)	750	∞	13,575 (13,636)	736 (734)

[a] All values given above are from S. Brody and M. Brody (1963) except those given in parentheses which are from S. Brody (1964a).

with Butler's 705-nm chlorophyll found by low-temperature absorption spectroscopy (see above, Section IV,A,2,*a*).

S. Brody and M. Brody (1963) also undertook an analysis of the number of forms of chlorophyll a in *Euglena* allowed to light-adapt for periods of time ranging from 6 to 80 hours. (Such cells do not contain P_a710, which is found only in old *Euglena*; see Section IV,A,1.) This analysis was based on interpreting the broad red emission envelope as consisting of several overlapping fluorescence bands. These workers determined the smallest possible number of forms giving rise to the envelope, by applying Weber's (1961) matrix method to fluorescence excitation and emission data.

Intensity of emission was measured at 5-nm intervals over the range 670–770 nm, so that as many as 21 excitation spectra were obtained. The excitation spectrum that corresponded to a particular wavelength in the emission spectrum, was punched onto IBM cards at 2-nm intervals over the range 400–664 nm resulting in 132 points for each excitation spectrum. All 2×2, 3×3, and 4×4 matrices (wavelengths of excitation versus wavelengths of emission) were calculated on an IBM 7090 computer. With this technique, when all 2×2 determinants are zero, there is only one fluorescence form present, when the 3×3's are zero, there are only two fluorescence forms, and so on. Since with experiments made at 77°K none of the 3×3's vanished completely but all the 4×4's did, the data of S. Brody and M. Brody (1963) suggested that three fluorescence components exist at this temperature. One they attributed to the monomer, the 673-nm absorption of which gives rise to fluorescence at 687 nm. They suggested that the dimer absorbs at 705 nm and gives rise to 720-nm fluorescence. As far as the nature of the third fluorescing component is concerned, the following must be considered. Since the longest wavelength absorption

maximum in cells light-adapted for 80 hours is 719 nm (as calculated from
the longest observed fluorescence maximum at 732 nm), at this stage of
development there is present an aggregate of effective size of 3.77 chlorophyll
a molecules; therefore, there must be present some fluorescent tetramer (but a
nonfluorescent trimer, if such an aggregate exists). Another possibility,
not considered in the above work, is that the fluorescence band with maximum at 698 nm (F698) seen clearly for *Chlorella* (M. Brody and S. Brody,
1961; S. Brody and M. Brody, 1963), but very weakly and erratically in
Euglena, arises from another special monomer (see immediately below);
if so, the third fluorescence form would correspond to a tetramer.*

In their 1963 work, S. Brody and M. Brody investigated more thoroughly
in *Euglena* the emission in the blue-green region of the spectrum which had
been noted earlier (M. Brody and Linschitz, 1961; M. Brody and S. Brody,
1961) in various algae and higher plants, and confirmed by Goedheer (1961)
with etiolated bean leaf. They found this emission from the blue-green
region to be especially evident in young cells at low temperature (Figs. 13,
14, and 15). As cells continue to green, and more chlorophyll is formed,
there is a decrease in fluorescence in this region. This emission in *Euglena*
was attributed to carotenoids by M. Brody and Linschitz (1961), on the
basis of similar emission and action spectra for carotenoids extracted from
Euglena (especially antheraxanthin). It should be noted, however, that
Goedheer (1961) attributed similar fluorescence in greening bean leaves to
FMN and DPNH derivatives.

In this same article (1963), S. Brody and M. Brody continued their studies
on the fluorescence band with maximum at 698 nm, which they had originally
reported in 1961 (M. Brody and S. Brody); in this same volume, Kok
(1963), Govindjee (1963), and Bergeron (1963) confirmed the presence of
the 698-nm fluorescence band (F698) in several photosynthetic organisms
at 77°K. Two of these workers, Govindjee and Bergeron, further postulated
that this pigment participates in the primary photochemistry of photosynthesis in system II in a manner analogous to P700 in system I (that is, that the
pigment giving rise to F698 might be a photochemically active chlorophyll,
receiving energy from accessory pigments and "antennae chlorophyll"
of the shorter wavelength system II).

S. Brody and M. Brody (1963) additionally reported that low-temperature
emission spectroscopy of solutions of specially prepared chlorophyll a

* The matrix method described above is subject to the following limitations: in order
for different fluorescence forms to be revealed, they must absorb directly at least several
percent of the light they receive, i.e., all energy cannot be transferred from the monomer.
If under the conditions with which S. Brody and M. Brody (1963) worked, the chlorophyll
giving rise to F698 did not fulfill this requirement, it could not have constituted one of the
fluorescence forms and the interpretation first presented would be most valid.

revealed the presence of a new band. In dilute solution in acetone, benzene, ethanol, ethyl ether or pyridine, emission could be observed around 698 nm. This work was further amplified by S. Brody and Broyde (1963). It was later suggested (Broyde and S. Brody, 1965, 1966) that this band was probably emitted by a modified chlorophyll monomer. S. Brody and M. Brody (1963) also pointed out the similarity of this band to the one observed *in vivo* at 698 nm. If their suggestion about the identity of the bands *in vivo* and *in vitro* is correct, F698 represents a new and unique form of chlorophyll unlike the other bands *in vivo*, which upon extraction yields the ordinary monomer of chlorophyll a. The 698-nm fluorescence was revealed by exhaustively washing crystalline chlorophyll a, containing F698, with petroleum ether which removed small traces of quenching materials. On the other hand, emission of F698 is quenched by nitrobenzene, *p*-phenylenediamine, and the residue of the petroleum ether washings of the crystalline chlorophyll. Because of its method of preparation, S. Brody and M. Brody (1963) suggested that the naturally occurring quencher (probably an isoprenoid quinone) is strongly complexed with the chlorophyll species giving rise to F698 *in vivo*.

The most comprehensive survey of the existence of F698 *in vivo* was made by Goedheer in 1964. He determined fluorescence emission spectra at temperatures between 20° and −196°C for a number of photosynthetic organisms including *Euglena*. Although he confirmed many of the low-temperature fluorescence observations made on this organism by M. Brody and Linschitz (1961) and S. Brody and M. Brody (1963), e.g., that the long-wavelength band at 720 nm is by far the dominant one in older cells, he was not able to observe the shift of this band because his studies were not of a time-dependent nature. Goedheer (1964) showed the presence of the third or middle band (F698) in many organisms in addition to the ones cited above. In young cells of blue-green and red algae the band was strong; in old cultures and in green algae it was weak. In green leaves and chloro plasts, and especially in *Euglena*, the long-wavelength band was much stronger than F698. Despite the fact that Goedheer (1964) also noted that F698 could not be detected in some preparations, his exhaustive comparative survey leaves very little doubt about the ubiquitous nature of F698. For more recent work on this pigment in other organisms and *in vitro*, see Krey and Govindjee (1964) and Cederstrand *et al.* (1966).

In 1965 Goedheer determined fluorescence action spectra with optically dense (absorption equivalent to 100% in peaks) as well as optically thin (absorption less than 50% in peaks) suspensions of *E. gracilis*. For these experiments he used light-grown cells that had been continuously cultured for 14–18 days at about 300 ft-c in air enriched with 5% CO_2 .

For room-temperature action spectra, he monitored total fluorescence emission at wavelengths greater than 705 nm. Figure 16 shows such a room-temperature action spectrum obtained with a thin suspension; there appears in the red band a maximum at 676 nm with a shoulder at 692 nm. The corresponding fluorescence emission spectrum of such algae, measured at room temperature, exhibits a maximum around 705 nm, while the usual 685-nm band is seen merely as a shoulder on its short-wavelength side—a condition reminiscent of the emission spectrum given by French and Elliot (1958; see also Fig. 10). (It should be remembered that the latter workers associated the 705 to 710-nm fluorescence emission band with C_a695.) From Fig. 16 it can also be seen that there is not a marked contribution of

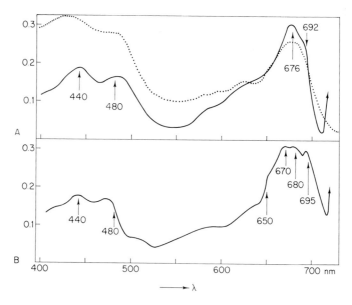

Fig. 16. Upper curves, room-temperature fluorescence action spectrum (unbroken line) and absorption spectrum (dotted line) for a dilute suspension of a 14-day culture of *Euglena*. Lower curve, liquid nitrogen temperature fluorescence action spectrum of dilute cell suspension of a 14-day culture of *Euglena*. Adapted from Goedheer (1965). Reproduced from *Biochim. Biophys. Acta* **102**, 83 (1965).

chlorophyll b to fluorescence at wavelengths more than 705 nm. The broad band with maxima at 440 and 480 nm can be ascribed to carotenoids.

For action spectra determinations with thin suspensions at liquid nitrogen temperature, Goedheer (1965) monitored total fluorescence at wavelengths greater than 720 nm. Such an action spectrum can be seen in Fig. 16; not only are maxima present at 670 and 680 nm, (these species seem to become active in exciting emission at low temperature), but there is also a marked band at 695 nm. The shoulder at 653 nm indicates action of chlorophyll b. In addition to the carotenoid bands seen at room temperature, a new band at 510 nm is seen at low temperature in some cultures.

For action spectrum determinations with dense suspensions at the temperature of liquid nitrogen, Goedheer (1965) monitored total fluorescence at wavelengths greater than 740 nm. Such an action spectrum differs markedly from those given above; it is flat from the blue region up to about 700 nm, where a band (with maximum at 702 nm) begins—this spectrum is very similar to the one given earlier by Butler (1961) for greening bean leaves.

To understand the shape of these action spectra better, the reader should recall the following.

(a) If all pigments transfer their absorbed light energy, with an efficiency approaching 100%, to the fluorescent pigments being monitored, the fluorescence action spectrum corresponds in shape with the absorption spectrum. In the case of dense suspensions, under such conditions, the action spectrum will be flat just as the absorption spectrum is (because absorption by most pigments would approach 100%). Even in dense suspensions, however, there are wavelengths at which light absorption is low—contributions from these particular pigments to fluorescence being not readily observable under most circumstances. When the absorption or action spectra become flat in regions of high optical density, the contributions of pigments of low optical density become apparent. Such is probably the case with the 702-705-nm band, which is not ordinarily seen in the long-wavelength tail of the chlorophyll band.

(b) If a particular fraction of the pigments does not transfer its excitation energy, or transfers it with low yield to the fluorescent pigment being monitored, there will be a lack of correspondence between the action spectrum and the absorption spectrum (as, for example, occurs in the region of carotenoid absorption).

In his 1965 paper, Goedheer gives an important reminder about the dependence of the shape of the fluorescence action spectrum upon the extent of absorption in the cell suspension: "It should be remembered that the exact location of the bands depends on absorption ratios and thus differs with different pigment density" (see Table IV; compare items b, c, and d, and compare also items e and f). Goedheer (1965) showed for other algae, also, that the higher the absorption the further the peaks shift to longer wavelengths.

As far as the positions of the long-wavelength emission maxima are concerned, as noted above, Brody and Brody had shown earlier that these shift during the greening process. In more recent works (S. Brody and M. Brody, 1965; M. Brody and S. Brody, 1966) they gave further information on fluorescence excitation spectra, both for *Euglena* and *in vitro* situations.

From the data of these experiments (Table IV, compare item a with items e and f) it seems as though long-wavelength action spectra peaks may also possibly be shifting slightly with greening.

In their 1965 paper, S. Brody and M. Brody attempted to test the hypothesis that the spectral properties of P700 *in vivo* can be mainly attributed to aggregated chlorophyll (rather than to a special chlorophyll–cytochrome complex as suggested by Butler, 1961) by determining with high concentrations of chlorophyll in various solvents whether or not the 705-nm band could be observed in the low-temperature action spectrum for emission at 736 nm. Similar measurements for fluorescence emitted at 736 nm were made with *E. gracilis* strain Z and a few other photosynthetic organisms. Measurements with ethanol containing high concentrations of chlorophyll a all revealed the presence of this band, as well as other bands that corresponded reasonably well with those observed in light-grown *Euglena* (Table IV).

In their 1966 paper, M. Brody and S. Brody presented data to show that aggregates exist *in vivo* and *in vitro* at room temperature, as well as at the temperature of liquid nitrogen. Action spectra peaks from this work, for *Euglena* and for chlorophyll a in pyridine, are given in Table IV.

These workers concluded from their experiments that position of long-wavelength action spectra peaks vary in solution with concentration of chlorophyll (Table IV; compare especially items h and i), just as they vary in *Euglena* with age (Table IV; compare items a and e), in both because of changing distribution of various populations of different size aggregates.

One other factor may have a small but noticeable effect on the location of peaks in action spectra. As the wavelength of the fluorescence being monitored is shifted toward the red (Table IV; items b and c) there will be an accompanying shift of a few nm to longer wavelengths in the location of the action spectrum peaks. This comes about because the longer wave-length-absorbing forms of chlorophyll also fluoresce at longer wavelengths; as one monitors farther into the red, the longer wavelength components giving rise to this fluorescence will be revealed.

b. Chloroplast Fragments. In 1963, Butler and Baker attempted to separate pigment systems in various photosynthetic organisms, including light-grown var. *bacillaris*, by the method of sonic oscillation and differential centrifugation of chloroplast fragments. On the basis of low-temperature absorption measurements with their smallest fragments (those left in the supernatant of a 173,000-g centrifugation), with which they found the chlorophylls in the same proportion as in intact chloroplasts, and on the basis of low-temperature fluorescence action spectra (for excitation at wavelengths longer than 730 nm) with these same fragments, with which they observed that energy transfer was the same as in intact chloroplasts, these workers concluded that no fractionation of pigments was achieved.

ACTION SPECTRA MAXIMA FOR EXCITING LONG WAVELENGTH FLUORESCENCE

A. In vivo

Wavelength of fluorescence monitored (nm)	Organism and experimental conditions (77°K)	Peak positions in action spectra (nm)						Reference[a]
		650–659 (A_b650)	660–669	670–679 (A_a673)	680–689 (A_a683)	690–699 (A_a695)	>700 (A_a705)	
a. 730	Strain Z, light-adapted for 80 hours	648	667	—	680	—	707	1
b. >705	Light-grown cells, 14-day old, dilute suspension[b]	650	—	676	—	692	—	2
c. >720	Light-grown cells, 14-day old, dilute suspension	653	—	670	680	695	—	2
d. >740	Light-grown cells, 14-day old, concentrated suspension	—	—	—	—	—	702	2
e. 736	Strain Z, light-grown	650	668	—	685	690	708	3
f. 735	Strain Z, light-grown, O.D. >2	652	—	670	685	690	710	4

B. In vitro

Wavelength of fluorescence monitored (nm)	Solvent and concentration of chlorophyll a (77°K)	Peak positions in action spectra (nm)					Reference[a]
		660–669	670–679	680–689	690–699	>700	
g. 736	Pyridine ($6 \times 10^{-2} M$)	662	677	684	—	715	1
h. 736	Ethanol ($6 \times 10^{-2} M$)	668	—	683	—	708	3
i. 736	Ethanol ($8 \times 10^{-2} M$)	—	670	685	—	710	3
j. 735	Pyridine ($8 \times 10^{-2} M$)	—	673	685	—	712	4

[a] Key to references: 1, S. Brody and M. Brody (1963); 2, Goedheer (1965); 3, S. Brody and M. Brody (1965); 4, M. Brody and S. Brody (1966).

[b] Spectrum measured at 293°K.

Their findings were in essential agreement with those of Brown (1961), who observed that the absorption spectrum of her smallest chloroplast fragments (obtained by repeated passage through a needle valve under high pressure, followed by differential centrifugation) was identical with that of whole cells (except in respect to P_a710 in aged cells) (see Section IV,A,1).

S. Brody *et al.* reported in 1965, however, that fractional centrifugation of chloroplast fragments produced by sonication yields samples of various sizes which do differ from each other, both in low-temperature fluorescence emission spectra and in fluorescence excitation spectra. They found that as the size of the chloroplast fragment decreases, so does the intensity of longest wavelength fluorescence (aggregate) relative to that of shortest wavelength fluorescence (monomer). In the case of *E. gracilis* strain Z, reduction in fragment size makes the monomer band much more readily observable that it is in whole chloroplasts or whole cells. S. Brody *et al.* (1965) agree with Butler and Baker (1963) and with Brown (1961) that comparison of whole chloroplasts with chloroplast fragments reveal no pronounced difference in absorption or fluorescence excitation spectra (at either room or liquid nitrogen temperature). However, S. Brody *et al.* (1965) suggest that the techniques used for evaluation are the limiting factors and that, in contrast, low-temperature fluorescence *emission* spectra are capable of revealing the production of fragments that differ in pigment ratio from whole chloroplasts. The latter workers base the efficacy of this method on the difference in concentration of monomer and aggregate, suggesting that fragments are produced that have little (if any) aggregate and that subsequently, the emission spectra will show attentuation of fluorescence from the aggregate and enhancement of fluorescence from the monomer (since little energy sink will be present to divert energy from the monomer).

In 1966 Brown made room-temperature determinations of fluorescence emission on chloroplast fragments from 3-week-old, light-grown cells of *E. gracilis* treated with sodium deoxycholate and separated by centrifugation into fractions containing different proportions of chlorophyll pigments, using a method reported earlier (Brown *et al.*, 1965a,b). Before addition of detergent, the fragments gave a main emission maximum at about 695 nm with a shoulder at 685 nm; the 710-nm maximum, so apparent in whole cells, was barely visible. Detergent was added and after several centrifugations, the final one (at 144,000 g) yielded a supernatant containing only C_a673 and a sediment slightly enriched in chlorophyll b and C_a695 (as determined by measurements with the derivative absorption spectrophotometer). This supernatant shows the fluorescence band at 685 nm as being emitted by C_a673, while the sediment emits the same three fluorescence bands as the original particles (the shoulder on the short-wavelength side is, however, reduced because of the small proportion of C_a673 in this fraction). Brown

(1966) assigns fluorescence bands to the various complexes in agreement with the interpretation given by Goedheer (1964, 1965) (see Section IV,B).

S. Brody *et al.* (1966), using absorption and low-temperature fluorescence spectroscopy, studied the effect of various reagents (some regularly used in chloroplast preparation) on the states of chlorophyll in chloroplast fragments of log-phase, light-grown strain Z. They observed that when aliquots of these fragments (produced by sonication and fractional centrifugation) had salts, sucrose, urea (0.1–4.5 M), or digestive enzymes added to them, or had their pH modified from neutrality, there followed a decrease in the fluorescence yield at 715–736 nm, an increase in the fluorescence yield at 685 nm, and a shift of the long-wavelength emission maximum of about 7 nm toward longer wavelengths.

It was also noted that when intensity of emission from the long-wavelength form was reduced by addition of salt, the presence of F698 became readily apparent. See Fig. 17 for the control compared to three samples containing different concentrations of NaCl. Accompanying these fluorescence changes is the appearance of an absorption band between 705 and 710 nm.

To other samples, buffers were added to achieve pH readings from 2.2 to 10; with these, fluorescence changes similar to those produced by salt, urea (and possibly sucrose) were seen to occur. In concentrated buffer at the lowest pH readings, pheophytin formation probably occurred, as judged by change in color of the fragments to a brownish-green.

Since the kinds of fluorescence changes described above were also produced by the action of digestive enzymes, S. Brody *et al.* (1966) concluded that the effect of these reagents was not a direct one on the chromophore, but a secondary one produced by conformational changes in chloroplast proteins; this conclusion was further supported by their observation that salts added to concentrated solutions of chlorophyll a produced fluorescence alterations opposite to those observed *in vivo*.

The changes in state of chlorophyll brought about by these reagents, particularly the ones that produce ionic or pH effects, are especially interesting in light of recent findings of Jagendorf and co-workers. In 1963, Jagendorf and Hind reported that for several seconds after illumination chloroplasts of higher plants were able to convert ADP, added in the dark, to ATP, probably because of light-induced formation of a large, high-energy pool. That this pool probably represents protons is supported by the findings of Jagendorf and Uribe (1966) that with the establishment of an appropriate pH gradient, ATP can be formed in the absence of illumination. The observations of S. Brody *et al.* (1966) suggest that the various methods used in the preparation and subsequent treatment of chloroplasts bring about modification in the states of chlorophyll which may, in turn, determine the kinds of photochemical or biochemical reactions that can occur.

3. Polarization Measurements

In his monograph, Wolken (1961) points out that *Euglena* chloroplasts show a faint lamination under the phase contrast microscope; in the polarizing microscope they also show both form and intrinsic birefringence. Because of birefringence, a regular ordered arrangement within chloroplasts was

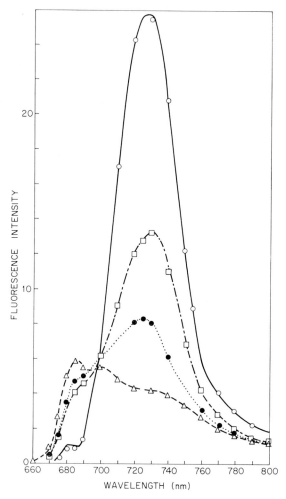

Fig. 17. Fluorescence emission spectra of *Euglena* chloroplast fragments excited at 436 nm, at 77°K. Intensities, while given on an arbitrary scale, are relative to each other. Curves represent fragments treated with different concentrations of NaCl; triangles, 1.5 *M*; solid circles, 0.15 *M*; squares, 0.12 *M*; open circles, control (absence of NaCl). Adapted from S. Brody *et al.* (1966).

postulated long before it was actually observed (Rabinowitch, 1945). Much of this birefringence is form (or morphic) birefringence resulting from the presence of layered arrays (lamellar structure); this type is more readily detected than intrinsic birefringence which arises from molecular order.

Before going on to considerations of orientations of chlorophyll molecules, a little more explanation and definition of terms is needed. The major techniques applied to studies of the orderliness of molecular arrays *in vivo* (as well as to the existence of lamellar structure) are based on these arrays showing some of the anisotropic properties of crystals. These properties arise because of variation in direction of certain characteristics of the molecule; the directions have a definite orientation with respect to each other. This anisotropy may be observed in the following phenomena: (1) dichroism (unequal or polarized absorption in two different directions), (2) birefringence (double refraction), and (3) polarized fluorescence (if molecules are oriented and are excited with nonpolarized light, fluorescence will be polarized; if they are excited with polarized light, fluorescence will also be polarized in the same direction). Optical studies of such phenomena were made by Goedheer (1954, 1955, 1957) on molecules of chlorophyll a oriented in ammonium oleate and on chlorophyll a in chloroplasts of photosynthetic organisms, including *Euglena*, but particularly *Mougeotia*. From a comparison of his *in vitro* studies with those *in vivo*, Goedheer (1954, 1955, 1957) was able to conclude that in the latter, chlorophyll molecules are closely packed in very thin layers, occupying about 10% of the total cross section of the chloroplast (implying lamellar structure), and are probably oriented.

Differences in shapes of dispersion curves of birefringence* of young and old *Mougeotia* were attributed to a deficiency in chlorophyll b in young cells; this dependence of shape on chlorophyll b content was further supported by studies on *Euglena*, in which species *E. gracilis* yielded curves similar to those of old chloroplasts, while curves of species *E. viridis* (which presumably does not contain chlorophyll b) resembled more closely those of young chloroplasts.

Not only did Goedheer conclude from his studies (1954, 1955, 1957) that chlorophyll a was laid down in thin layers, he suggested that the thickness of the layers was about the same magnitude as the thickness of the porphyrin heads of the chlorophyll molecules—about 4 Å. He not only confirmed (see Rabinowitch, 1945) that the planes of the porphyrin heads of the chlorophylls were oriented preferably parallel to the lamellae but, in addition,

---

* Because the disposition of pigments *in vivo* was difficult to determine from traditional measurements of dichroism, Goedheer additionally made measurements of anomalous dispersion of birefringence. This phenomonon is observed as a striking change in birefringence in the wavelength regions enclosing the absorption bands.

he determined experimentally the direction of the oscillators giving rise to the absorption bands in the chlorophyll molecules (see below).

If we refer back to the structure of chlorophyll a and related compounds (Section II) we note that molecules exist that have "round-field" spectra (with no predominant long axis in the conjugated ring system), for example, porphin (Fig. 1a); in such molecules, transitions in two perpendicular oscillator directions lead to the same energy. In contrast, with molecules which have "long-field" spectra, such as tetrahydroporphin (Fig. 1b), the degeneracy is removed and each transition corresponds to a single direction either parallel or perpendicular to the longest axis of the conjugated system. If we compare chlorophyll a (Fig. 1c) with these molecules we note that in symmetry of conjugated ring systems chlorophyll a lies in between them. Goedheer pointed out, however, that the absorption spectrum of chlorophyll a has the main characteristics of a long-field spectrum. Pheophytin a seems to have a slightly more round-field spectrum, whereas the change to chlorophyll b (which involves the conversion of the methyl group of carbon atom 3 into a formyl group, with subsequent addition of a double bond) seems to increase even more the round-field characteristics; in protochlorophyll a (in which a double bond is introduced between carbons 7 and 8), these are even more pronounced.

Goedheer verified experimentally in his polarization studies the direction of the oscillators or transitions giving rise to the absorption bands in the chlorophyll a molecule. [These directions were calculated earlier by Longuet-Higgins et al., (1950).] While both the red and blue transitions would lie in the plane of the porphyrin head (and therefore in the plane of the lamellae) perpendicular to each other, the red oscillator (corresponding to the smaller energy transition) would be along the direction of the short axis of the conjugated ring system.

Those studies of Goedheer, which showed that some orientation of chlorophyll molecules probably does occur, were further extended in the studies of Olson and co-workers (1961, 1962, 1964a,b) on dichroism and polarized fluorescence. For their work they used E. gracilis var. bacillaris. In 1961, Olson et al. concluded that excitation with unpolarized light (at 436 nm) results in fluorescence that is highly polarized at wavelengths of about 700 nm. The chloroplasts viewed on edge showed bright emission when oriented with the long axis of the profile parallel to the vibration plane of the analyzer prism. Their observation of this correspondence between the plane of polarization and the long dimension of the chloroplast supports the suggestion of Goedheer that the plane of the porphyrin head of the emitting chlorophyll molecule lies close to the plane of the lamellae. In 1962, Olson et al. reinforced their earlier finding—that the polarized emission came from a form of chlorophyll which has a longer absorption maximum than 690 nm—with further evidence from dichroism (polarized absorption) studies. In these studies, photographs were taken at 695 nm; and again the chloroplasts viewed on edge were seen to exhibit maximum extinction when observed with the long axis of their profile parallel to the vibration plane of the analyzer prism. At 695 nm Olson *et al.* estimated a dichroic ratio greater than 4, a value much larger than to be expected on the basis of

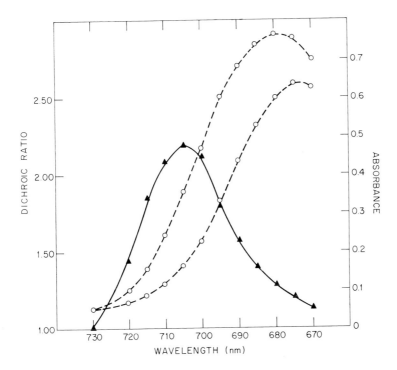

Fig. 18. Spectral dependence of dichroism of a *Euglena* chloroplast, where the upper dashed curve shows the enhanced absorption in the plane of polarization parallel to the lamellar direction; the lower dashed curve shows the enhanced absorption in the plane of polarization perpendicular to the lamellar direction. The ratio of the upper curve to the lower curve—the dichroic ratio—is given by the solid curve. Adapted from Olson *et al.* (1964a). Reproduced from *Biochim. Biophys. Acta* **88**, 318 (1964).

dichroism of lamellar structure. While these workers could not observe or measure dichroism in the 680-nm absorption peak (because of high absorbancy), at shorter wavelengths, 630–660 nm, where extinction is comparable to the 690 to 710-nm region, no dichroism was observed.

In 1961 they made observations on polarized fluorescence which showed that excitation energy was for the most part transferred from the unoriented chlorophyll a molecules to the oriented molecules.* Their 1962 work showed that the absorption band of the oriented chlorophyll (with maximum at 690–710 nm) is strategically located to accept excitation energy by resonance transfer from unoriented chlorophyll a.

An extended study of this dichroism effect was reported by Olson *et al.*

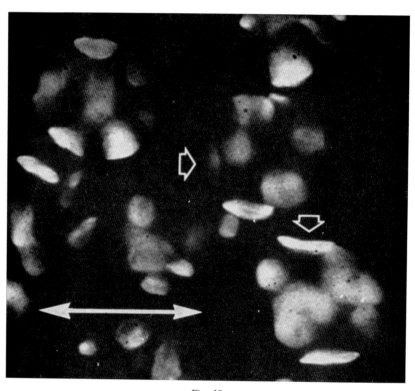

Fig. 19

Figs. 19 and 20. Bifluorescence (polarized fluorescence) of *Euglena* chloroplasts excited by unpolarized light (436 nm) and observed at 716 nm. Plane of polarization is indicated by double-headed arrows. The short, open arrows indicate typical edge-viewed chloroplasts which lie parallel to one of the two orthogonal planes of polarization of the analyzer. Note increased brightness of polarized emission when the chloroplast lies parallel to a polarization plane. Adapted from Olson *et al.* (1964b). Reproduced from *Biochim. Biophys. Acta* **88**, 331. (1964).

* Since these oriented molecules comprise only a few percent of the total chlorophyll, they probably could not satisfy the structural requirements for separation of charges in the first steps of photosynthesis. Such crystalline structure was postulated (Katz, 1949; Calvin, 1961) in theories involving chloroplasts acting as semiconductors (see also Arnold and Sherwood, 1957).

in 1964(a). None could be observed in the chloroplasts of nonintact or damaged cells, but whole chloroplasts extruded into viscous serum albumin retained this property for several hours. The spectral dependence of dichroism was measured and the maximum wavelength was found to be near 705 nm (Fig. 18).

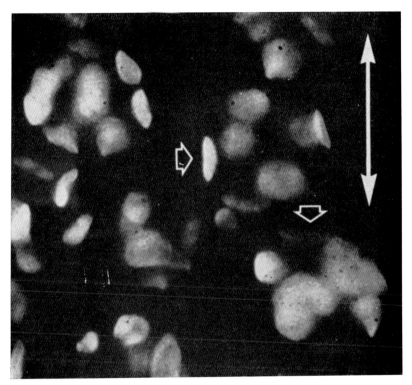

Fig. 20

The spectral properties of the oriented chlorophyll a suggest that this pigment is identical with one or all of the following: French and Brown's C_a695, Kok's P700, the chlorophyll aggregate of Brody and Brody that fluoresces at long wavelengths, and Butler's low-temperature absorption band at 705 nm. Data that may be considered additional support for the third assignment comes from the 1964(b) work of Olson *et al.* who in an extension of their earlier (1961) studies on polarized emission (bifluorescence) of *Euglena* chloroplasts found the band maximum to be near 716 nm (Figs. 19 and 20). [See Clayton (1965) for arguments in support and in conflict with this oriented chlorophyll being P700.]

Olson *et al.* (1964a) further proposed that the particular chlorophyll orientation they observed *in vivo*, in turn, depends upon the orientation of protein macromolecules to which the chromophores are attached, in correspondence with the *in vitro* orientation of chlorophyll molecules in materials such as ammonium oleate (which orient by virtue of their having hydrophilic and hydrophobic poles).

The material discussed in Section IV,A,1–3 is summarized in Table V; included are the different forms of chlorophyll (and derivatives) in *Euglena*.

Table V

FORMS OF CHLOROPHYLL IN *Euglena*

Method used for detection	Wavelength[a]						References[b]
Derivative absorption spectroscopy	C_a673 (670–673)	C_a683 (680–683)	C_a695	—	—	P_a710 (705–710)	*I*(C_a673, 683, 695) *2, 3* (P_a710)
Low-temperature absorption spectroscopy	—	—	—	—	C_a705	—	*4*
Light-induced absorption changes	—	—	—	P700	—	—	*2, 3*
Absorption of oriented chlorophyll	—	—	—	—	705 (690–710)	—	*5*
Low-temperature fluorescence excitation spectroscopy	A_a673 (667–676)	A_a683 (676–685)	A_a695 (690–702)	—	A_a705 (702–710)	—	*6*

[a] Figures in parentheses represent reported range.
[b] Key to references: *1*, French and Elliot (1958); *2*, Brown (1960); *3*, Brown and French (1961); *4*, Butler and Baker (1963); *5*, Olson *et al.* (1962, 1964a); *6*, See Table IV,A.

B. RELATIONSHIPS BETWEEN THE FORMS AND THEIR ROLE IN THE TWO PHOTOACTS OF PHOTOSYNTHESIS

On the basis of his 1964 and 1965 studies, as well as earlier studies (both his and other workers), Goedheer assigned to the chlorophyll a forms seen *in vivo* the fluorescence bands indicated in Table VI. Other interpretations and designations are possible, of course, and some will be presented here.

As far as Goedheer's first assignment, of F685 (system II) to C_a673 is concerned, there can be little disagreement. The correspondence between absorption at 673 nm and fluorescence at 685 nm was recognized long ago, on the basis of fluorescence observations at early stages of greening (when no other chlorophyll is present), and on the basis of analogy with fluorescence of dilute solutions of chlorophyll a *in vitro* (in which only monomer is present).

Table VI

THE DIFFERENT FORMS OF CHLOROPHYLL a IN *Euglena*: THEIR ASSOCIATED EMISSION BANDS AND SYSTEM OF PARTICIPATION IN THE TWO PHOTOACTS OF PHOTOSYNTHESIS

Forms of chlorophyll a	Fluorescence emission bands and system of photosynthesis[a]		Forms of chlorophyll a
	Postulated by Goedheer	Postulated by Brody and Brody	
C_a673	F685; system II	F_M685; system II	C_a673
C_a683	F696; system I		C_a683
C_a695^b	F720; system I	F_A710–740; system I	C_a705^b
C_a705^b	F740; system I		C_a695^b
		F698; system II	

[a] See text (Section IV,B) for details and literature citations.
[b] See text (Section IV, B) for discussion of these forms, including possible identity of C_a695, C_a705, and P700.

Goedheer's third and fourth assignments of F720 (system I) to C_a695, and F740 (system I) to C_a705, respectively, can be considered together. With reference to the fourth assignment the following should be noted. When Goedheer found the long-wavelength emission band with maximum at 740 nm in bean leaves and chlorophyll preparations [in substantiation of the work of Litvin *et al.* (1960) and M. Brody and S. Brody, (1961)] he suggested that its corresponding absorption band is probably located at a wavelength longer than C_a695 which he assumed gave rise to 720-nm fluorescence in algae—on this basis he tentatively assigned F740 to C_a705. In conflict with this designation, however, are the findings of the Brodys and their colleagues (M. Brody and Linschitz, 1961; M. Brody *et al.*, 1965; S. Brody and M. Brody, 1963) who showed, especially with greening *Euglena*, that the long-wavelength emission maximum shifts from about 717 nm in "young cells" to 732–734 nm in 80-hour cells. S. Brody and M. Brody (1963) and M. Brody *et al.* (1965) additionally suggested that the maxima for the corresponding absorption bands must also shift with increase in populations of larger aggregates. With this in mind, it is perhaps better to assign F710–740 to similarly shifting absorption bands ~695–705 nm (see below); in this form the assignment is in essential agreement with one made several years earlier, by S. Brody (1958) and S. Brody and M. Brody (1961a,b, 1963), namely that of F720 (system I) to C_a705.

In Goedheer's second assignment he ascribes fluorescence at 696 nm (F698) to C_a683, placing them also in system I. At variance with this assignment, however, are the observations that emission at 698 nm *in vivo* is of low intensity and that the form of chlorophyll a designated C_a683 constitutes about half the total chlorophyll. Especially if F698 *in vivo* is identical with F698 *in vitro*, Goedheer's assignment is questionable, because this special monomeric form of chlorophyll is present in very low concentration *in vivo* [probably constituting considerably less than 5% of the total; see S. Brody and M. Brody (1963); Broyde and S. Brody (1966)].

We will now go on to a different assignment of fluorescence emission to C_a683, recognizing that this leaves no absorption band assignment to F698 *in vivo*; hopefully one will be made in the near future. As noted above, several other workers (S. Brody and M. Brody, 1963; Bergeron, 1963; Govindjee, 1963) attributed F698 to system II, suggesting that the absorption band giving rise to it acts as does P700 in system I.*

In considering another assignment of fluorescence to C_a683, it should be recalled that Krasnovsky and Kosobutskaja (1952) attributed this long-wavelength absorption band to aggregation. S. Brody and M. Brody (1961b, see *their* Figs. 3 and 4; 1963) further suggested that both C_a683 and C_a705 represent absorption bands of long-wavelength fluorescing aggregates, and assigned these bands to system I. That such a relationship exists, and further, that energy absorbed by C_a683 is transferred to C_a705 (from which it may be lost as fluorescence at ~720 nm) is based on four observations. The first of these was made by S. Brody and M. Brody (1963, 1965) and M. Brody and S. Brody (1966)—who found that bands corresponding to C_a683 and C_a705 appear in action spectra for exciting emission from the aggregate *in vivo* and *in vitro* (this observation can, however, be interpreted simply in terms of energy transfer between two different species of chlorophyll). The second observation is that the aggregate (at least *in vitro*) has two overlapping absorption bands in the red region of the spectrum (S. Brody and M. Brody, 1961b; Broyde *et al.*, 1968). Third, Butler (1965) found only a symmetrical absorption band at 673 nm with dark-grown bean leaves that had been illuminated for 2 hours; after this time both chlorophyll b and C_a683 appeared (absorption spectroscopy) and the low-temperature

---

* It is possible, of course, that two separate and distinct "reaction centers" of chlorophyll do not exist (Franck and Rosenberg, 1964); the photochemical reactions would then occur alternately at the same reaction site (perhaps P700).

fluorescence excitation spectrum showed a band with maximum at 705 nm. Fourth, the experiments of Brown *et al.* (1965a,b) with detergent have shown that C_a673 comes down on one particle, while C_a683 and C_a695 (see below) come down together on another.

Relationships between the different forms of chlorophyll a and postulates about their associated emission bands and participation in the two photoacts of photosynthesis, as discussed in this Section, are summarized in Table VI.

The reader may recall that P_a710 is found in old cultures of *Euglena*, and that it has been variously attributed to pheophytin, pheophorbides, and related degradation products of chlorophyll. Information on emission from cells containing P_a710, especially at low temperatures, is scanty and no special bands have been assigned to it. Although fluorescence of pheophytin and related compounds has been reported *in vitro* (Smith and Benitez, 1955), comparable studies have not been made *in vivo*.

Because of its spectral properties P_a710 could be an extremely efficient and probably wasteful sink for either system I or system II energy. Fortunately, "downhill" transfer of energy depends on more than just satisfying spectral requirements and, in addition, certain spatial requisites exist; since fluorescence bands have not been attributed to P_a710 *in vivo*, these may not be met.

Butler and Baker (1963) found evidence for the existence of C_a705 as well as C_a695 in *Euglena*. On the basis of additional observations, they suggested that C_a695 is not generally found in all plants, as is C_a705. They further implied that C_a705 and C_a695 are identical in *Euglena*; because they had seen the 705-nm absorption band only at low temperature, they reasoned that it might have undergone a shift from 695 nm at room temperature. However, since recent room-temperature measurements with *Euglena* revealed the presence of the 705-nm band in the spectrum for exciting long-wavelength fluorescence (M. Brody and S. Brody, 1966), it seems likely that factors additional to temperature determine peak position. Data from several experiments are given in Table IV, from which it may be seen that in *Euglena* at 77°K, fluorescence action spectra reveal the presence of the 695-nm band or the 705-nm band or both. (In accordance with the pigment designations used in the present work, these excitation or action spectra maxima are denoted as A_a695, A_a705, etc.) Since it may well be that C_a695 and C_a705 are interconvertible or identical forms, we might ask what relationship, if any, these two forms bear to P700. One possibility is that all three are identical. (Recall the experiments made in collaboration with Kok by Brown in 1960 and Brown and French in 1961, in which evidence was given to show that P700 and C_a695 are the same.) However, while at 77°K P700 is bleached by light, C_a705 is not (Kok, 1963). On the other hand, algal mutants, which lack C_a705 as determined at low temperature (Butler and

Bishop, 1963), also do not show the light-induced absorption change in P700 at room temperature.

We should now consider some consequences of postulating relationships between the "different" long-wavelength absorbing forms of chlorophyll a. If they are identical (i.e., $C_a 695 = C_a 705 = P700$), these bands plus $C_a 683$ may represent one aggregate and therefore other aggregates having different (but not yet determined) absorption maxima must exist; shifts in populations of these could give rise to F710–F740. It is also possible that these long-wavelength forms represent the same size aggregate but that some molecules experience special orientations or environments that yield small changes in their spectral properties, leading to the F710–F740 shift. (Some, for example, might remain relatively amorphous while others take on a more orderly semicrystalline array.)

On the other hand, the three long-wavelength bands might correspond to different size aggregates (with $C_a 683$ representing the shorter wavelength absorption partner of one or all); changes in population of these could then lead to the F710–F740 shift.

In the above considerations all bands cited have been designated aggregates. While much data have been given in support of this stand, it should be additionally noted that aggregation might be expected to result in those semicrystalline properties that give rise to long-wavelength polarized emission.

As can be judged from this Section (IV,A,B), the question about the number of forms of chlorophyll a *in vivo* and their functions in photosynthesis is far from resolved, in spite of much progress from recent experiments (many of which were made with *Euglena*).

V. Concentration of Chlorophyll a

A. In the Chloroplast—Determination Based on Electron Microscopy

In his monograph, Wolken (1961) gave an estimate of the concentration of chlorophyll a in the chloroplast of log-phase, light-grown *E. gracilis* var. *bacillaris*. By extraction, he first determined the number of chlorophyll molecules per cell to be 5.1×10^9; he then divided this by 5 (his figure for the average number of chloroplasts per cell from electron microscope studies) to yield a value of 1.02×10^9 for the number of chlorophyll molecules per chloroplast. Measurements of chloroplast dimensions allowed him to calculate an average value of 6.6×10^{-11} ml for the volume of the chloroplast. Dividing the number of chlorophyll molecules per chloroplast by the number of milliliters per chloroplast yielded the number of chlorophyll molecules per milliliter; conversion to moles per liter resulted in a concentration of 0.025 for chlorophyll distributed homogeneously in the chloroplast.

B. On the Lamellae—Determination Based on Fluorescence Spectroscopy

M. Brody et al. (1965), using E. gracilis strain Z, determined chlorophyll concentration on the lamellae at various periods of time during greening. They used a method entirely different from Wolken's (1961), one which involved no estimate of chloroplast number or volume or lamella number, and which was based on low-temperature fluorescence emission spectroscopy.

Dark-grown cells, harvested in the log phase of growth, were allowed to adapt in light of about 100 ft-c, for periods up to 80 hours. Most of the studies of M. Brody et al. (1965) were brought to an end at this time, when cells had a full complement of lamellae, since under their experimental conditions pheophytin formation was found to begin at approximately 100 hours (at the end of the log period of growth). Nevertheless, they did compare the spectral properties of greening cells to cells grown continuously in the light.

For the most part, the calculations and conclusions presented in the paper of M. Brody et al., (1965) were based on observations of the two major emission bands seen in Euglena at 77°K, the shortest and longest ones—F685 and F715-740. F698, the middle band, was not observed in greening cells or was observed only erratically.

It should be noted that with cells light-adapted for 80 hours or less, no band at 695 nm (A_a695) is found in the action spectrum for sensitizing long-wavelength fluorescence (Fig. 11), in agreement with the observation that C_a695 is only present in aged cells (Section IV,A,1).

In this study (in which an IBM 1620 computer was used to automatically correct the data for spectral response of the fluorescence apparatus and aid in many of the calculations), three major trends were observed with greening cells. First, the increase in fluorescence of the long-wavelength form compared to the short-wavelength form (F_A/F_M) (Fig. 21) was seen to generate an S-shaped curve (Fig. 22) with a steep, steplike rise at about 10 hours (see Table VII). The significance of this relationship was already discussed in Section III,C.

The second trend, also noted earlier (S. Brody and M. Brody, 1963, and Section IV,A,2,a), is that although the long-wavelength emission maximum is first observed at 717 nm, it shifts progressively toward longer wavelengths with greening, reaching a final position of 734 nm in 80-hour cells (Fig. 24). These workers also noticed a similar shift in long-wavelength (low-temperature) emission maximum with increasing concentration of chlorophyll

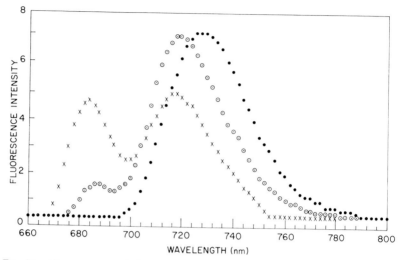

Fig. 21. Fluorescence emission spectra of *Euglena* at 77°K, excited at 436 nm; cells light-adapted for various periods of time. Six-hour curve given by crosses, 17-hour curve given by open (dot-containing) circles, 63-hour curve given by solid circles. Adapted from M. Brody *et al.* (1965).

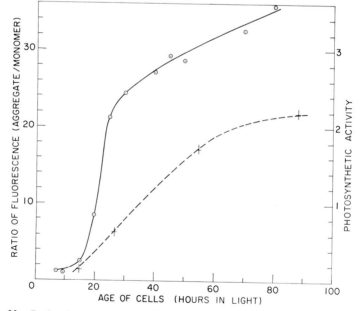

Fig. 22. Ratio of long-wavelength (F_A) to short-wavelength (F_M) fluorescence at 77°K (solid line), and photosynthetic activity (broken line) of dark-grown *Euglena* as functions of hours in the light. Adapted from M. Brody *et al.* (1965).

in ethanol (Fig. 24). The limiting value of 734 nm *in vivo* at 80 hours occurs when about 1.1×10^9 chlorophyll molecules per cell are found. Since formation of lamellae is complete between 72 and 95 hours, M. Brody *et al.* (1965) suggested that the size and geometry of the fluorescent aggregate has reached its final value at this time. However, if one compares F_A/F_M for 80-hour cells and for cells grown continuously in the light, values of 35 and 257 are found, respectively. It would be interesting to know if this 7.5-fold difference in F_A/F_M originates from increase in chlorophyll concentration or from increase in efficiency of energy transfer to the aggregate. A 2.7-fold increase in "equivalent molar chlorophyll concentration" (see below) could account for this difference, but analytical determination of total chlorophyll content per cell indicated that only a 2.3-fold increase actually occurred. Therefore, while most of the increase in F_A/F_M was accounted for by concentration changes, the remainder was attributed to increased efficiency of energy transfer between monomeric and aggregated states.

In order to determine chlorophyll a concentration on the lamellae, M. Brody *et al.* (1965) made use of a reference curve which relates F_A/F_M, at 77°K, to concentration of chlorophyll in ethanol. They then assumed that F_A/F_M *in vivo* are the same at similar concentrations of chlorophyll a, and

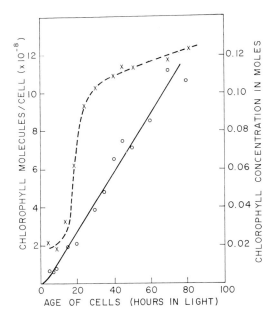

Fig. 23. Total number of chlorophyll molecules per cell (solid line) and "equivalent concentration" of chlorophyll *in vivo* (broken line) as functions of the number of hours dark-grown *Euglena* have been in the light. Adapted from M. Brody *et al.* (1965).

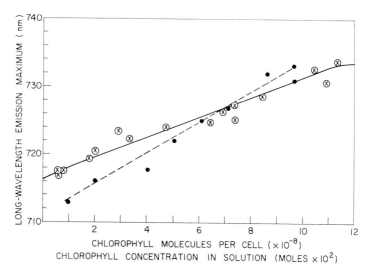

Fig. 24. Long-wavelength emission maximum, at 77°K, as a function of chlorophyll a concentration in ethanolic solution (broken line, solid circles) and as a function of total number of chlorophyll molecules per cell in *Euglena* (solid line, circles with crosses). Emission sensitized at 435 nm. Adapted from M. Brody *et al.* (1965).

Table VII

CALCULATIONS FOR TOTAL LAMELLAR AREA AS A FUNCTION OF AGE IN *E. gracilis*[a]

Age (hours)	Total chl. molecules per cell × 10⁻⁸	Ratio fluor. (F_A/F_M)	Equivalent molar conc. in solution	Equivalent unit area per molecule (Å²)	Total lamellar area (cm² × 10⁵)
5	0.65	1.47	0.022	2350	1.5
7	0.63	1.32	0.022	2350	1.5
9	0.81	1.01	0.020	2490	2.0
15	1.89	2.45	0.033	1770	3.34
20	2.02	8.49	0.062	1170	2.37
25	3.39	20.1	0.094	892	3.02
30	3.95	24.5	0.103	840	3.32
40	6.51	27.1	0.108	814	5.30
45	7.49	29.4	0.113	772	5.79
50	7.09	28.7	0.112	792	5.61
70	11.1	32.7	0.119	762	8.45
80	10.6	35.0	0.123	745	7.9
∞[b]	25	257	0.334	381	9.5

[a] From M. Brody *et al.* (1965).
[b] Light-grown cells.

compared F_A/F_M in vivo, at 77°K, to the reference curve in order to obtain an "equivalent concentration" for chlorophyll in vivo. Figure 23 shows equivalent chlorophyll concentration in moles (derived from the reference curve) for greening Euglena cells. It also can be seen from Table VII that the equivalent molar concentration on the first lamella (formed between 5 and 9 hours) is about 0.020 M; in 80-hour cells it is 0.123 M; and in cells continuously cultured in light it is 0.334 M.

The third trend noted in this work was the tendency for Euglena to develop higher concentrations of chlorophyll a on the lamellae than other photosynthetic organisms studied (based on the observation that F_A/F_M was highest in this form). M. Brody et al. (1965) suggested that although the factors that limit chlorophyll synthesis in vivo are unknown, it would be reasonable to assume that in Euglena some concentration-dependent feedback mechanism is either absent or imperfect (limitation of concentration perhaps being determined by rate of photodestruction or restriction of lamellar area).

C. ADDITIONAL CHLOROPLAST PARAMETERS—CALCULATIONS BASED ON CHLOROPHYLL CONCENTRATION AS DETERMINED FROM FLUORESCENCE EMISSION SPECTROSCOPY AND OTHER TECHNIQUES

1. Lamellar Area Occupied by a Single Chlorophyll Molecule and Total Lamellar Area as Functions of Greening

M. Brody et al. (1965) used their data on equivalent molar concentration (expressed as moles per liter) to determine chlorophyll concentration per unit area of lamellae (moles per square centimeter), from which they calculated the area occupied by a single chlorophyll molecule (Å² per molecule). For cells grown continuously in the light, they calculated an area of 381 Å² for each chlorophyll molecule. Their calculations were based on the assumption that chlorophyll on the lamellae is similar to a two-dimensional solution.

The product of the total number of chlorophyll molecules per cell (Fig. 23) and the area occupied per molecule equals total lamellar area per cell (cm² × 10⁻⁵). Table VII shows the results of these calculations, based on fluorescence data from cells in various stages of greening.

Wolken (1961) had given a value of 222 Å² for the lamellar area occupied by a single chlorophyll molecule. His calculations of area were based on electron microscope studies using the following equation

$$A = \frac{8nd^2}{\pi N}$$

where n = the number of dense layers (lamellae), taken by him to be 21 (he assumed there are $2n$ interfaces available for chlorophyll molecules);

d = length (diameter) of chloroplast (6.5 μ); and N is the average number of chlorophyll molecules per chloroplast (1.02 $\times$ 10⁹), based on his estimate of 5 chloroplasts per cell. Agreement between, the value of 381 Å² found by M. Brody *et al.* (1965) and Wolken's (1961) value of 222 Å² would be even better if the newer figure of 12 lamellae and 10 chloroplasts [as given in the electron microscope studies of Gibbs (1960) and Ben-Shaul *et al.* (1964)] were substituted in Wolken's calculations, i.e., such a substitution increases the area given by Wolken to 254 Å².

2. Number of Lamellae in an Idealized Chloroplast

M. Brody *et al.* (1965) found the total lamellar area in light-grown cells to be 9.5 $\times$ 10⁻⁵ cm² per cell (Table VII). Using this area in Wolken's formula, in conjunction with the newer value of 10 chloroplasts per cell, these workers calculated the number of lamellae in the "idealized" chloroplast of light-grown cells to be about 9. In this idealized situation, lamellae are circular and equal in size; if lamellae are elliptical or incised, the actual number would be greater than nine. Also, if pheophytin or some other substance were contributing to long-wavelength fluorescence in light-grown cells, the number would again be larger.

That this indirect technique of M. Brody *et al.* (1965) based on fluorescence emission leads to reasonable results, can be seen, for example, in a comparison of their data on number of lamellae with recent electron microscope findings—which yield 8 to 16 lamellae per chloroplast (Ben-Shaul *et al.*, 1964; Gibbs, 1960).

3. Number of Proplastids in Dark-Grown Cells

Again using their data (Table VII) for total lamellar area in greening cells, M. Brody *et al.* (1965) extrapolated the function to time zero. They did this in order to deduce several characteristics of the proplastids, recognizing, however, that at time zero neither chlorophyll or lamellae exist. This extrapolation leads to a lamellar area of 0.85 $\times$ 10⁻⁵ cm². In order to calculate the average number of proplastids, n, present at time zero, they took as the area of the first lamella the total surface area of the inner membrane of the spherical proplastid, the diameter of which was given as 1.3 μ by Ben-Shaul *et al.* (1964). Using the equation n $\times$ area of one proplastid $\times$ 2 = lamellar area at time zero, n was found to be:

$$\frac{0.85 \times 10^{-5} \text{ cm}^2 \times 10^8 \text{ cm}^2}{2\pi(1.3)^2} = 80$$

This is about double the number determined by Lyman *et al.* (1961) and Epstein and Schiff (1961) on the basis of photoinactivation experiments and fluorescence microscopy. In the work of Epstein and Schiff (1961) it is implicitly assumed that, at minimum, one ultraviolet-labile chlorophyll precursor and one fluorescent entity are present in each proplastid. On the basis of their own findings, M. Brody *et al.* (1965) suggest the possibility that there exist proplastids lacking a fluorescent entity or chlorophyll precursor; they further propose that such "deficient" proplastids could contribute to chloroplast development by coalescing with "complete" proplastids.

Since the estimate of proplastid number given by M. Brody *et al.* (1965) (unlike that of Epstein and Schiff, 1961) is based on effective chlorophyll concentration and related lamellar size, it is of interest to note that, unknown to M. Brody *et al.* (1965) at the time of their writing, two other workers had re-estimated target numbers in *E. gracilis* to give values higher than those reported by Epstein and Schiff—values much closer to the one reported for proplastids by M. Brody *et al.* (1965). In 1963, Cook gave figures of about 60 to 80 (there being some dependence on time in cell division cycle), and Petropulos (1964) suggested that the data of Lyman *et al.* (1961) could be reinterpreted to give proplastid numbers of approximately 60 for dark-grown cells and about 25 for light-grown cells. Although it is evident that more work must be done in this area, it is probably safe to assume that the studies of Schiff and co-workers have set a lower limit of about 30 to 40 on the number of proplastids. (See also Chapter 10)

4. Number of Chlorophyll-Bearing Discs per Lamella

Epstein and Schiff (1961) and Ben-Shaul *et al.* (1964) had given a model for lamellae formation, which involves the blebing-off of discs from the inner membrane of the proplastid followed by fusion of these discs to yield lamellae. M. Brody *et al.* (1965) used this model, in conjunction with their data on the lamellar area of cells light-adapted for 5–7 hours (Table VII), to calculate the number of discs comprising the first lamella. To do this they took 1.5×10^{-5} cm² for the average value of total lamellar area and divided it by 2 (since at this stage of development both surfaces probably have chlorophyll deposited on them); from the data of Ben-Shaul *et al.* (1964) on 5-hour cells they took 2.55 μ for proplastid diameter and 30 to 40 as the number of chlorophyll-forming proplastids. They then calculated the number of discs, D, by setting

$$\frac{1.5 \times 10^{-5} \text{ cm}^2}{2} = D(30 \text{ to } 40) \, \pi(1.27)^2 \times 10^{-8} \text{ cm}^2$$

with the result that D was found to be equal to 3.6 to 4.8. M. Brody *et al.* (1965) concluded that the first lamella is composed of about four discs on which chlorophyll is deposited on all surfaces. The value of D observed in electron microscope studies (Ben-Shaul *et al.*, 1964) is 3.6. M. Brody *et al.* (1965) also give their interpretation of how young chlorophyll-bearing discs in *Euglena* are converted into the lamellae characteristic of the mature state. They suggest that if these discs do not undergo fusion, but instead bifurcate to form lamellae, only the outer lamellae surfaces would be covered with chlorophyll, as shown in Fig. 25. Gibbs (1960) and also Moriber *et al.* (1963) demonstrated that the lamellae reported by Wolken (1961) are actually composed of several (usually four) discs. However, the reasonable agreement between the value of 9.5×10^{-5} cm^2 given by M. Brody *et al.* (1965) for total lamellar area (in which no estimate of chloroplast or lamellar number is involved), and that given by Wolken (1961), 11×10^{-5} cm^2, seems to suggest that even if each one of Wolken's dense bands is composed of two to five discs the preponderance of chlorophyll in mature *Euglena* is located only on the outer surfaces of what Wolken called a lamella.

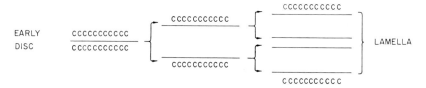

Fig. 25. A diagramatic interpretation of how the early chlorophyll-bearing discs in *Euglena* give rise to lamellae as seen in the mature state; if the discs do not fuse, but instead bifurcate, to form the lamellae, only the outer surfaces of the lamellae will be covered with chlorophyll as shown. Adapted from M. Brody *et al.* (1965).

VI. Additional Remarks

In addition to the literature already cited, the following recent books, review articles, and symposia reports contain material pertainent to the subject of this chapter: Clayton, 1963; Duysens, 1964; Kok, 1965; Olson, 1963.

After the present literature survey was completed, a monograph, "The Chlorophylls" was published Vernon and Seeley, 1966; many of its chapters contain material relevant to the subject of the present chapter, however, the work of the following contributors should be particularly called to the readers attention: S. Aronoff, p. 3; H. H. Strain and W. A. Svec, p. 22; A. S. Holt, p. 111; J. C. Goedheer, p. 147, 399; W. L. Butler, p. 343; N. K. Boardman, p. 437; L. Bogorad, p. 481; M. B. Allen, p. 511; L. P. Vernon and B. Ke, p. 569; R. K. Clayton, p. 609.

A similar situation exists in respect to *Current Topics in Bioenergetics* (Sanadi, 1966); here the reader is referred to the chapters by W. L. Butler, p. 49 and B. Kok and G. Cheniae, p. 2. Also published later was a paper by Murata *et al.* (1966). In this work, Murata *et al.* report their studies of low-temperature fluorescence emission and action spectra of chlorophyll a in several photosynthetic organisms including *E. gracilis*. From these, they assign to the different forms of chlorophyll a *in vivo* fluorescence emission bands (and systems of participation in photosynthesis) different from those of Goedheer (1964, 1965) (and Brown, 1960), but in essential agreement with those of Brody and Brody (1963) (see Section IV,B).

References

Albers, V. M., and Knorr, H. V. (1937). *Plant Physiol.* **12**, 833.
Allen, M. B., French, C. S., and Brown, J. S. (1960). *In* "Comparative Biochemistry of Photoreactive Systems" (M. B. Allen, ed.), p. 33. Academic Press, New York.
Arnold, W., and Sherwood, H. K. (1957). *Proc. Natl. Acad. Sci. U.S.* **43**, 105.
Ben-Shaul, Y., Schiff, J. A., and Epstein, H. T. (1964). *Plant Physiol.* **39**, 231.
Ben-Shaul, Y., Epstein, H. T., and Schiff, J. A. (1965). *Can. J. Botany* **43**, 129.
Bergeron, J. A. (1963). *In* "Photosynthetic Mechanisms in Green Plants," Publ. 1145, p. 527. Natl. Acad. Sci—Natl. Res. Council. Washington, D. C.
Boardman, N. K., and Anderson, J. M. (1964). *Nature* **203**, 166.
Bogorad, L. (1960). *In* "Comparative Biochemistry of Photoreactive Systems" (M. B. Allen, ed.), p. 227. Academic Press, New York.
Bogorad, L. (1962). *In* "The Physiology and Biochemistry of the Algae" (R. A. Lewin, ed.), p. 385. Academic Press, New York.
Bogorad, L. (1965). *In* "The Chemistry and Biochemistry of Plant Pigments" (T. W. Goodwin, ed.), Part I, p. 29. Academic Press, New York.
Brawerman, G., and Chargaff, E. (1959). *Biochim. Biophys. Acta* **31**, 178.
Bril, C. (1965). *Carnegie Inst. Wash. Yrbook* **64**, 370.
Brody, M., and Brody, S. (1961). *Abstr. 5th Intern. Congr. Biochem., Moscow, 1961*, p. 443.
Brody, M., and Brody, S. (1962). *In* "The Physiology and Biochemistry of the Algae" (R. A. Lewin, ed.), p. 3. Academic Press, New York.
Brody, M., and Brody, S. (1966). *Biochim. Biophys. Acta* **112**, 54.
Brody, M., and Emerson, R. (1959a). *Am. J. Botany* **46**, 433.
Brody, M., and Emerson, R. (1959b). *J. Gen. Physiol.* **43**, 251.
Brody, M., and Linschitz, H. (1961). *Science* **133**, 705.
Brody, M., Brody, S., and Levine, J. H. (1965). *J. Protozool.* **12**, 465.
Brody, S. (1958). *Science* **128**, 838.
Brody, S. (1964a). *J. Theoret. Biol.* **7**, 352.
Brody, S. (1964b). *Nature* **204**, 470.
Brody, S., and Brody, M. (1961a). *Nature* **189**, 547.
Brody, S., and Brody, M. (1961b). *Biochim. Biophys. Acta* **54**, 495.
Brody, S., and Brody, M. (1961c). *Arch. Biochem. Biophys.* **95**, 521.
Brody, S., and Brody, M. (1963). *In* "Photosynthetic Mechanisms in Green Plants," Publ. 1145, p. 455. Natl. Acad. Sci.—Natl. Res. Council, Washington, D. C.

Brody, S., and Brody, M. (1965). *Arch. Biochem. Biophys.* **110**, 583.
Brody, S., and Broyde, S. B. (1963). *Nature* **199**, 1097.
Brody, S., Brody, M., and Levine, J. H. (1965). *Biochim. Biophys. Acta* **94**, 310.
Brody, S., Ziegelmair, C. A., Samuels, A., and Brody, M. (1966). *Plant Physiol.* **41**, 1709.
Brown, J. S. (1959). *Carnegie Inst. Wash. Yrbook* **58**, 331.
Brown, J. S. (1960). *Carnegie Inst. Wash. Yrbook* **59**, 330.
Brown, J. S. (1961). *Carnegie Inst. Wash. Yrbook* **60**, 366.
Brown, J. S. (1962). *Carnegie Inst. Wash. Yrbook* **61**, 352.
Brown, J. S. (1963a). *In* "La Photosynthese," Publ. 119, p. 377. C.N.R.S., Paris.
Brown, J. S. (1963b). *Photochem. Photobiol.* **2**, 159.
Brown, J. S. (1963c). *Biochim. Biophys. Acta* **75**, 299.
Brown, J. S. (1963d). *Carnegie Inst. Wash. Yrbook* **62**, 361.
Brown, J. S. (1964). *Carnegie Inst. Wash. Yrbook* **63**, 480.
Brown, J. S. (1966). *Biochim. Biophys. Acta* **120**, 305.
Brown, J. S., and Bril, C. (1965). *Carnegie Inst. Wash. Yrbook* **64**, 373.
Brown, J. S., and Duranton, J. (1964). *Biochim. Biophys. Acta* **79**, 209.
Brown, J. S., and French, C. S. (1961). *Biophys. J.* **1**, 539.
Brown, J. S., Bril, C., and Urbach, W. (1965a). *Carnegie Inst. Wash. Yrbook* **64**, 374.
Brown, J. S., Bril, C., and Urbach, W. (1965b). *Plant Physiol.* **40**, 1086.
Broyde, S. B., and Brody, S. (1965). *Biochem. Biophys. Res. Commun.* **19**, 444.
Broyde, S. B., and Brody, S. (1966). *Biophys. J.* **6**, 353.
Broyde, S. B., Brody, S., and Brody, M. (1968). *Biochim. Biophys. Acta* **153**, 183.
Bruinsma, J. (1963). *Photochem. Photobiol.* **2**, 241.
Butler, W. L. (1961). *Arch. Biochem. Biophys.* **93**, 413.
Butler, W. L. (1962). *Biochim. Biophys. Acta* **64**, 309.
Butler, W. L. (1965). *Biochim. Biophys. Acta* **102**, 1.
Butler, W. L., and Baker, J. E. (1963). *Biochim. Biophys. Acta* **66**, 206.
Butler, W. L., and Bishop, N. I. (1963). *In* "Photosynthetic Mechanisms in Green Plants," Publ. 1145, p. 91. Natl. Acad. Sci.—Natl. Res. Council, Washington, D.C.
Butler, W. L., and Briggs, W. R. (1966). *Biochim. Biophys. Acta* **112**, 45.
Butler, W. L., and Norris, K. H. (1960). *Arch. Biochem. Biophys.* **87**, 31.
Calvin, M. (1961). *J. Theoret. Biol.* **1**, 258.
Cederstrand, C. N., Rabinowitch, E. I., and Govindjee (1966). *Biochim. Biophys. Acta* **120**, 247.
Chance, B., and Sager, R. (1957). *Plant Physiol.* **32**, 548.
Clayton, R. K. (1963). *Ann. Rev. Plant Physiol.* **14**, 159.
Clayton, R. K. (1965). "Molecular Physics in Photosynthesis." Ginn (Blaisdell), Boston, Massachusetts.
Cohen-Bazire, G., and Stanier, R. Y. (1958). *Nature* **181**, 250.
Cook, J. R. (1963). *Photochem. Photobiol.* **2**, 407.
Dutton, H. L., and Manning, W. M. (1941). *Am. J. Botany* **28**, 516.
Dutton, H. L., Manning, W. M., and Duggar, B. M. (1943). *J. Phys. Chem.* **47**, 308.
Duysens, L. N. M. (1951). *Nature* **168**, 548.
Duysens, L. N. M. (1952). Ph. D. Thesis, Utrecht, The Netherlands.
Duysens, L. N. M. (1961). *In* "Progress in Photobiology"; Proc. 3rd Intern. Congr. Photobiol., Copenhagen, 1960, (B. C. Christiensen and B. Buchmann, eds.), p. 135.
Duysens, L. N. M. (1964). *Progr. Biophys.* **14**, 1.
Duysens, L. N. M., and Amesz, J. (1962). *Biochim. Biophys. Acta* **64**, 243.
Emerson, R. (1958). *Ann. Rev. Plant Physiol.* **9**, 1.
Emerson, R., and Arnold, W. (1932). *J. Gen. Physiol.* **15**, 391.

Emerson, R., and Lewis, C. M. (1942). *J. Gen. Physiol.* **25**, 579.

Emerson, R., and Lewis, C. M. (1943). *Am. J. Botany* **30**, 165.

Emerson, R., Chalmers, R., Cederstrand, C. N., and Brody, M. (1956). *Abstr. Natl. Acad. Sci., Science* **123**, 676.

Emerson, R., Chalmers, R., and Cederstrand, C. (1957). *Proc. Natl. Acad. Sci. U.S.* **43**, 133.

Epstein, H. T., and Schiff, J. A. (1961). *J. Protozool.* **8**, 427.

Fischer, H. (1940). *Naturwissenschaften* **28**, 401.

Franck, J. (1955). *Dædalus* **86**, 17.

Franck, J. (1958). *Proc. Natl. Acad. Sci. U.S.* **44**, 941.

Franck, J., and Rosenberg, J. (1964). *J. Theoret. Biol.* **7**, 276.

Frei, Y. F. (1960). *Carnegie Inst. Wash. Yrbook* **59**, 333.

Frei, Y. F. (1962). *Biochim. Biophys. Acta* **57**, 82.

French, C. S. (1956). *Carnegie Inst. Wash. Yrbook* **55**, 251.

French, C. S. (1957). *Proc. Instr. Soc. Am., Northern Calif. Sect., Berkeley* p. 83.

French, C. S. (1958a). *In* "Photobiology, Biology Colloquium" (R. W. Newburgh, ed.), p. 52. Oregon State College Press, Corvallis, Oregon.

French, C. S. (1958b). *Brookhaven Symp. Biol.* **11**, 65.

French, C. S. (1960a). *In* "Handbuch der Pflanzenphysiologie" (W. Ruhland, ed.), Vol. V, Part 1, p. 252. Springer, Berlin.

French, C. S. (1960b). *Carnegie Inst. Wash. Yrbook* **59**, 309.

French, C. S., and Elliot, R. F. (1958). *Carnegie Inst. Wash. Yrbook* **57**, 278.

French, C. S., and Harper, G. E. (1957). *Carnegie Inst. Wash. Yrbook* **56**, 281.

French, C. S., Brown, J. S., Allen, M. B., and Elliot, R. F. (1959). *Carnegie Inst. Wash. Yrbook* **58**, 327.

Gibbs, S. P. (1960). *J. Ultrastruct. Res.* **4**, 127.

Godnev, T. N., Rotfarb, R. M., and Akulovich, N. K. (1963). *Photochem. Photobiol.* **2**, 119.

Goedheer, J. C. (1954). *Proc. 1st Intern. Congr. Photobiol., Amsterdam, 1954*, p. 345.

Goedheer, J. C. (1955). *Biochim. Biophys. Acta* **16**, 471.

Goedheer, J. C. (1957). Ph. D. Thesis, Utrecht, The Netherlands.

Goedheer, J. C. (1961). *Biochim. Biophys. Acta* **53**, 422.

Goedheer, J. C. (1964). *Biochim. Biophys. Acta* **88**, 304.

Goedheer, J. C. (1965). *Biochim. Biophys. Acta* **102**, 73.

Govindjee, (1963). *In* "Photosynthetic Mechanisms in Green Plants," Publ. 1145, p. 318. Natl. Acad. Sci.—Natl. Res. Council, Washington, D. C.

Granick, S., and Mauzerall, D. (1961). *In* "Metabolic Pathways" (D. M. Greenberg, ed.), Vol. 2, p. 525. Academic Press, New York.

Greenblatt, C. L., and Schiff, J. A. (1959). *J. Protozool.* **6**, 23.

Holden, M. (1965). *In* "The Chemistry and Biochemistry of Plant Pigments" (T. W. Goodwin, ed.), p. 462. Academic Press, New York.

Holt, A. S. (1965). *In* "The Chemistry and Biochemistry of Plant Pigments" (T. W. Goodwin, ed.), p. 3. Academic Press, New York.

Jacobs, E. E., Holt, A. S., Kronhout, R., and Rabinowitch, E. I. (1957). *Arch. Biochem. Biophys.* **72**, 495.

Jagendorf, A., and Hind, G. (1963). *In* "Photosynthetic Mechanisms in Green Plants," Publ. 1145, p. 599. Natl. Acad. Sci.—Natl. Res. Council, Washington, D. C.

Jagendorf, A., and Uribe, E. (1966). *Proc. Natl. Acad. Sci. U.S.* **55**, 494.

Kamen, M. D. (1963). "Primary Processes in Photosynthesis." Academic Press, New York.

Katz, E. (1949). *In* "Photosynthesis in Plants" (J. Franck and W. E. Loomis, eds.), p. 287. Iowa State Univ. Press, Ames, Iowa.

Kok, B. (1959). *Plant Physiol.* **34**, 185.

Kok, B. (1963). *In* "Photosynthetic Mechanisms in Green Plants," Publ. 1145, p. 45. Natl. Acad. Sci.—Natl. Res. Council, Washington, D. C.

Kok, B. (1965). *In* "Plant Biochemistry" (J. Bonner and J. E. Varner, eds.), p. 904. Academic Press, New York.

Kok, B., and Gott, W. (1960). *Plant Physiol.* **35**, 802.

Kok, B., and Hoch, G. (1961). *In* "Light and Life" (W. D. McElroy and B. Glass, eds.), p. 397. Johns Hopkins Press, Baltimore, Md.

Krasnovsky, A. A., and Kosobutskaja, L. M. (1952). *Dokl. Akad. Nauk SSSR* **85**, 177.

Krasnovsky, A. A., and Kosobutskaja, L. M. (1955). *Dokl. Akad. Nauk SSSR* **104**, 440.

Krasnovsky, A. A., Vojnovskaja, K. K., and Kosobutskaja, L. M. (1952). *Dokl. Akad. Nauk SSSR* **85**, 389.

Krey, A., and Govindjee (1964). *Proc. Natl. Acad. Sci. U.S.* **52**, 1568.

Krinsky, N., and Goldsmith, T. H. (1960). *Arch. Biochem. Biophys.* **91**, 271.

Krinsky, N., Gordon, A., and Stern, A. I. (1964). *Plant Physiol.* **39**, 441.

Lewis, S. C. (1963). Ph. D. Thesis, Brandeis Univ., Waltham, Massachusetts.

Liro, J. I. (1909). *Ann. Acad. Sci. Fennicae, Ser. A* **1**, 1.

Litvin, F. F., Krasnovsky, A. A., and Rikhireva, G. T. (1960). *Dokl. Akad. Nauk SSSR* **135**, 287.

Longuet-Higgins, H. C., Rector, C. W., and Platt, J. R. (1950). *J. Chem. Phys.* **18**, 1174.

Lyman, H., Epstein, H. T., and Schiff, J. A. (1961). *Biochim. Biophys. Acta* **50**, 301.

McRae, L. G., and Kasha, M. (1958). *J. Chem. Phys.* **28**, 721.

Madsen, A. (1963). *Physiol. Plantarum* **16**, 470.

Moriber, L. G., Hershenov, B., Aaronson, S., and Bensky, B. (1963). *J. Protozool.* **10**, 80.

Murata, N., Nishimura, M., and Takamiya, A. (1966). *Biochim. Biophys. Acta* **126**, 234.

Myers, J. (1946). *J. Gen. Physiol.* **29**, 419.

Myers, J. (1963). *In* "Photosynthetic Mechanisms in Green Plants," Publ. 1145, p. 301. Natl. Acad. Sci.—Natl. Res. Council, Washington, D. C.

Myers, J., and French, C. S. (1960). *J. Gen. Physiol.* **43**, 723.

Newton, J. W., and Levine, L. (1959). *Arch. Biochem. Biophys.* **83**, 456.

Nishimura, M., and Huzisige, H. (1959). *J. Biochem.* **46**, 225.

Olson, R. A. (1963). *In* "Photosynthetic Mechanisms in Green Plants," Publ. 1145, p. 545. Natl. Acad. Sci—Natl. Res. Council, Washington, D.C.

Olson, R. A., Butler, W. L., and Jennings, W. H. (1961). *Biochim. Biophys. Acta* **54**, 615.

Olson, R. A., Butler, W. L., and Jennings, W. H. (1962). *Biochim. Biophys. Acta* **58**, 144.

Olson, R. A., Jennings, W. H., and Butler, W. L. (1964a). *Biochim. Biophys. Acta* **88**, 318.

Olson, R. A., Jennings, W. H., and Butler, W. L. (1964b). *Biochim. Biophys. Acta* **88**, 331.

Petropulos, S. F. (1964). *Science* **145**, 392.

Rabinowitch, E. I. (1945). "Photosynthesis," Vol. I. Wiley (Interscience), New York.

Rabinowitch, E. I. (1951). "Photosynthesis," Vol. II, Part 1. Wiley (Interscience), New York.

Rabinowitch, E. I. (1956). "Photosynthesis," Vol. II, Part 2. Wiley (Interscience), New York.

Rosenberg, A., and Pecker, M. (1964). *Biochemistry* **3**, 254.

Sanadi, D. R., ed. (1966). *Current Topics Bioenergetics* **1**.

Schiff, J. A. (1963). *Carnegie Inst. Wash. Yrbook* **62**, 375.

Schiff, J. A., and Epstein, H. T. (1965). *In* "Reproduction: Molecular, Subcellular and Cellular" (M. Locke, ed.), p. 131. Academic Press, New York.

Schiff, J. A., Lyman, H., and Epstein, H. T. (1961). *Biochim. Biophys. Acta* **51**, 340.

Shibata, K. (1957). *J. Biochem.* **44**, 147.

Shibata, K., Benson, A. A., and Calvin, M. (1954). *Biochim. Biophys. Acta* **15**, 461.
Shlyk, A. A., Kaler, V. L., Vlasenok, L. I., and Gaponenko, V. I. (1963). *Photochem. Photobiol.* **2**, 129.
Sistrom, W. R., Griffith, M., and Stanier, R. Y. (1956). *J. Cellular Comp. Physiol.* **48**, 473.
Smith, J. H. C., and Benitez, A. (1955). *In* "Modern Methods of Plant Analysis" (K. Paech and M. V. Tracey, eds.), Vol. IV, p. 141. Springer, Berlin.
Smith, J. H. C., and French, C. S. (1963). *Ann. Rev. Plant Physiol.* **14**, 181.
Stern, A. I., Schiff, J. A., and Epstein, H. T. (1964a). *Plant Physiol.* **39**, 220.
Stern, A. I., Epstein, H. T., and Schiff, J. A. (1964b). *Plant Physiol.* **39**, 226.
Strell, M., and Kalojanoff, A. (1962). *Ann. Chem.* **652**, 218.
Tanada, T. (1951). *Am. J. Botany* **38**, 276.
Vernon, L. P., and Seeley, G. R., eds. (1966). "The Chlorophylls." Academic Press, New York.
Virgin, H. I. (1960). *Physiol. Plantarum* **13**, 155.
Virgin, H. I., Kahn, A., and von Wettstein, D. (1963). *Photochem. Photobiol.* **2**, 83.
von Wettstein, D. (1961). *Can. J. Botany* **39**, 1537.
Warburg, O., and Negelein, E. (1923). *Z. Physik. Chem.* **106**, 191.
Weber, G. (1961). *Nature* **190**, 27.
Wolff, J. B., and Price, L. (1957). *Arch. Biochem. Biophys.* **72**, 293.
Wolken, J. J. (1956a). *J. Protozool.* **3**, 211.
Wolken, J. J. (1956b). *J. Comp. Physiol.* **48**, 349.
Wolken, J. J. (1958). *Brookhaven Symp. Biol.* **11**, 87.
Wolken, J. J. (1959). *Ann. Rev. Plant Physiol.* **10**, 71.
Wolken, J. J. (1961). "*Euglena.* An Experimental Organism for Biochemical and Biophysical Studies." Rutgers Univ. Press, New Brunswick, New Jersey.
Wolken, J. J. (1963). *In* "Photosynthetic Mechanisms in Green Plants," Publ. 1145, p. 575. Natl. Acad. Sci.—Natl. Res. Council, Washington, D. C.
Wolken, J. J., and Mellon, A. D. (1956). *J. Gen. Physiol.* **39**, 675.
Wolken, J. J., Mellon, A. D., and Greenblatt, C. L. (1955). *J. Protozool.* **2**, 89.
Woodward, R. B., Ayer, W. A., Beaton, J. M., Bickelhaupt, F., Bonnett, R., Buchschacher, P., Closs, G. L., Dutler, H., Hannah, J., Hauck, F. P., Ito, S., Langemann, A., LeGoff, E., Leimgruber, W., Lwowski, W., Sauer, J., Valenta, Z., and Volz, H. (1960). *J. Am. Chem. Soc.* **82**, 3800.

CHAPTER 10

THE CONTINUITY
OF THE CHLOROPLAST IN *EUGLENA**

Jerome A. Schiff and H. T. Epstein

* Reprinted, with minor revisions, from the 24th Annual Symposium of the Society for Developmental Biology organized by Dr. Herbert Stern: "Reproduction: Molecular, Subcellular and Cellular," edited by Michael Locke; Academic Press, New York, 1965.

I. Introduction—The Two Aspects of Organelle Continuity

Eucaryotic cells contain several organelles conspicuously delimited from the surrounding cytoplasm at the level of resolution of the light microscope. This characteristic separates the vast bulk of living organisms from the procaryotic group represented by blue-green algae and bacteria, and provides us with the problem of the origins of various organelles such as chloroplasts and mitochondria.

For convenience, two aspects of the problem can be distinguished. The first concerns the developmental origins of the organelle in question including a description of its formation from simpler precursor bodies together with a consideration of the control mechanisms governing the inception and orderly programming of the process. A second aspect concerns the continuity of the organelle from generation to generation and raises questions concerning the localization of information for the formation of organelle constituents and the mode of inheritance of this information during the reproductive cycle. Carried far enough back in time, this aspect includes speculations regarding the evolutionary origins of the organelle.

In discussing these questions, we will be primarily concerned with organelle continuity in *E. gracilis* var. *bacillaris* and with the chloroplast of this organism. Chloroplast development and inheritance in other organisms, particularly higher plants, has been reviewed extensively (Gibor and Granick, 1964; Granick, 1961, 1963; Rhoades, 1946; Cleland, 1962).

Much of the pioneering work on *Euglena* has been performed by Pringsheim, Lwoff, Hutner, Provasoli, and their collaborators. Through their efforts, the two strains of *Euglena* most popular for research were isolated and obtained in axenic culture; defined media were devised which support luxuriant growth of the organism in a wide pH range (pH 3–9) on a variety of substrates. Their work also emphasized the suitability of *Euglena* for studies of chloroplast development by demonstrating that the formation of this organelle was light-dependent and that various agents would interfere with the ability of the cells to form plastids. This work is ably summarized in reviews (Hutner and Provasoli, 1951, 1955). The preceding applies only to two strains of *E. gracilis* since many other species of *Euglena* do not posses these characteristics. These two strains are *E. gracilis* var. *bacillaris* and *E. gracilis* strain Z. Since the strains are very similar, *Euglena* will be used to designate them in the subsequent discussion whenever there is no reason to think that the findings reported are unique to one strain or the other. A useful *Euglena* bibliography will be found in Wolken (1961).

II. The Developmental Aspect of Chloroplast Continuity*

A. THE *Euglena* CHLOROPLAST

The fully developed chloroplast characteristic of light-grown cells of *Euglena* consists of about 12 lamellae each composed of 2 to 4 closely appressed pairs of membranes called discs (Gibbs, 1960; Epstein and Schiff, 1961; Ben-Shaul *et al.*, 1964) as illustrated in Figs. 1 and 4. As is characteristic of algal chloroplasts in general, there is a centrally located pyrenoid region which appears more dense in electron micrographs and in which the lamellae appear to be somewhat reduced in thickness. Plates of paramylum, the carbohydrate reserve of *Euglena* (a β-1:3 glucan) (Kreger and Meeuse, 1952; Clarke and Stone, 1960) flank the exterior of the pyrenoid and the entire plastid is surrounded by a double membrane. In the fluorescence microscope (where, under illumination with blue light, the chlorophyll emits a red fluorescence) most of the chlorophyll appears to be distributed in the lamellar regions with very little or no fluorescence within the pyrenoid region. Figure 1 also shows another algal characteristic shared by *Euglena*, the absence of grana regions in the chloroplast characteristic of higher plant chloroplasts.

B. THE LIGHT REQUIREMENT FOR CHLOROPHYLL AND CHLOROPLAST FORMATION

We are accustomed to thinking of the formation of chlorophyll and chloroplasts in plants as a light-dependent process but in fact, many organisms form chlorophyll and chloroplasts in the dark. The angiosperms, in general, and *Euglena* and *Ochromonas* (Gibbs, 1962) require light for the formation of plastid structures and chlorophyll, but certain gymnosperms and several algae such as *Chlorella* and *Chlamydomonas* do not. Indeed it may be true that the majority of algae resemble *Chlorella* and *Chlamydomonas* in this respect although an experimental test of this requires that the organism in question be capable of organotrophic growth on a reduced carbon source in the dark. Organisms that cannot utilize organic substrates cannot be adequately tested.

Those organisms that require light for chloroplast development and chlorophyll formation all appear to utilize light energy for the conversion of protochlorophyll(ide) a to chlorophyll(ide) a and careful action spectra in higher plants match the absorption spectrum of protochlorophyll(ide).

* *Editor's Note:* This topic is further covered in Chapters 1, 5, 6, and 11.

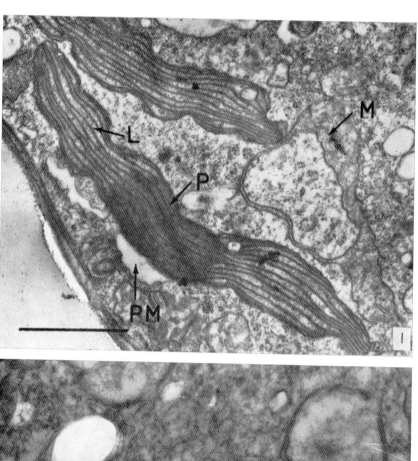

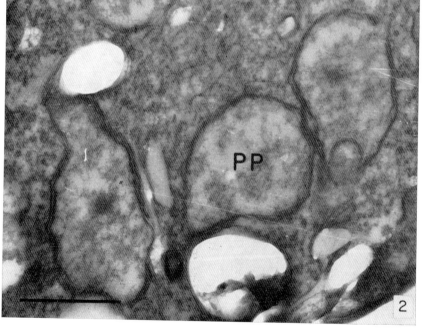

(In those cases in which careful studies have been carried out, protochloro-phyllide has been shown to be the compound converted photochemically to chlorophyllide a. In *Euglena*, however, and several other organisms, it has not been determined whether protochlorophyll or protochlorophyllide is the photochemically reduced precursor. While it is likely that proto-chlorophyllide will also turn out to be the precursor in these cases, the designation "protochlorophyll(ide)" will be used to indicate the ambiguity.) This photochemical step has been studied in a holochrome particle extracted from beans, and much of the pioneering work was done in Smith's laboratory (J. H. C. Smith, 1958). While the action spectra measured for *Euglena* are consistent with those for higher plants, (Nishimura and Huzisige, 1959; Wolken *et al.*, 1955) more data are necessary to be certain. Due to the small amounts of protochlorophyll(ide) in dark-grown organisms, most action spectra have measured the effectiveness of various wavelengths in bringing about an accumulation of chlorophyll over a period of time. It would be very desirable, however, to have action spectra for the transformation of the initial protochlorophyllide to chlorophyllide since other photochemical transformations (possibly with different action spectra) may subsequently intervene.

From organisms that do not require light for chloroplast and chlorophyll formation, mutants can be isolated that require light. Thus, mutants of *Chlamydomonas* and *Chlorella* are known that are yellow when grown in the dark and become green only on exposure to light (Sager, 1958). If it is assumed that these mutants are the result of a single mutation in each case, it seems likely that the wild-type organisms contain both the standard light-induced protochlorophyll(ide)-to-chlorophyll(ide) step and an enzyme system for carrying out this transformation in the dark. Mutation would then have eliminated the dark enzyme leaving only the light-induced alter-native, and rendering the mutant light-dependent for chloroplast and chlorophyll formation.

Fig. 1.   Cell of wild-type *Euglena* grown in the light. (Ben-Shaul *et al.*, 1964.)
Abbreviations used here and in subsequent figures: B, basal body; C, chloroplast; D, disc; E, endosome; ER, endoplasmic reticulum; G. Golgi body; GU, gullet; L, lamella; M, mitochondrion; N, nucleus; NP, nuclear pore; P, pyrenoid; PE, pellicle; PM, para-mylum; PP, proplastid; PV, pinocytotic vesicle. Marker indicates 1 μ. Here and in sub-sequent figures, the organism is *E. gracilis* var. *bacillaris*.

Fig. 2.   Wild-type *Euglena* grown in the dark. (Ben-Shaul *et al.*, 1965.) (Key to abbreviations in legend of Fig. 1.)

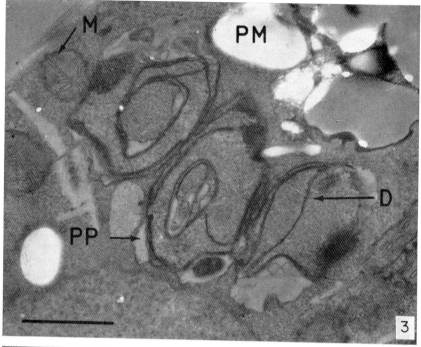

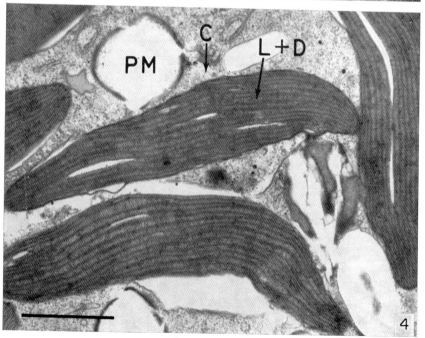

C. THE PROPLASTID IN DARK-GROWN *Euglena*

After many generations of growth in the dark, *Euglena* cells lose all of their chlorophyll and contain only protochlorophyll(ide) (Nishimura and Huzisige, 1959; Schiff *et al.*, 1961b) as the detectable green pigment. Early electron micrographs revealed that these cells contain proplastids about 1 μ in diameter which seem to lack extensive internal structure (Epstein and Schiff, 1961; Ben-Shaul *et al.*, 1964), (Fig. 2). Improvement of fixation procedures, however, has permitted the detection of one or two internal membranes in many of the proplastids which are occasionally organized for part of their length into a more complex structure (Fig. 3), and particles the size of ribosomes can also be seen (Liss *et al.*, 1965). Rough counts with the fluorescence microscope indicate that there are about 30 proplastids per cell (Epstein and Schiff, 1961; Epstein *et al.*, 1960). Extensive tubular structures, such as the prolamellar body found in certain proplastids of higher plants (von Wettstein, 1961) seem to be absent (Ben-Shaul *et al.*, 1964).

D. CHLOROPLAST DEVELOPMENT IN *Euglena*

When dark-grown cells of *Euglena* are exposed to light, chloroplast development ensues whether the cells are dividing or not. By keeping the cells under nondividing conditions on a "resting" medium it has been possible to study chloroplast development uncomplicated by cell division (Stern *et al.*, 1964a).

The morphological events of this process may be summarized as follows (Epstein and Schiff, 1961; Ben-Shaul *et al.*, 1964): (1) Membranes (which later form discs) are invaginated from the inner proplastid membrane; (2) These discs eventually fuse with each other along their length to form lamellae consisting of 2 to 4 discs; (3) The pyrenoid region differentiates after about 18–24 hours of development; (4) The maximum number of lamellae is formed by about 72 hours of development and chloroplast development is complete. The kinetics of this process are summarized in Fig. 5. The rise and fall in the number of discs reflects the initial formation of discs reaching a maximum number, cessation of disc formation, and fusion of discs to form lamellae. Lamella formation is linear from about 14 hours to maturity.

Fig. 3. Wild-type *Euglena* grown in the dark. (Liss *et al.*, 1965). (Key to abbreviations in legend of Fig. 1.)

Fig. 4. Wild-type *Euglena* grown in the light. (Liss *et al.*, 1965.) (Key to abbreviations in legend of Fig. 1.)

All parameters seem to increase by about a factor of 3 between 10 and 14 hours of development. This has been interpreted as a fusion of three proplastids to form one chloroplast at this point in development, which is consistent with some radiation data to be subsequently presented. The possibility also exists that proplastids are already linked in the dark-grown cells, in groups of three, by fine membrane connections, but in the fluorescence

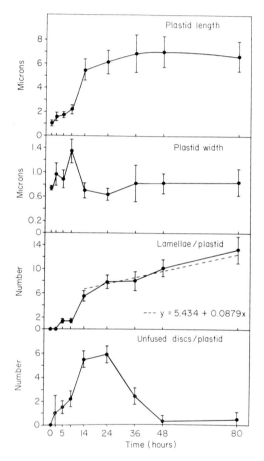

Fig. 5. Kinetics of the formation of discs and lamellae; and plastid lengths and widths during chloroplast development in *Euglena.* Zero time represents dark-grown cells immediately before induction of development with light. Time is measured from hours of development after dark-grown cells are exposed to light. In all cases, the points represent the means of several observations and the flags show the 95% confidence intervals of the means. The dotted line was fitted by least squares to the linear portion of lamella development. (Ben-Shaul *et al.*, 1964).

microscope appear singular because the protochlorophyll(ide) is concentrated in the larger parts of the structure. If this were true, it would offer an alternative explanation to the fusion of proplastids, which is consistent with all the relevent data. The pattern of development in *Euglena* appears to be quite different from that in higher plants and other algae which have been studied (Gibbs, 1962; von Wettstein, 1961; Sager, 1958).

E. DEVELOPMENTAL PHYSIOLOGY OF THE CHLOROPLAST IN *Euglena*

1. *Pigments.* After its initial formation on light induction of dark-grown cells (Nishimura and Huzisige, 1959; Schiff *et al.*, 1961b), chlorophyll a increases slowly up to about 10 hours (Stern *et al.*, 1964a). After 10 hours (Fig. 6) the rate of chlorophyll a formation increases dramatically and becomes essentially parallel to the rate at which lamellae are being formed. Chlorophyll b is difficult to measure because even in fully developed cells it constitutes only a small proportion of the total chlorophyll.

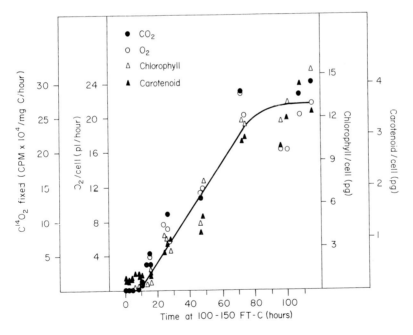

Fig. 6. Kinetics of the appearance of chlorophyll, carotenoids, photosynthetic oxygen evolution, and photosynthetic carbon dioxide fixation during chloroplast development in *Euglena*. As in Fig. 5 (data on comparable cells), zero time represents measurements on dark-grown cells; time is measured from inception of light-induced chloroplast development. (Stern *et al.*, 1964a.)

The dark-grown cell contains appreciable carotenoid (Stern *et al.*, 1964a; Krinsky and Goldsmith, 1960) although the proportion of the total cell content localized in the proplastid is not known. On light induction of chloroplast development the increase of carotenoids parallels that of chlorophyll a (Fig. 6) (Stern *et al.*, 1964a). The carotenoids of the dark-grown cell are: β-carotene, echinenone, euglenanone, cryptoxanthin, zeaxanthin, *trans*-antheraxanthin, *cis*-antheraxanthin, trollein, and hydroxyechinenone (Krinsky and Goldsmith, 1960). At about 4 hours of chloroplast development neoxanthin appears for the first time and continues to increase during development (Krinsky *et al.*, 1964). The fact that neoxanthin appears approximately at the inception point of photosynthetic competence is pregnant with speculative possibilities.

2. *Photosynthesis.* The first event that can be measured by gas exchange is the large irreversible increase in the rate of oxygen uptake when dark-grown cells are exposed to light (Schiff, 1963). This undoubtedly represents an increase in respiration for mobilization of energy for the synthesis of chloroplast constituents. Superimposed on this large irreversible change is a small reversible photoinduced uptake of oxygen. As development of the chloroplast proceeds, this reversible uptake is gradually compensated until by about 4 hours of development it has become balanced by photoinduced oxygen evolution. From this point onward there is an increasing net photosynthetic oxygen evolution (Fig. 6). The inception point for photosynthesis, therefore, can be assumed to be somewhat prior to 4 hours of development. Photosynthetic carbon dioxide fixation also becomes apparent at about 6 hours of development (Stern *et al.*, 1964a). By 15 hours (Fig. 6) of development the photosynthetic quotient is 1.0 and remains at this value during the remainder of development. In general, the rate of photosynthesis during development parallels the formation of pigments and lamellae (Stern *et al.*, 1964a) (Figs. 5 and 6). The optimum light intensity for development in *Euglena* is about 100 ft-c; higher or lower intensities yield lower amounts of chlorophyll. Low intensities also lead to abnormal development (Stern *et al.*, 1964b; Ben-Shaul *et al.*, 1964).

3. *Protein Synthesis.* Since chloroplast development takes place normally on a medium devoid of nitrogen and carbon sources, it is of interest to know whether the formation of the chloroplast involves *de novo* protein synthesis or, alternatively, whether the proteins of the chloroplasts already exist in the dark-grown cells and are merely packaged into chloroplasts on light induction. Several enzyme activites have been shown to be associated with the chloroplast fraction of light-grown cells (Smillie, 1963).

One way of attacking the problem is to measure enzyme activities during development. TPN-Triose phosphate dehydrogenase (Fuller and Gibbs, 1959; Brawerman and Konigsberg, 1960), TPN-transhydrogenase (Lazzarini and Woodruff, 1964; Lazzarini and San Pietro, 1963), and ribulose di-phosphate carboxylase (Fuller and Gibbs, 1959) all appear during development. By spectroscopic determination, it has been possible to show that cytochrome 552, the chloroplast-localized cytochrome of *Euglena* is formed during development (Nishimura, 1959; Wolken and Gross, 1963; Perini *et al.*, 1964a,b) at a rate that maintains the ratio of cytochrome to chlorophyll at 1:400, the value characteristic of the mature chloroplast (Perini *et al.*, 1964b). This suggests that photosynthetic units are being constructed and completed as individual units during development. The number of chlorophyll molecules per cytochrome is consistent with the currently accepted size of the photosynthetic unit.

Another approach involves the preparation of antibodies to the proteins of fully mature chloroplasts by injecting acetone powders of purified chloro-plasts into rabbits and isolating the antiserum (Lewis *et al.*, 1965). It is then possible to detect a number of antigen–antibody reactions by means of the agar diffusion methods developed by Ouchterlony. Using these methods, investigations have shown that there is a progressive increase in the number of antigens in the cell that react with the antichloroplast antibodies as chloroplast development proceeds. These results suggest that new proteins are being formed during chloroplast development (Lewis *et al.*, 1965). Considered together, this evidence suggests that the induction of chloroplast development by light resembles a mass induction of adaptive enzymes. Many new proteins and enzyme activities appear during development and since this occurs on a medium lacking carbon and nitrogen, these molecules must be synthesized either from internal pools of intermediates or from the breakdown of existing macromolecules.

4. *RNA and Ribosomes during Development.* Extensive work on this problem has been performed using *E. gracilis* strain Z (Smillie and Krotkov, 1960). Previous findings had indicated that exposure of dark-grown organisms to light brings about synthesis of chloroplast proteins and an increase and change in cellular RNA (Brawerman *et al.*, 1962a; A. O. Pogo *et al.*, 1962). Further explorations showed that the chloroplasts have distinctive ribosomes (Brawerman, 1963) which can be distinguished from their cytoplasmic counterparts on the basis of base composition and sedimentation characteristics. It was further shown that intact chloroplasts from *Euglena* can incorporate amino acids into protein (Eisenstadt and Brawerman, 1963). Ribosomes isolated from both chloroplasts and cytoplasm could incorporate amino acids into protein when provided with necessary cofactors and intermediates (Eisenstadt and Brawerman, 1964a,b). The evidence suggests that both the cytoplasm and chloroplasts of *Euglena* have protein synthesizing systems of the usual type found in other systems.

5. *Miscellaneous Compounds.* Differences in lipid content and type of lipid have been found between light-grown and dark-grown cells (Rosenberg, 1963). α-Linolenic acid seems to be characteristic of the *Euglena* chloroplast since it is found in that fraction of the light-grown cells, but is absent or present only in a very small amount in dark-grown cells and in cells which cannot form plastid structures (Erwin and Bloch, 1962). Ergosterol on the other hand, appears not to be chloroplast-associated since it is found in comparable amounts in dark-grown, light-grown, and mutant cells (Stern *et al.*, 1960). As in other systems, iron is necessary for chloroplast development and iron deficiency can impede chlorophyll formation (Price and Carell, 1964). Aminotriazole inhibits chlorophyll formation in *Euglena* (Aaronson and Scher, 1960). Utilizable carbon sources appear to repress chloroplast development to some extent (App and Jagendorf, 1963).

6. *Control Mechanisms.* Possible control mechanisms for chloroplast development will be considered in the last section of this chapter.

F. The Return of the Chloroplast to the Proplastid Condition

This is a process most easily studied in unicellular organisms since in multicellular organisms the plastids exist in a highly determinate structure, the leaf. In *Euglena*, however, the chloroplast is capable of returning to the proplastid condition on dark adaptation (Ben-Shaul *et al.*, 1965). In dividing cells, lamellae dissociate into discs which are progressively lost from the plastids at a rate of about 0.3 per generation, somewhat less than the rate predicted from simple dilution of chloroplast constituents among daughter cells (0.5 per generation). Chlorophyll, however, is initially lost at a rate of about 0.5 per generation. This observation suggests that when the light is turned off, chlorophyll synthesis stops immediately (as required by the known light requirement for the protochlorophyll(ide) to chlorophyll(ide) step) but that some discs and lamellae continue to be made at a low rate. This evidence leads to the interpretation that synthesis of the messenger RNA for the production of the constituents of these structures may be repressed in darkness, but that the messenger has a sufficiently long lifetime to persist for a generation or two to permit the synthesis of constituents at a diminishing rate as the available messenger becomes diluted among daughter cells. After about 144 hours of darkness (8 generations) the chloroplast has regressed all the way to the proplastid condition (Ben-Shaul *et al.*, 1965).

Under nondividing conditions a different situation prevails (Ben-Shaul *et al.*, 1965). There is virtually no loss of structure over the course of 144 hours even though about 38% of the chlorophyll has been lost completely and another 50% has been converted to pheophytin (see Greenblatt and Schiff, 1959; Brown, 1963). This suggests that chlorophyll per se is not a determinant of the lamellar structures, a conclusion also reached by other workers with different material (von Wettstein, 1961).

Thus, chloroplast development from the proplastid on light induction takes place in both dividing and nondividing cells in an identical manner. The reverse process, conversion of chloroplasts to proplastids in darkness, takes place in dividing cells but not in nondividing cells. An explanation of these differences can be sought in control mechanisms which adapt *Euglena* to its ecological situation. The organism is a facultative phototroph or organotroph growing equally well by photosynthetic fixation of carbon dioxide or at the expense of reduced organic compounds in the medium. The dark-grown organisms containing only proplastids can live and multiply if a reduced carbon source is available to them. If no carbon source is available they will cease to divide but will live for quite a while. It is of great adaptive advantage for the organism, under these conditions, to be able to form chloroplasts as soon as light is available and to adopt a phototrophic mode of existence. Even in the presence of organic compounds, when the organism can divide, photosynthesis might still be a more efficient method of energy utilization. Thus, the organism is capable of forming chloroplasts either under dividing or nondividing conditions. Consider now the organism with fully developed chloroplasts. If light becomes limited two alternatives are available. If the medium is devoid of reduced carbon sources and growth is impossible in darkness the organism maintains its plastids which would be advantageous at the first reappearance of light. Should the medium contain reduced sources of carbon the organism divides and rapidly loses the excess baggage of the chloroplast, by returning them to the proplastid condition, while it exists as an efficient organotroph. During the course of evolution control mechanisms have apparently been selected in *Euglena* which efficiently adapt it to prevailing environmental conditions (Ben-Shaul et al., 1965).

III. The Replicative Aspect of Chloroplast Continuity*

A. DEFINITION OF THE PROBLEM

On the basis of available information from many organisms, it is possible to make some general models of chloroplast inheritance. Figure 7 shows three extremes for the purposes of discussion. In the first alternative, information for the construction of a plastid resides in the nucleus which codes for production of everything else in the cell as well. This model predicts

* *Editor's Note:* This topic is further covered in Chapter 11.

that the chloroplast (or proplastid, or any other organelle) is constructed *de novo* in each generation from information supplied by the nucleus. The large numbers of mutations in maize, barley, and other organisms which affect chloroplast phenotypes and which behave in a perfectly Mendelian fashion can be used in support of this model. As we will see later, however, other interpretations of this data are possible.

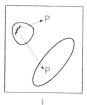 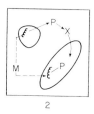 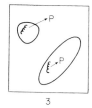

Fig. 7. Simplified hypothetical schemes for possible genetic interactions between organelles. In all cases, the circular structure represents the nucleus and the ellipse depicts the chloroplast. In alternative 1, an informational unit in the nucleus codes for the proteins of the entire cell including the chloroplast. Alternative 3 represents the other extreme in which the nucleus and chloroplast have independent informational units, the nuclear unit codes for generalized cell protein, and the chloroplast unit determines chloroplast proteins. Alternative 2 is necessitated by genetic studies with higher plants and shows two additional modes of interaction. The nucleus may code for a protein(s) which manufacture nutrients (X) required by the chloroplast. Alternatively, the nucleus may manufacture a mutagen (M) which irreversibly mutates the chloroplast informational unit.

The third alternative visualizes independent informational units in the nucleus and in the plastid. The unit in the nucleus codes for proteins produced in the nucleus and cytoplasm exclusive of the organelle in question. The organelle itself contains an informational unit which codes for its own proteins. When the cell replicates, the two informational units are replicated independently, leading to the possibility of autonomous chloroplast division.

In between these two extremes of interpretation are the possibilities for genetic interaction between the nucleus and the organelle shown in the second alternative of Fig. 7. These possibilities have been suggested by experiments with higher plants. Rhoades (1946) discovered a mutant affecting chloroplast phenotype in maize which he called *iojap*. The *iojap* gene is chromosomal and behaves in a Mendelian manner. Plants homozygous for the mutant gene produce abnormal chloroplasts. These abnormalities persist and are perpetuated, however, when the chloroplasts are crossed back into plants having a normal genetic constitution. Rhoades suggested, therefore, that the nucleus and plastid might have different genomes but that a mutant gene in the nucleus could produce a mutagen which irreversibly mutated the genome of the plastids which then continue to replicate the abnormality even after the nuclear constitution was returned to normal. Similar and even more complex interactions have been found in other plants, particularly *Oenothera* (Cleland, 1962).

Nuclear mutations affecting chloroplast phenotypes but which are entirely normal in Mendelian behavior (cited above in connection with alternative 1) can also be reinterpreted here. It is possible that the nucleus and plastid have independent genomes but that during the course of evolution the plastid has become nutritionally dependent on the rest of the cell for one or more metabolites (represented by "X" in alternative 2). A nuclear mutation that prevented the formation of these nutrients would lead to chloroplast abnormalities even though there was no direct informational dependence of the chloroplast on the nucleus.

In any case, the weight of the evidence seems to suggest separate genomes in nucleus and plastid. The rest of this chapter will be concerned with evidence that the behavior of the *Euglena* system is consistent with this interpretation.

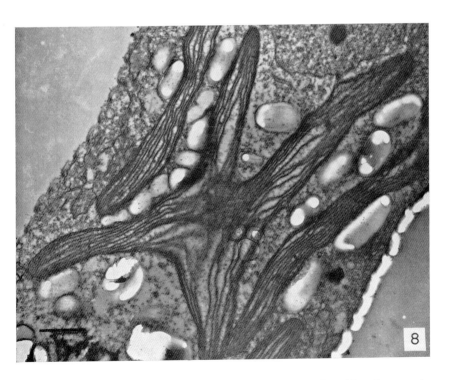

Fig. 8. Wild-type *Euglena* grown in the light in which a dividing chloroplast may be seen.

B. Cytological Evidence for Chloroplast Division

The fact that chloroplasts of algae divide has been known for many years and is well documented (Bold, 1951). In *E. deses*, for example, Gojdics was able to show that the cell divided first, apportioning the chloroplast complement approximately equally to the two daughter cells (Godjics, 1934). After cell division was completed each chloroplast divided to restore the original plastid complement. An electron micrograph of a dividing chloroplast in *E. gracilis* var. *bacillaris* is shown in Fig. 8. Since the chloroplast returns to the proplastid condition in this organism, and the number of

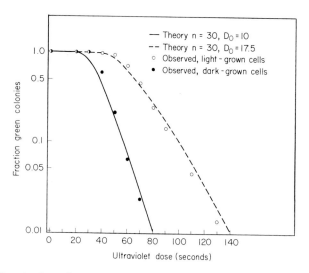

Fig. 9. Inactivation of green colony-forming ability in *Euglena* by ultraviolet light. The points represent experimental findings and the curves were calculated from target theory, multiplicity (*n*) of 30. D_0 is the dose required for a single inactivation. Light-grown and dark-grown cells show the same multiplicity but differ in D_0. (Lyman *et al.*, 1961.)

proplastids remains approximately constant from generation to generation in the dark and since the dark-grown cells are always capable of chloroplast formation, it seems reasonable to assume that the proplastids in this species are also capable of division.

C. Blockage of Green Colony–Forming Ability by Ultraviolet Light

If light-grown or dark-grown cells of *E. gracilis* var. *bacillaris* are exposed to ultraviolet light and are plated under nonphotoreactivating conditions, but with light induction to permit chloroplast formation, the number of green colonies formed decreases as the ultraviolet dose is increased (Pringsheim, 1958; Lyman *et al.*, 1959, 1961). Increasing numbers of nongreen colonies replace the green colonies that are lost (Fig. 9). Thus, ultraviolet light brings about a loss of the ability to become green in the progeny of cells that had received the radiation. It is possible to bring about 100% conversion of the progeny to the nongreen condition at ultraviolet doses that are too low to have any effect whatsoever on viability. Loss of viability begins at doses 10 times greater than the maximum doses required for inactivation of green colony–forming ability (compare Figs. 10 and 12) (Lyman *et al.*, 1961; Hill *et al.*, 1966b).

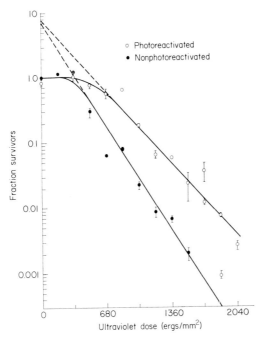

Fig. 10. Ultraviolet inactivation and photoreactivation of viability (colony–forming ability) in *Euglena*. The extrapolations indicate a multiplicity of about 8 for inactivation in this particular experiment. (Hill *et al.*, 1966b.)

The first question that arose concerned the numbers of ultraviolet-sensitive entities controlling this process. Target analysis of the inactivation curves revealed that the curves for dark-grown and light-grown cells both fitted multiplicities of about 30 (Fig. 9) (Lyman *et al.*, 1961). This has since been verified by computer analysis of many experiments (Hill *et al.*, 1966a). This number agreed very nicely with the number of proplastids in the dark-grown cells estimated by fluorescence microscopy. The fact that light-grown cells having about 10 chloroplasts also showed ultraviolet multiplicities of 30 led us to the hypothesis that in the formation of 10 chloroplasts from 30 proplastids during light-induced development, proplastids fused in three's to form single chloroplasts conserving the ultraviolet-sensitive entities present in each proplastid. Evidence consistent with this interpretation was

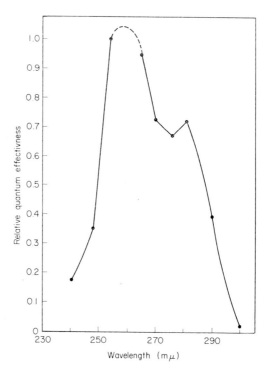

Fig. 11. Action spectrum for ultraviolet inactivation of green colony–forming ability in *Euglena*. (Lyman *et al.*, 1961.)

presented above in the discussion of chloroplast development. On the basis of these facts and the lack of lethality in this ultraviolet range, we suggested that the ultraviolet-sensitive sites were cytoplasmic (Lyman *et al.*, 1961). Gibor and Granick (1962b) confirmed this by elegant experiments with an ultraviolet microbeam and were able to show that high doses of ultraviolet delivered selectively to the nucleus killed the cells, but low doses delivered to the surrounding cytoplasm, with the nucleus shielded, reproduced the phenomena we had described. It appears likely then, that the ultraviolet-sensitive entities affecting green colony–forming ability are localized in the plastids themselves.

The second question concerned the chemical nature of the ultraviolet-sensitive chromophore. An action spectrum for the ultraviolet inactivation revealed that the absorbing chromophore had peaks in the regions of 260 and 280 mμ, suggesting the participation of a nucleoprotein (Fig. 11) (Lyman *et al.*, 1961).

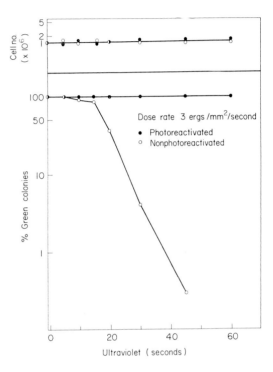

Fig. *12.*   Ultraviolet inactivation and photoreactivation of green colony–forming ability in light-grown cells of *Euglena* (lower curves). The upper part of the figure shows that the ultraviolet doses employed have no effect on cell viability as measured by viable cell numbers estimated from total colony count ("cell no." in upper part of figure). (Lyman *et al.*, 1961.)

As is true of ultraviolet inactivation in many other systems, the inactivation of green colony–forming ability in *Euglena* can be reversed by treatment with long-wavelength ultraviolet and blue light if given soon after inactivating ultraviolet (Schiff *et al.*, 1961a). This photoreactivation of green colony–forming ability can result in 100% reversal in *Euglena* (Fig. 12). This is a very high efficiency when compared with other systems (Jagger, 1958) and with the photoreactivation of viability in *Euglena* itself (Fig. 10) (Hill *et al.*, 1966b), and suggests that processes resembling multiplicity reactivation in bacteriophages may be occurring, resulting in cooperation among damaged entities in a single cell. This interpretation and others are discussed fully elsewhere (Hill *et al.*, 1966a,b,c). (For some anomalies in *E. gracilis* strain Z, see Cook, 1963.)

Figure 10 also shows that multiplicities for inactivation of viability in *Euglena* are of the order of four to eight, consistent with other unpublished data from our laboratory using X-rays. This suggests that the nuclear chromosomal complement in our strain of *E. gracilis* var. *bacillaris* is polyploid and helps to explain why the plastid system is so much more sensitive to ultraviolet than is viability.

The action spectrum for photoreactivation of green colony–forming ability in *Euglena* (Fig. 13) (Schiff *et al.*, 1961a) is very similar to that described for

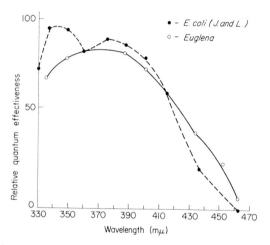

Fig. 13. Action spectrum for photoreactivation of green colony–forming ability in *Euglena* compared with photoreactivation in *Escherichia coli* measured by Jagger and Latarjet (1956). The rest of the visible spectrum (green to red) is completely inactive. (Schiff *et al.*, 1961a.)

photoreactivation of viability of *E. coli* and of photoreactivation of ultra-violet-inactivated bacteriophage T2 in the same organism (Kelner, 1951; Jagger and Latarjet, 1956). Since this system is known to involve the in-activation and repair of DNA it became possible to consider the possibility of plastid-localized DNA nucleoproteins that control the ability of the cells to produce green colonies.

It became important to know whether ultraviolet acted by preventing the replication of plastid entities or whether it merely prevented the develop-ment of proplastids into chloroplasts. An experiment was devised in which dark-grown cells were irradiated with a dose of ultraviolet that would produce 100% inactivation of green colony–forming ability when plated under nonphotoreactivating conditions. An aliquot of these cells was placed on a resting medium which prevented cell division, and the cells were exposed to red light which induces chloroplast and chlorophyll formation without causing photoreactivation. Fluorescence microscopy revealed that all of the irradiated cells produced normal chlorophyll and chloroplasts, indicating that chloroplast *development* was not blocked by ultraviolet. When the cells that had formed chloroplasts were plated however, they formed 100% nongreen colonies, indicating that ultraviolet blocks the *replication* of chloroplast-forming entities at the time of cell division (Schiff *et al.*, 1961b).

The experiments with ultraviolet and photoreactivation lead to the assumption that the dark-grown cells contain about 30 DNA–protein entities localized in the approximately 30 proplastids. On light induction, the 30 proplastids develop into 10 chloroplasts by fusion in three's with the conservation of the 30 DNA–protein entities now localized 3 to a chloroplast. Irradiation of either the dark-grown or light-grown cells with ultraviolet results in blockage of either proplastid or chloroplast replication, respectively, at the time of cell division. This would predict then, that ultraviolet inactivation and loss of green colony–forming ability by a cell should be synonymous with the loss of that cell's plastids and their contained DNA entities.

D. Cytology of Ultraviolet Mutant Cells

Cells incapable of chloroplast and chlorophyll production produced through ultraviolet treatment have never reverted to chloroplast–forming competence in the 8 years they have been carried in culture. In addition, fluorescence microscopy reveals no red-fluorescing structures of any kind, indicating the absence of protochlorophyll(ide) as well.

To confirm the absence of plastid structures, an extensive program of electron microscopy of *Euglena* mutants was undertaken. Improvement of fixation and embedding procedures (Liss *et al.*, 1965) now results in an image of proplastids and chloroplasts which stand out clearly and show enough individuality not to be confused with other organelles (Figs. 3 and 4). Other structures improve in resolution as well, including the endoplasmic reticulum (Fig. 14) (Liss *et al.*, 1965). Using these new methods, we have carefully examined the light-grown cells and dark-grown cells of all of our mutants and find that in the case of chlorophyll-free mutants induced by ultraviolet, streptomycin, and heat, there are no detectable chloroplasts or proplastids (Liss *et al.*, 1965). Representative pictures are shown in Figs. 15–20. Gibor and Granick (1962a) have treated mutants of this type from *E. gracilis* strain Z with δ-aminolevulinic acid by freeze-thawing the

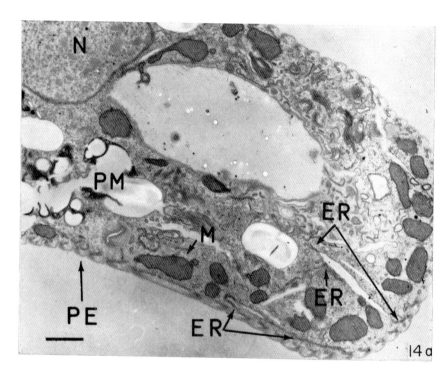

Fig. 14a. Y₃BUD, a yellow, ultraviolet-induced mutant of *Euglena* grown in the dark. Note investment of pellicle by the endoplasmic reticulum and its continuation centrally. (Liss *et al.*, 1965.) (Key to abbreviations in legend of Fig. 1.)

Fig. 14b. Y₃BUD, a yellow, ultraviolet-induced mutant of *Euglena* grown in the light. Note connection of endoplasmic reticulum and nuclear membrane, and endoplasmic reticulum investment of pellicles of the exterior and of the gullet. (Liss *et al.*, 1965.) (Key to abbreviations in legend of Fig. 1.)

Fig. 14c. W₃BUL, a white, ultraviolet-induced mutant of *Euglena* grown in the light. Pinocytotic vesicles can be seen in association with the gullet. The questionable structures are believed (on the basis of many observations) to be either abnormal mitochondria or amyloplasts. (Liss *et al.*, 1965.) (Key to abbreviations in legend of Fig. 1.)

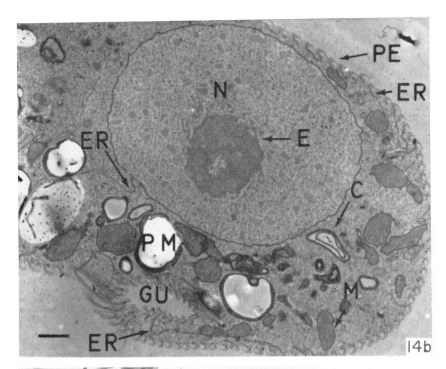

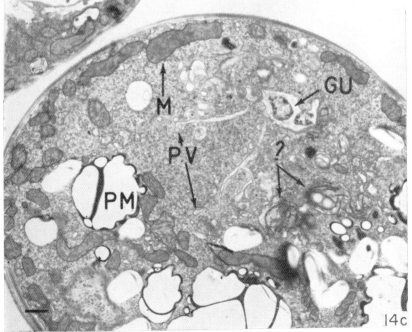

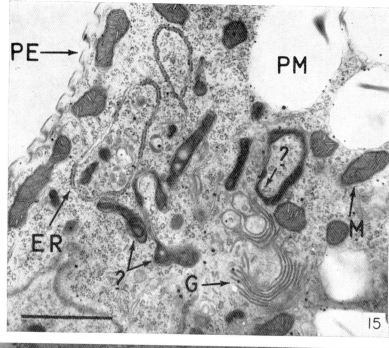

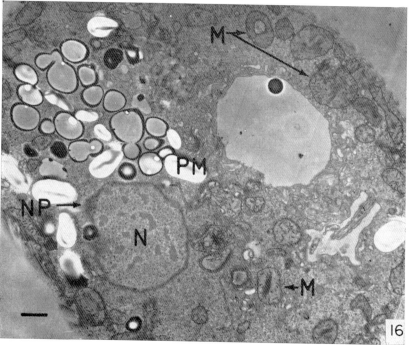

cells in a solution of the compound. They report that red-fluorescing centers can be detected in the cells after this treatment and interpret this to mean that plastids, or remnants of their structure, persist in the mutants. (See also Siegesmund *et al.*, 1962, and Moriber *et al.*, 1963.) No emission spectra are reported, however, for these red-fluorescing centers and it remains possible that they are mitochondrial sites of protoporphyrin synthesis for heme and cytochrome production rather than centers which form magnesium-containing tetrapyrroles, since both classes of compounds fluoresce red.

On the basis of our own work cited above and to be detailed below, we consider it unlikely that plastid or proplastid structures persist in clones of certain mutants of *E. gracilis* var. *bacillaris* induced with ultraviolet, heat, or streptomycin.

In addition to these mutants induced by ultraviolet, streptomycin, or heat which lack the ability to form any plastid structures or chlorophyll, others have been isolated which are blocked at some stage of development. All of these have proplastids in the dark (like wild type, Fig. 4) but display interesting abnormalities which should be of considerable use in studying the physiological basis of development (Liss *et al.*, 1965). For example, pale-green mutants (P_1) have been isolated which lack patches of lamellae and make less chlorophyll than wild type (Figs. 21 and 22) (Stern *et al.*, 1964a). Olive-green mutants have abnormally large plastids with discontinuous lamellae and many unfused discs as in O_1 (Figs. 23 and 24). Another olive-green mutant, O_2 (Figs. 25 and 26) produces structures strangely reminiscent of the grana of higher plant chloroplasts. Yellow mutants have been obtained which are blocked rather early in development and form only small abnormal plastids. Y_1 and Y_3 (Figs. 27–30) are examples (Stern *et al.*, 1964a).

The mutant cells also display a phenomenon noted for dark-grown cells (Lefort, 1964); there is a great hypertrophy of mitochondrial structures of bewildering diversity. It is possible that the presence or absence of an active chloroplast controls the development of mitochondrial structures for compensatory respiratory activity.

It is also possible that the mutagenic agent used in each of the cases to produce mutants in chloroplast phenotype also produced mutations in some of the mitochondria yielding some abnormal forms. Evidence for mitochondrial DNA will be discussed below.

Fig. 15. W$_3$BUL, a white, ultraviolet-induced mutant of *Euglena* grown in the dark. Structures marked with question marks are unknown but do not appear (on the basis of many observations) to be proplastids. (Liss *et al.*, 1965.) (Key to abbreviations in legend of Fig. 1.)

Fig. 16. W$_3$BUL, a white, ultraviolet-induced mutant of *Euglena* grown in the light. Note diversity of mitochondrial morphology, nuclear pores, and the absence of plastid-related structures. (Liss *et al.*, 1965.) (Key to abbreviations in legend of Fig. 1.)

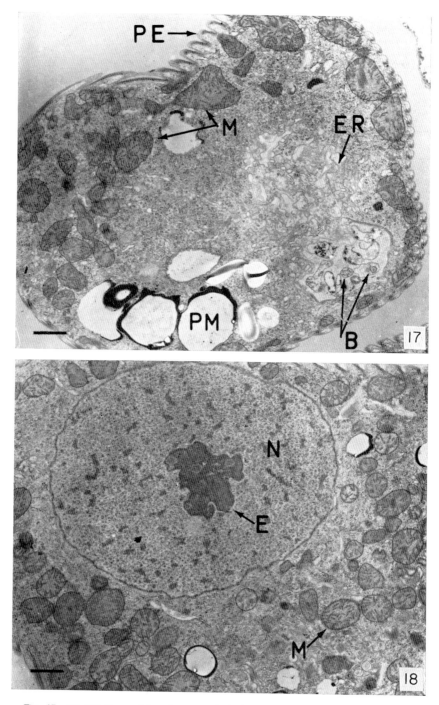

Fig. 17. $W_{10}BS_mL$, a white, streptomycin-induced mutant of *Euglena* grown in the dark. Note absence of plastid-related structures and the extensive smooth endoplasmic reticulum. (Liss *et al.*, 1965.) (Key to abbreviations in legend of Fig. 1.)

Fig. 18. $W_{10}BS_mL$, a white, streptomycin-induced mutant of *Euglena* grown in the light. Note absence of plastid-related structures. (Liss *et al.*, 1965.) (Key to abbreviations in legend of Fig. 1.)

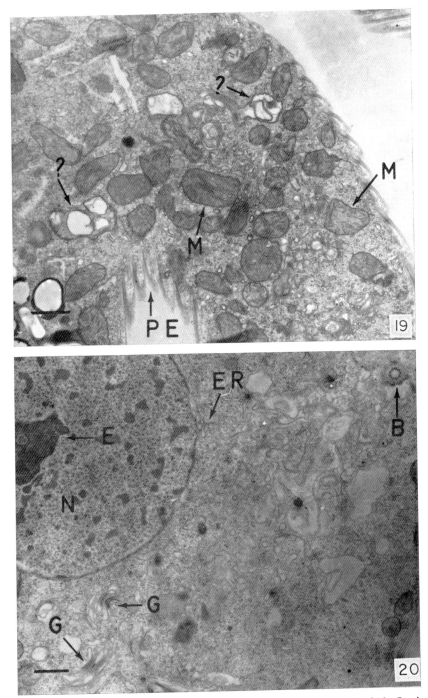

Fig. 19. W₈BHL, a white, heat-induced mutant of *Euglena* grown in the dark. On the basis of many observations, the structures with question marks do not resemble proplastids; they may be amyloplasts. (Liss *et al.*, 1965.) (Key to abbreviations in legend of Fig. 1.)

Fig. 20. W₈BHL, a white, heat-induced mutant of *Euglena* grown in the light. Note absence of plastid-related structures and presence of basal body, connection of endoplasmic reticulum and nuclear envelope, and Golgi lamellae with dense intercisternal elements. (Liss *et al.*, 1965.) (Key to abbreviations appears in legend of Fig. 1.)

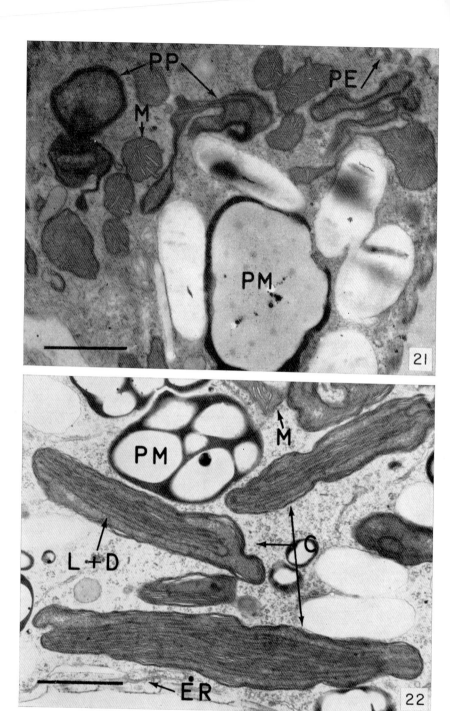

Fig. 21. Proplastids of P_1BXL, a pale-green, X-ray–induced mutant of *Euglena* grown in the dark. (Liss *et al.*, 1965.) (Key to abbreviations in legend of Fig. 1.)

Fig. 22. Plastids of P_1BXL, a pale-green, X-ray–induced mutant of *Euglena* grown in the light. (Liss *et al.*, 1965.) (Key to abbreviations in legend of Fig. 1.)

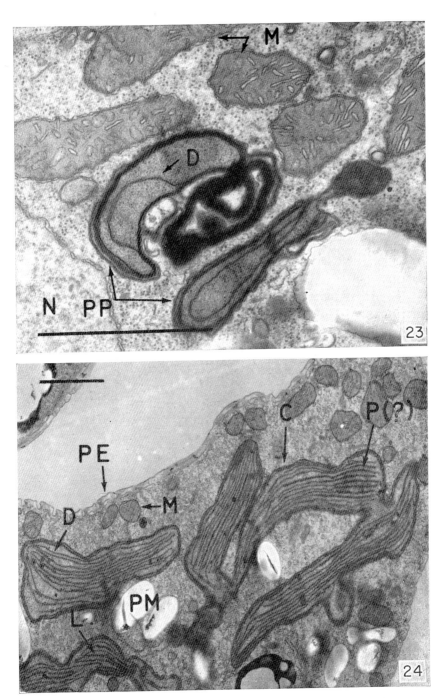

Fig. 23. Proplastids of O₁BS, an olive-green, spontaneous mutant of *Euglena* grown in the dark. (Liss *et al.*, 1965.) (Key to abbreviations in legend of Fig. 1.)

Fig. 24. Plastids of O₁BS, an olive-green, spontaneous mutant of *Euglena* grown in the light. Note junctions between plastids on right. (Liss *et al.*, 1965.) (Key to abbreviations in legend of Fig. 1.)

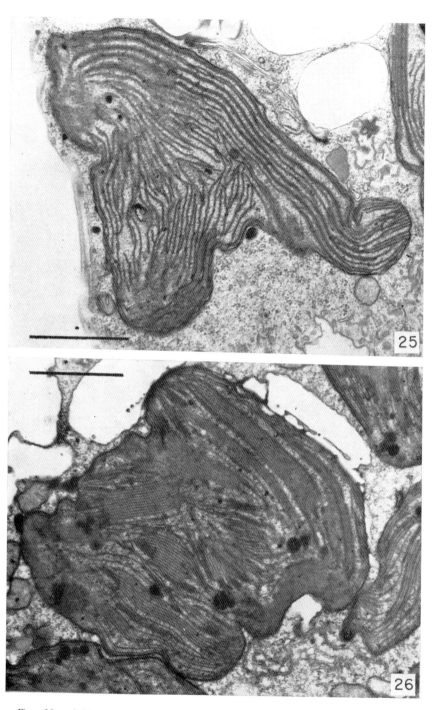

Figs. 25 and 26. Two representative examples of plastids in O₂BX, an olive-green, X-ray–induced mutant of *Euglena* grown in the light. (Liss *et al.*, 1965.) (Key to abbreviations in the legend of Fig. 1.)

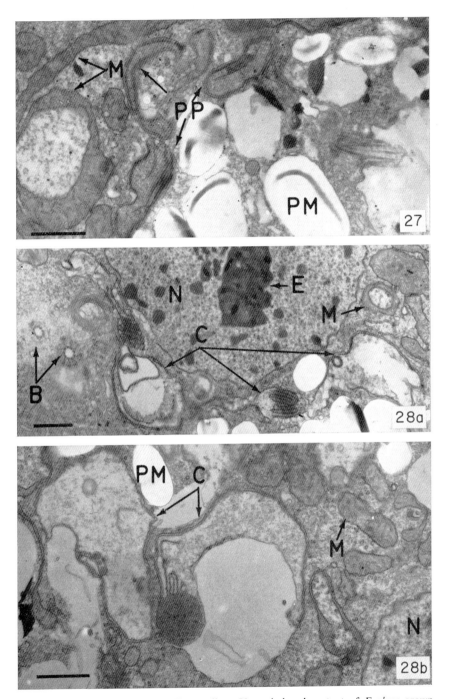

Fig. 27. Proplastids of Y_1BXD, a yellow, X-ray–induced mutant of *Euglena* grown in the dark. (Liss *et al.*, 1965.) (Key to abbreviations in legend of Fig. 1.)

Figs. 28a and 28b. Representative plastids of Y_1BXD, a yellow, X-ray–induced mutant of *Euglena* grown in the light. Note that the limiting membrane of the three plastids in Fig. 28a is continuous. (Liss *et al.*, 1965.) (Key to abbreviations in legend of Fig. 1.)

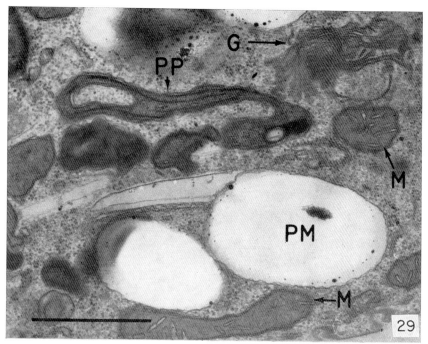

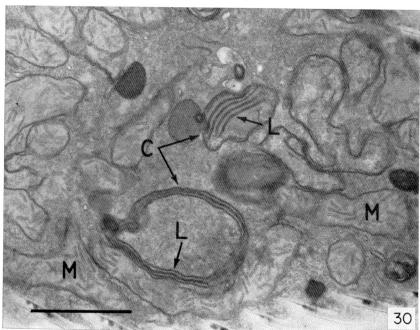

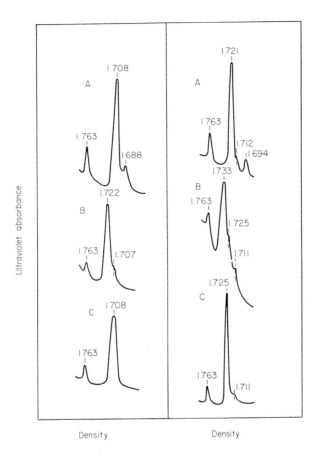

Fig. 31. Left: Microdensitometer tracings of ultraviolet photographs of DNA from *E. gracilis* var. *bacillaris* banded in cesium chloride density gradients. A, Light-grown wild-type cells, native DNA (13 µg); B, Light-grown wild-type cells, heat denatured DNA (13 µg); C, W$_3$BUL, native DNA (11 µg) (mutant lacking chloroplasts produced by treatment with ultraviolet). Right: Microdensitometer tracings of ultraviolet photographs of DNA banded in cesium chloride density gradients. A, *Chlamydomonas reinhardi* Y$_1$, native DNA (6.4 µg); B, *Chlamydomonas reinhardi* Y$_1$, heat-denatured DNA (6.4 µg); C, *Polytoma obtusum*, native DNA (7 µg).
In all cases, the band of density 1.763 is an added DNA of known density to calibrate the gradient. (Leff *et al.*, 1963.)

Fig. 29. Proplastids of Y$_3$BUD, a yellow, ultraviolet-induced mutant of *Euglena* grown in the dark. (Liss *et al.*, 1965.) (Key to abbreviations in legend of Fig. 1.)

Fig. 30. Plastids of Y$_3$BUD, a yellow, ultraviolet-induced mutant of *Euglena* grown in the light. (Liss *et al.*, 1965.) (Key to abbreviations in legend of Fig. 1.)

E. DNA of the Chloroplast and Other Organelles

The experiments with ultraviolet light described above suggested very strongly that a plastid-localized species of DNA exists in *Euglena*. Evidence in support of this was forthcoming from a comparison of the banding profiles of *Euglena* DNA in cesium chloride density gradients (Leff *et al.*, 1963). As may be seen in Fig. 31, light-grown cells display two bands of different densities, one at 1.708 and a satellite band at 1.688. Both of these are double-stranded since heat denaturation brings about the expected shifts to higher densities. Corresponding DNA preparations from ultraviolet mutants (Fig. 31) that lack plastid structures entirely, retained the main

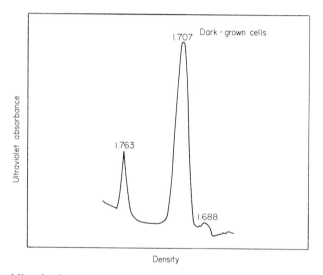

Fig. 32. Microdensitometer tracing of ultraviolet photographs of DNA from dark-grown wild-type cells of *E. gracilis* var. *bacillaris*. The band at 1.763 is added DNA of known density to calibrate the gradient. (Edelman *et al.*, 1964.)

band at density 1.708 but showed no detectable satellite DNA. This suggested that the main band (1.708) is probably nuclear DNA while the satellite (1.688) is probably chloroplast-associated DNA. A similar situation was found in a comparison of *Chlamydomonas* DNA with its aplastidic counterpart, *Polytoma* (Fig. 31) (Leff *et al.*, 1963).

This interpretation was further strengthened by the finding that dark-grown cells in *Euglena* that contain proplastids also contain the 1.688 satellite band (Fig. 32) (Edelman *et al.*, 1964).

Soon after this initial demonstration of satellite DNA, it became possible to show that the 1.688 satellite was highly enriched in the chloroplast fraction of light-grown cells of both *E. gracilis* var. *bacillaris* (Fig. 33) (Edelman *et al.*, 1964; Ray and Hanawalt, 1964) and strain Z (Brawerman and Eisenstadt, 1964b).

It then became apparent that there were actually two DNA satellites in light-grown and dark-grown cells of wild-type *Euglena* (Fig. 34) (Edelman *et al.*, 1965; Ray and Hanawalt, 1965). The satellite at density 1.691 had been overlooked previously because the concentrations of DNA used in ultracentrifugation had been too low to permit its detection in the ultraviolet

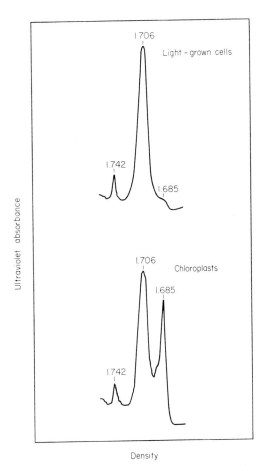

Fig. 33. Enrichment of satellite DNA of density 1.685 in the chloroplast fraction of light-grown cells of *E. gracilis* var. *bacillaris* compared with whole cell DNA. The curves show microdensitometer tracings of the ultraviolet absorption photographs of DNA separated in cesium chloride density gradients. In both cases, 1.742 represents added DNA of known density to calibrate the gradient. (Edelman *et al.*, 1964.)

mutant cells. Wild-type *Euglena* cells contain, therefore, three types of DNA; main band DNA (1.707) which is associated with the nucleus, and two satellites: S_c (1.686) associated with the chloroplast fraction and with the ability of the cells to make chloroplasts, and another satellite S_x (1.691) which is associated with the small particle fraction of the cells containing the mitochondrial cytochromes (Edelman *et al.*, 1965). Since *Euglena* mitochondria have now been shown to contain membrane-bounded DNA of density 1.691 (Edelman, *et al.*, 1966) S_x DNA can now be designated S_m

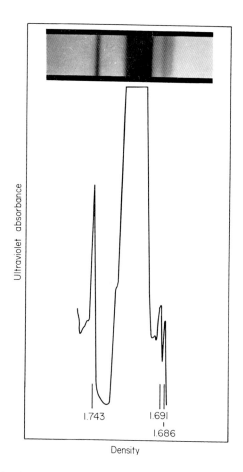

Fig. 34.   Microdensitometer tracing of ultraviolet absorption photograph of DNA from light-grown cells of *E. gracilis* var. *bacillaris* separated on a cesium chloride density gradient. The moderate overloading of DNA in the gradient permits the resolution of two satellites. The band at 1.743 is added density standard DNA to calibrate the gradient. The overloaded band is main band DNA. (Edelman *et al.*, 1965.)

DNA. As may be seen from Fig. 35 (column A, unstarred), all strains of *Euglena* capable of forming proplastids or a partial chloroplast, contain S_c in addition to S_x and main band. Treatment of any of these strains with ultraviolet and isolation of colorless clones results in a loss of S_c (Fig. 35, column A, starred). All strains incapable of forming plastid structures lack S_c but contain S_x and main band (Fig. 35, column B, unstarred). As expected, treatment of these cells with ultraviolet produces no further alteration. This demonstrates that S_c is definitely correlated with the cells' ability to produce proplastids and chloroplasts and is consistent with the cytological evidence presented before for plastid loss in mutant cells produced by ultraviolet (Edelman *et al.*, 1965).

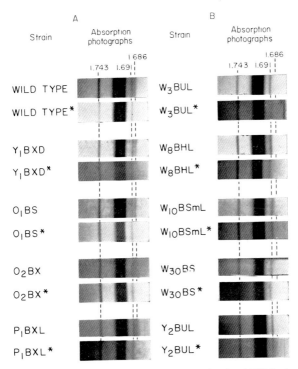

Fig. 35. The DNA's of *Euglena* mutants. Band of density 1.743 is density standard DNA added to calibrate gradient. All strains in column A are capable of developing at least a partial chloroplast and possess both satellite bands, S_x (1.691) and S_c (1.686). All strains in column B are incapable of even partial chloroplast development and contain only satellite band S_x (1.691). All strains in both columns A and B when subjected to treatment with ultraviolet light (indicated by asterisk) yield strains which lack S_c (1.686) but retain S_x (1.691). (Edelman *et al.*, 1965.) Since *Euglena* mitochondria have now been shown to contain membrane-bounded DNA of density 1.691 (Edelman *et al.*, 1966) S_x DNA can now be designated S_m DNA.

Table I

DNA OF *E. gracilis*

Source and method	Main band		S_c		S_x^b		Reference
	A+T	G+C[a]	A+T	G+C	A+T	G+C	
E. gracilis var. *bacillaris* (density)	52	48	74	26	69	31	Edelman et al., 1964, 1965
E. gracilis var. *bacillaris* (thermal denaturation)	45	55	70	30	—	—	Edelman et al., 1964
E. gracilis var. *bacillaris* (analysis)	47	53	76	24	—	—	Ray and Hanawalt, 1964
E. gracilis strain Z (density)[c]	51	49	76	24	67	33	Brawerman and Eisenstadt, 1964b
E. gracilis strain Z (analysis)	49	51	75	25	—	—	Brawerman and Eisenstadt, 1964b
E. gracilis strain Z (thermal denaturation)[c]	47–52	48–53	74–79	21–26	—	—	Brawerman and Eisenstadt, 1964b
Molecular weight, as isolated (sedimentation)	$20–40 \times 10^6$		$20–40 \times 10^6$		$2.6–3.6 \times 10^6$		Ray and Hanawalt, 1964, 1965
Denaturation studies	Double-stranded		Double-stranded		Double-stranded		Edelman et al., 1965
Density (gm/cm³)	1.707		1.686		1.691		See above references

[a] Includes approximately 2.3% methyl cytosine (Ray and Hanawalt, 1964; Brawerman et al., 1962b).

[b] Since *Euglena* mitochondria have now been shown to contain membrane-bounded DNA of density 1.691 (Edelman et al., 1966) S_x DNA can now be designated S_m DNA.

[c] Calculated from data given in reference.

Table I summarizes the properties of the three types of DNA from *Euglena* cells. *Euglena gracilis* var. *bacillaris* and *E. gracilis* strain Z are quite similar in the densities found for main band and S_c. In var. *bacillaris*, the base compositions and molecular weights as isolated vary considerably among the three types of DNA.

Consistent with these findings, bromouracil incorporation by *Euglena* brings about an increase in plastid mutations (Scher and Collinge, 1965). Azathymine incorporation affords ultraviolet protection, presumably by reducing the probability of thymine dimer formation (Lyman and Smillie, 1963). Since *Euglena* mitochondria have now been shown to contain membrane-bounded DNA of density 1.691 (Edelman *et al.*, 1966) S_x DNA can now be designated S_m DNA.

F. ORGANELLE-ASSOCIATED DNA IN OTHER SPECIES

Since the original demonstration by Ris and Plaut (1962) of DNA fibrils in chloroplasts, satellite DNA's from many chloroplast-containing species have been described. These are summarized in Table II. As may be seen, the base compositions of satellite DNA's attributed to the chloroplast vary widely from species to species as do the main band DNA's. Nass and Nass (1963) demonstrated DNA fibrils in mitochondria of chick embryo tissue, and the DNA was subsequently isolated by Rabinowitz *et al.* (1965). Luck and Reich (1964) have provided convincing evidence that this organelle is self-replicating in *Neurospora* and contains its own type of DNA. Table III summarizes the base compositions of satellite DNA's from species lacking chloroplasts.

G. LOCALIZATION OF INFORMATION FOR CHLOROPLAST CONSTITUENTS

The experiments reviewed above for *Euglena* and other species seem to leave no doubt that a DNA exists in the chloroplast and in other organelles such as mitochondria. The evidence from studies with ultraviolet on chloroplast continuity in *Euglena* are consistent with the interpretation that the information for the construction of the *Euglena* chloroplast or proplastid resides in the organelle itself. The existing data do not indicate, however, how much of the information is contained within the organelle. Since sexual fusion has not been observed in *Euglena* and attempts to find an infecting virus or transformation have been uniformly unsuccessful, it has been impossible to study the various modes of inheritance in *Euglena* in the usual way. In those species in which this type of genetic analysis has been possible (e.g., maize and *Oenothera*) interrelationships between the nucleus and the chloroplast are strongly suggested by the data. All we can say at present

Table II

DNA of Chloroplast-Containing Species and Related Organisms

Group	Species	Main band[a] Density	A+T	G+C	Satellites Density	A+T	G+C	Density	A+T	G+C	References
Euglenophyta	E. gracilis var. bacillaris	1.707	52	48	1.686[b]	74	26	1.691[c]	69	31	Table I
	E. gracilis strain Z	1.708	51	49	1.684[b]	75	25	1.692	67	33	Table I
Chlorophyta	Chlamydomonas reinhardi	1.726(?)	38	62	1.702[b,d]	61	39	—	—	—	Sager and Ishida, 1963
	Chlamydomonas reinhardi	1.723	36	64	1.695[e]	64	36	—	—	—	Chun et al., 1963
	Chlamydomonas reinhardi	1.721	38	62	1.694[e]	65	35	1.712	47	53	Leff et al., 1963
	Polytoma obtusum	1.725	35	65	—	—	—	1.711	48	52	Leff et al., 1963
	Chlorella ellipsoidea	1.716	43	57	1.695[b]	64	36	—	—	—	Chun et al., 1963; Iwamura and Kuwashima, 1964; Iwamura, 1960
Chrysophyta	Ochromonas danica	1.708	52	48	1.691	69	31	—	—	—	Edelman et al., 1963
Tracheophyta	Beta vulgaris	1.695	64	36	1.705[e]	54	46	1.719[e]	40	60	Chun et al., 1963
	Spinacia oleracea	1.695	64	36	1.705[e]	54	46	1.719[e]	40	60	Chun et al., 1963
	Vicia faba	A : G = 1.54			A : G = 1.67[b]			—	—	—	Kirk, 1963

[a] In all cases, main band DNA is attributed to the nucleus.
[b] Shown to be associated with chloroplasts.
[c] Shown to be associated with mitochondria.
[d] Possible error in calculation of density in original paper.
[e] Attributed to chloroplasts.

SPECIES LACKING CHLOROPLASTS BUT CONTAINING DNA SATELLITES

Group	Species	Main band			Satellites			Reference
		Density	A + T	G + C	Density	A + T	G + C	
Vertebrates	Mouse (fibroblast)	1.702	57	43	1.691	68	32	Kit, 1961; Chun and Littlefield, 1963
	Calf (thymus)	1.699	60	40	1.713	46	54	Schildkraut et al., 1962
	Guinea pig	1.697	62	38	1.703	56	44	Kit, 1961
	Chick (heart, liver)	1.698	61	39	1.707[a]	52	48	Rabinowitz et al., 1965
	Salmon (sperm)	1.703	56	44	1.688	71	29	Schildkraut et al., 1962
Arthropods	Cancer (7 species)	1.699-	41-	57-	1.677-	1-	99-	Sueoka, 1961
		1.701	43	59	1.683	3	97	M. Smith, 1964
	Balanus nubilis	1.706	53	47	1.714	45	55	M. Smith, 1964
Protozoa	Paramecium aurelia	1.689	70	30	1.696[b]	63	37	Smith-Sonneborn et al., 1963
	Blastocrithidia culicis	1.715	44	56	1.696	63	37	Mandel, 1965
	Crithidia fasciculata (Anoph.)	1.713	46	54	1.698	61	39	Mandel, 1965
	Crithidia fasciculata (Culex)	1.717	42	58	1.693	66	34	Schildkraut et al., 1962
	Crithidia oncopelti	1.709	50	50	1.699	60	40	Marmur et al., 1963
					1.691[c]	68	32	
	Naegleria gruberi S	1.693	66	34	1.683	76	24	Mandel, 1965
					1.702	57	43	
Fungi	Leishmania enrietti	1.721	43	57	1.699[d]	64	36	DuBuy et al., 1965
	Physarum polycephalum	1.703	56	44	1.714	45	55	Braun et al., 1965
	Blastocladiella emersonii	1.725	34	66	1.710	49	51	Comb et al., 1964
	Neurospora crassa	1.712	47	53	1.701[a]	58	42	Luck and Reich, 1964
Bacteria	Halobacterium (2 species)	1.727	32	68	1.718	41	59	Joshi et al., 1963
	Serratia marcescens	1.718	42	58	1.709[e]	50	50	Marmur et al., 1961
					1.703[e]	56	44	
	Proteus mirabilis	1.698	61	39	1.710[e]	49	51	Wohlhieter et al., 1964

[a] Attributed to mitochondria.
[b] Attributed to κ particles.
[c] Attributed to an endosymbiont.
[d] Attributed to the kinetoplast.
[e] Attributed to an episome.

is that at least part (a crucial part) of the information required to construct a chloroplast or proplastid resides in the organelle itself. It is possible that varying degrees of organelle autonomy exist in various species. If appropriate genetic and biochemical techniques become available it may be possible to assess whether the complete informational autonomy of the plastids (which is consistent with the present data) is indeed true in organisms such as *Euglena* or whether some genetic interaction with the nucleus is present as in higher plants. At the very least, the replication of organelles such as the chloroplast is responsive to overall signals for cell division which coordinate the division of the cytoplasmic organelles, nucleus, and of the cell itself.

IV. Possible Control Mechanisms for Chloroplast Development and Replication*

Figure 36 shows a model which we have constructed to relate the various facts known about chloroplast development and replication in *Euglena*. At worst it is a useful mnemonic device; at best it may serve as a working hypothesis. At the left are the dark-grown cells which have about 30

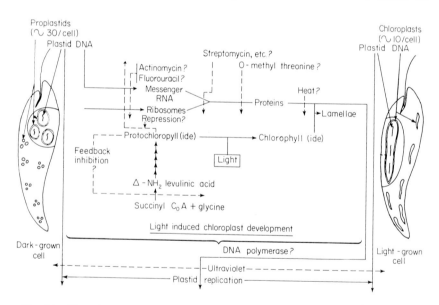

Fig. 36. Hypothetical model for control of chloroplast development and replication in *Euglena*. The details are explained in the text.

---

* *Editor's Note:* This topic is further covered in Chapters 11 and 12.

proplastids containing protochlorophyll(ide) and DNA. Maintained in darkness, these cells divide and the proplastids replicate to keep the numbers constant from one generation to the next. This implies that the DNA contained in each proplastid replicates itself in each cell generation, presumably via a DNA polymerase enzyme contained in the plastid itself. We assume that small amounts of this enzyme are present during growth in the dark to allow the continuity of the proplastid in dark-grown cultures.

Similarly, at the right of the diagram, is the light-grown cell which contains about 10 chloroplasts. Since both dark-grown and light-grown cells have multiplicities of about 30 for ultraviolet inactivation of replication, we assume that 3 proplastids have fused during the transition from dark to light with conservation of the DNA. Each chloroplast then would contain three of the DNA units formerly present in each proplastid. When the chloroplast divides during light growth of the cells, these DNA's are replicated as in the dark-grown cells. Since our experiments clearly showed that ultraviolet specifically blocks the transmission of plastid-forming ability to daughter cells at the time of cell division we have indicated the site of action of ultraviolet as being on DNA replication.

Now let us consider the developmental process from proplastid to chloroplast during light induction. The proplastids contain small amounts of protochlorophyll(ide) (about 1/5,000 the amount of pigment compared with the chlorophyll which will eventually be formed). It is well known that the action spectrum for light induction of chloroplast formation from proplastids in *Euglena* and higher plants is the absorption spectrum of protochlorophyll(ide) and that the light-induced conversion of protochlorophyll(ide) to chlorophyll(ide) is a necessary step in chlorophyll biosynthesis. The small amounts of protochlorophyll(ide) present (much less than would be expected from an intermediate accumulating behind a dark block) suggest that the formation of protochlorophyll in dark-grown cells is under feedback control. By analogy to other feedback inhibitions, protochlorophyll(ide) might be expected to act as an inhibitor of the first enzyme of the pathway, δ-aminolevulinic synthetase. On light conversion of protochlorophyll(ide) to chlorophyll(ide), the steady-state concentration of protochlorophyll(ide) would be quite low and would unblock the first step of the pathway leading to protochlorophyll(ide) synthesis. It is quite possible in fact that the protochlorophyll(ide) holochrome isolated by J. H. C. Smith (1958) is a masked δ-aminolevulinic synthetase. Regulation of this type for heme biosynthesis has already been described (Burnham and Lascelles, 1963). This picture suggests that all of the enzymes in protochlorophyll(ide) synthesis are already present in the proplastid and indeed we know that cells of *Euglena* kept in the dark can maintain their protochlorophyll(ide) content generation after generation. Unpublished experiments by Roth in our laboratory indicate that the behavior of protochlorophyll(ide) is consistent with this picture of feedback inhibition. Illumination of dark-grown cells of *Euglena* for a period of time results in conversion of all of the protochlorophyll(ide) to chlorophyll(ide). If left in the dark, these cells will resynthesize protochlorophyll(ide) to approximately the same level as before and then cease. After conversion with light again, the same thing occurs. This can be done many times in succession, suggesting that light unblocks protochlorophyll(ide) synthesis by converting the inhibitory protochlorophyll(ide) to chlorophyll. Resynthesis of protochlorophyll(ide) then occurs until the original level is reached and the biosynthesis is turned off once more. Carell and Kahn (1964) have described some enzymes of porphyrin synthesis in *Euglena*.

The illumination of protochlorophyll(ide) does far more than mediate chlorophyll production. As described earlier, light induction results in the formation of many chloroplast-specific proteins. This suggests that the conversion of protochlorophyll(ide) to chlorophyll(ide) results in the derepression of plastid DNA, permitting the synthesis of RNA messengers. Evidence for template RNA in chloroplasts has appeared (Brawerman and Eisenstadt, 1964a). Consistent with this is the finding that fluorouracil (Smillie, 1963; Evans and Smillie, 1962) inhibits chloroplast development if given sufficiently soon after light induction. The system becomes insensitive to fluorouracil after about 24 hours of development indicating that all of the necessary RNA has been synthesized by this time. Actinomycin D is also partially inhibitory (B. G. T. Pogo and Pogo, 1964; McCalla and Allan, 1964). As noted before, a unique species of ribosome exists in *Euglena* plastids (Brawerman, 1963). Thus, if messenger is produced from plastid DNA it could associate with plastid ribosomes to form a protein synthesizing system. Hadacidin, an inhibitor of adenine biosynthesis, blocks chloroplast development if given within the first 24 hours of development (Mego, 1964).

O-Methyl threonine blocks plastid development (perhaps by replacing isoleucine, thereby forming nonsense proteins, or perhaps by inhibiting amino acid synthesis) and is reversible by isoleucine (Aaronson and Bensky, 1962; Gray and Hendlin, 1962).

It has been known for some time that treatment with streptomycin and other compounds results in cell clones incapable of chloroplast formation (Provasoli *et al.*, 1948; Rosen and Gawlik, 1961; Zahalsky *et al.*, 1962; Ebringer, 1962a,b,c; McCalla, 1962). As indicated before, this results from the loss of plastid DNA and structure from the treated cells during subsequent cell division. In this respect its action resembles that of ultraviolet. Unpublished work by Wilensky in our laboratory, however, has shown that the same concentrations of streptomycin, unlike ultraviolet, also block chloroplast development from the proplastid. The evidence from bacterial systems suggests that streptomycin interferes at the attachment of messenger to the ribosomes resulting in coding ambiguities (Spotts and Stanier, 1961; Cox *et al.*, 1964; Davies *et al.*, 1964). Applied to the *Euglena* chloroplast system we might suppose that streptomycin's primary action is to block chloroplast-specific protein synthesis in a similar manner. If one of the proteins produced by this system were the DNA polymerase for the plastid DNA, then interference with development by streptomycin might result in eventual loss of plastid DNA through lack of enough enzyme for its replication. Streptomycin would therefore eventually lead to complete elimination of the plastid structures and DNA from the cells as observed.

Temperatures above 34°C also result in plastid and plastid DNA elimination from *Euglena* cells (Pringsheim and Pringsheim, 1952; Brawerman and Chargaff, 1960). It is possible that some enzymes involved in DNA replication in the plastid are sensitive to denaturation at these relatively low temperatures.

In short, there seems to be no reason not to consider chloroplast induction by light as a complex coordinated type of enzyme induction employing the usual translation and transcription mechanisms described for other systems. As with the most favorable systems for study (bacteria, particularly, *Escherichia coli*) our greatest ignorance is of the mechanisms of repression, derepression, and control of protein synthesis.

V. Speculations Concerning the Evolution of the Chloroplast

Having provided a positive answer to the question of chloroplast autonomy through replication we confront the question of the origin of the organelle being replicated. Basically, we have the two alternatives often voiced for the origin of viruses. The first alternative visualizes that a portion of the nuclear DNA became detached as a separate entity sometime in the distant past. This episome then proceeded to replicate in the cytoplasm independently of the nucleus and eventually evolved into the structure we call a chloroplast.

The second alternative supposes that at some point in evolution cells resembling primitive animal cells and primitive photosynthetic bacteria or blue-green algae existed contemporaneously. Primitive photosynthetic cells of this type invaded the envelopes of the primitive animal-like cells and established themselves as endosymbionts. Eventually these photosynthetic invaders lost their cell walls, and perhaps to some extent became nutritionally dependent for growth factors on the host cell. Replicating along with the host they gradually became subject to precise control of division by the host cell, and became habituated as chloroplasts.

There is very little evidence for choosing among these alternatives (and the many others which could be proposed). The fact that chloroplast DNA's of many species are so different in base composition from their cells' nuclear DNA would speak against the first alternative, but arguments could be advanced that the nuclear DNA of average composition could be quite heterogeneous along its length so that a detached piece might have a different base composition from the average for the nuclear DNA as a whole. Also, we could argue that the episomal DNA, having become detached, could continue to be changed in composition through evolution resulting in a different base composition from the nucleus.

In regard to the second alternative, there would be no problem of DNA composition since the invader would not have to have the same DNA composition as the host. Also, it is possible to discern possible steps in the habituation of endosymbionts occurring today. Many cases of endosymbiotic algae inhabiting animal cells are known. In these cases the endosymbiont retains its wall and can often be grown independently of the host. In the case of *Cyanophora paradoxa* (Hall and Claus, 1963) a blue-green alga has become habituated in an animal cell, has lost its wall, and divides along with the host. It is a small step from here to becoming an organelle.

The heterogeneity of base composition of chloroplast DNA's (see Table II) among several species, however, would indicate that if their origin were through invasion and habituation, there must have been several different cases of invasion rendering the origins of chloroplasts in different species polyphyletic. It is possible, of course, that there was only one invasion and that subsequent evolution has changed the base composition of the invader in different host cells.

Although one cannot choose among these and other alternatives, any comprehensive theory of the origin of life and its connection with cellular evolution must eventually account for the origin and evolution of autonomously replicating organelles.

VI. Conclusion

Much has been learned about chloroplast development and inheritance in many systems. The *Euglena* system has been particularly rewarding because chloroplast and proplastid replication are more sensitive to experimental interference than is cell viability. With the findings that chloroplast replication and development involve the replication and reading of an autonomous code, this area of development has entered the mainstream of molecular biology only to find itself confronted by this area's major problem, the mechanism of control. Perplexity likes company, however, and the interesting work is just beginning.

ACKNOWLEDGMENTS

Findings from the authors' laboratory reported in this paper arose from research supported by grant RG-6344 from the National Institutes of Health. The expert technical assistance of Miss Nancy O'Donoghue is gratefully acknowledged. We also thank Dr. Marvin Edelman for his help in compiling the DNA summary tables.

References

Aaronson, S., and Bensky, B. (1962). *J. Gen. Microbiol.* **27**, 75.
Aaronson, S., and Scher, S. (1960). *J. Protozool.* **7**, 156.
App, A. A., and Jagendorf, A. T. (1963). *J. Protozool.* **10**, 340.
Ben-Shaul, Y., Schiff, J. A., and Epstein, H. T. (1964). *Plant Physiol.* **39**, 231.
Ben-Shaul, Y., Epstein, H. T., and Schiff, J. A. (1965). *Can. J. Botany* **43**, 129.
Bold, H. C. (1951). *In* "Manual of Phycology" (G. M. Smith, ed.), pp. 207–208. Chronica Botanica, Waltham, Massachusetts.
Braun, R., Mittermayer, C., and Rusch, H. (1965). *Proc. Natl. Acad. Sci. U.S.* **53**, 924.
Brawerman, G. (1963). *Biochim. Biophys. Acta* **72**, 317.
Brawerman, G., and Chargaff, E. (1960). *Biochim. Biophys. Acta* **37**, 221.
Brawerman, G., and Eisenstadt, J. M. (1964a). *J. Mol. Biol.* **10**, 403.
Brawerman, G., and Eisenstadt, J. M. (1964b). *Biochim. Biophys. Acta* **91**, 477.
Brawerman, G., and Konigsberg, N. (1960). *Biochim. Biophys. Acta* **43**, 374.
Brawerman, G., Pogo, A. O., and Chargaff, E. (1962a). *Biochim. Biophys. Acta* **55**, 326.
Brawerman, G., Hufnagel, D. A., and Chargaff, E. (1962b). *Biochim. Biophys. Acta* **61**, 340.
Brown, J. S. (1963). *Biochim. Biophys. Acta* **75**, 299.
Burnham, B. F., and Lascelles, J. (1963). *Biochem. J.* **87**, 462.
Carell, E. F., and Kahn, J. S. (1964). *Arch. Biochem. Biophys.* **108**. 1,
Chun, E. H. L., and Littlefield, J. W. (1963). *J. Mol. Biol.* **7**, 245.
Chun, E. H. L., Vaughan, M. H., Jr., and Rich, A. (1963). *J. Mol. Biol.* **7**, 130.
Clarke, A. E., and Stone, B. A. (1960). *Biochim. Biophys. Acta* **44**, 161.
Cleland, R. E. (1962). *Advan. Genet.* **11**, 147.
Comb, D., Brown, R., and Katz, S. (1964). *J. Mol. Biol.* **8**, 781.
Cook, J. R. (1963). *Photochem. Photobiol.* **2**, 407.
Cox, E., White, J. R., and Flaks, J. G. (1964). *Proc. Natl. Acad. Sci. U.S.* **51**, 703.
Davies, J., Gilbert, W., and Gorini, L. (1964). *Proc. Natl. Acad. Sci. U.S.* **51**, 883.
DuBuy, H., Mattern, C., and Riley, F. (1965). *Science* **147**, 754.
Ebringer, L. (1962a). *J. Antibiot. (Tokyo)* **A15**, 113.
Ebringer, L. (1962b). *Naturwissenschaften* **14**, 334.
Ebringer, L. (1962c). *J. Protozool.* **9**, 373.
Edelman, M., Schiff, J. A., and Epstein, H. T. (1963). Unpublished results.
Edelman, M., Cowan, C. A., Epstein, H. T., and Schiff, J. A. (1964). *Proc. Natl. Acad. Sci. U.S.* **52**, 1214.
Edelman, M., Epstein, H. T., and Schiff, J. A. (1966). *J. Mol. Biol.* **17**, 463.
Edelman, M., Schiff, J. A., and Epstein, H. T. (1965). *J. Mol. Biol.* **11**, 769.
Eisenstadt, J. M., and Brawerman, G. (1963). *Biochim. Biophys. Acta* **76**, 319.
Eisenstadt, J. M., and Brawerman, G. (1964a). *Biochim. Biophys. Acta* **80**, 463.
Eisenstadt, J. M., and Brawerman, G. (1964b). *J. Mol. Biol.* **10**, 392.
Epstein, H. T., and Schiff, J. A. (1961). *J. Protozool.* **8**, 427.
Epstein, H. T., Boy, de la Tour, E., and Schiff, J. A. (1960). *Nature* **185**, 825.

Erwin, J., and Bloch, K. (1962). *Biochem. Biophys. Res. Commun.* **9**, 103.

Evans, W. R., and Smillie, R. M. (1962). *Plant Physiol.* Suppl. **37**, xxxviii.

Fuller, R. C., and Gibbs, M. (1959). *Plant Physiol.* **34**, 324.

Gibbs, S. P. (1960). *J. Ultrastruct. Res.* **4**, 127.

Gibbs, S. P. (1962). *J. Cell Biol.* **15**, 343.

Gibor, A., and Granick, S. (1962a). *J. Protozool.* **9**, 327.

Gibor, A., and Granick, S. (1962b). *J. Cell Biol.* **15**, 599.

Gibor, A., and Granick, S. (1964). *Science* **145**, 890.

Gojdics, M. (1934). *Trans. Am. Microscop. Soc.* **53**, 299.

Granick, S. (1961). In "The Cell" (J. Brachet and A. E. Mirsky, eds.), Vol. 2, pp. 489–602. Academic Press, New York.

Granick, S. (1963). In "Cytodifferentiation and Macromolecular Synthesis" (M. Locke, ed.). pp. 144–169. Academic Press, New York.

Gray, R. A., and Hendlin, D. (1962). *Plant Physiol.* **37**, 223.

Greenblatt, C. L., and Schiff, J. A. (1959). *J. Protozool.* **6**, 23.

Hall, W. T., and Claus, G. (1963). *J. Cell Biol.* **19**, 551.

Hill, H., Schiff, J. A., and Epstein, H. T. (1966a). *Biophys. J.* **6**, 125.

Hill. H., Schiff, J. A., and Epstein, H. T. (1966c). *Biophys. J.* **6**, 373.

Hill, H., Epstein, H. T., and Schiff. J. A. (1966b). *Biophys. J.* **6**, 135.

Hutner, S., and Provasoli, L. (1951). *Biochem. Physiol. Protozoa* **1**, 29.

Hutner, S., and Provasoli, L. (1955). *Biochem. Physiol. Protozoa* **2**, 17.

Iwamura, T. (1960). *Biochim. Biophys. Acta* **42**, 161.

Iwamura, T., and Kuwashima, S. (1964). *Biochim. Biophys. Acta* **82**, 678.

Jagger, J. (1958). *Bacteriol. Rev.* **22**, 99.

Jagger, J., and Latarjet, R. (1956). *Ann. Inst. Pasteur* **91**, 858.

Joshi, J., Guild, W., and Handler, P. (1963). *J. Mol. Biol.* **6**, 34.

Kelner, A. (1951). *J. Gen. Physiol.* **34**, 835.

Kirk, J. T. O. (1963). *Biochim. Biophys. Acta* **76**, 417.

Kit, S. (1961). *J. Mol. Biol.* **3**, 711.

Kreger, D. R., and Meeuse, B. J. D. (1952). *Biochim. Biophys. Acta* **9**, 699.

Krinsky, N. I., and Goldsmith, T. (1960). **91**, 271.

Krinsky, N. I., Gordon, A., and Stern, A. I. (1964). *Plant Physiol.* **39**, 441.

Lazzarini, R. A., and San Pietro, A. (1963). *Plant Cell Physiol.* (*Tokyo*) Special Issue, pp. 453.

Lazzarini, R. A., and Woodruff, M. (1964). *Biochim. Biophys. Acta* **79**, 412.

Leff, J., Mandel, M., Epstein, H. T., and Schiff, J. A. (1963). *Biochem. Biophys. Res. Commun.* **13**, 126.

Lefort, M. (1964). *Compt. Rend.* **258**, 4318.

Lewis, S., Schiff, J. A., and Epstein, H. T. (1965). *J. Protozool.* **12**, 281.

Liss, R., Schiff, J. A., and Epstein, H. T. (1965). Unpublished.

Luck, D. J. L., and Reich, E. (1964). *Proc. Natl. Acad. Sci. U.S.* **52**, 931.

Lyman, H., and Smillie, R. M. (1963). *Plant Physiol.* **38**, iii.

Lyman, H., Epstein, H. T., and Schiff, J. A. (1959). *J. Protozool.* **6**, 264.

Lyman, H., Epstein, H. T., and Schiff, J. A. (1961). *Biochim. Biophys. Acta* **50**, 301.

McCalla, D. R. (1962). *Science* **137**, 225.

McCalla, D. R., and Allan, R. K. (1964). *Nature* **201**, 504.

Mandel, M. (1965). *Chem. Zool.* **1** (in press), can't complete.

Marmur, J., Rownd, R., Falkow, S., Baron, L. S., Schildkraut, C., and Doty, P. (1961). *Proc. Natl. Acad. Sci. U.S.* **47**, 972.

Marmur, J., Cahoon, M. E., Shimura, Y., and Vogel, H. J. (1963). *Nature* **197**, 1228.

Mego, J. L. (1964). *Biochim. Biophys. Acta* **79**, 221.
Moriber, L. G., Hershenov, B., Aaronson, S., and Bensky, B. (1963). *J. Protozool.* **10**. 80.
Nass, M., and Nass, S. (1963). *J. Cell Biol.* **19**, 593.
Nishimura, M. (1959). *J. Biochem.* (*Tokyo*) **46**, 219.
Nishimura, M., and Huzisige, H. (1959). *J. Biochem.* (*Tokyo*) **46**, 225.
Perini, F., Kamen, M. D., and Schiff, J. A. (1964a). *Biochim. Biophys. Acta* **88**, 74.
Perini, F., Schiff, J. A., and Kamen, M. D. (1964b). *Biochim. Biophys. Acta* **88**, 91.
Pogo, A. O., Brawerman, G., and Chargaff, E. (1962). *Biochemistry* **1**, 128.
Pogo, B. G. T., and Pogo, A. O. (1964). *J. Cell Biol.* **22**, 296.
Price, C. A., and Carell, E. F. (1964). *Plant Physiol.* **39**, 862.
Pringsheim, E. (1958). *Rev. Algologique* [N.S.] **4**, 41.
Pringsheim, E., and Pringsheim, O. (1952). *New Phytologist* **51**, 65.
Provasoli, L., Hutner, S. H., and Schatz, A. (1948). *Proc. Soc. Exptl. Biol. Med.* **69**, 279.
Rabinowitz, M., Sinclair, J., DeSalle, L., Haselkorn, R., and Swift, H. (1965). *Proc. Natl. Acad. Sci. U.S.* **53**, 1126.
Ray, D. S., and Hanawalt, P. C. (1964). *J. Mol. Biol.* **9**, 812.
Ray, D. S., and Hanawalt, P. C. (1965). *J. Mol. Biol.* **11**, 760.
Rhoades, M. M. (1946). *Cold Spring Harbor Symp. Quant. Biol.* **11**, 202.
Ris, H., and Plaut, W. (1962). *J. Cell Biol.* **13**, 383.
Rosen, W. G., and Gawlik, S. R. (1961). *J. Protozool.* **8**, 90.
Rosenberg, A. (1963). *Biochemistry* **2**, 1148.
Sager, R. (1958). *Brookhaven Symp. Biol.* **11**, 101.
Sager, R., and Ishida, M. R. (1963). *Proc. Natl. Acad. Sci. U.S.* **50**, 725.
Scher, S., and Collinge, J. C. (1965). *Nature* **205**, 828.
Schiff, J. A. (1963). *Carnegie Inst. Wash. Year Book* **62**, 375.
Schiff, J. A., Lyman, H., and Epstein, H. T. (1961a). *Biochim. Biophys. Acta* **50**, 310.
Schiff, J. A., Lyman, H., and Epstein, H. T. (1961b). *Biochim. Biophys. Acta* **51**, 340.
Schildkraut, C. L., Mandel, M., Levisohn, S., Smith-Sonneborn, J. E., and Marmur, J. (1962). *Nature* **196**, 795.
Siegesmund, K. A., Rosen, W. G., and Gawlik, S. R. (1962). *Am. J. Botany* **49**, 137.
Smillie, R. M. (1963). *Can. J. Botany* **41**, 123.
Smillie, R. M., and Krotkov, G. (1960). *Arch. Biochem. Biophys.* **89**, 83.
Smith, J. H. C. (1958). *In* "The Photochemical Apparatus—Its Structure and Function" (R. C. Fuller *et al.*, eds.), pp. 296–302. Brookhaven Natl. Lab., Upton, N. Y.
Smith, M. (1964). *J. Mol. Biol.* **9**, 17.
Smith-Sonneborn, J., Green, L., and Marmur, J. (1963). *Nature* **197**, 385.
Spotts, C. R., and Stanier, R. Y. (1961). *Nature* **192**, 633.
Stern, A. I., Schiff, J. A., and Klein, H. P. (1960). *J. Protozool.* **7**, 52.
Stern, A. I., Schiff, J. A., and Epstein, H. T. (1964a). *Plant Physiol.* **39**, 220.
Stern, A. I., Epstein, H. T., and Schiff, J. A. (1964b). *Plant Physiol.* **39**, 226.
Sueoka, N. (1961). *J. Mol. Biol.* **3**, 31.
von Wettstein, D. (1961). *Can. J. Botany* **39**, 1537.
Wohlhieter, J. A., Falkow, S., Cirarella, R. V., and Baron, L. S. (1964). *J. Mol. Biol.* **9**, 576.
Wolken, J. J. (1961). *Euglena*. Rutgers Univ. Press, New Brunswick, New Jersey.
Wolken, J. J., and Gross, J. A. (1963). *J. Protozool.* **10**, 189.
Wolken, J. J., Mellon, A. D., and Greenblatt, C. L. (1955). *J. Protozool.* **2**, 89.
Zahalsky, A. C., Hutner, S. H., Keane, M., and Burger, R. M. (1962). *Arch. Mikrobiol.* **42**, 46.

CHAPTER 11

CHLOROPLAST INHERITANCE

Aharon Gibor and Helen A. Herron

I. Introduction

A. ADVANTAGES OF *Euglena* FOR STUDIES OF CHLOROPLAST INHERITANCE

No sexual stages in the life cycle of *Euglena* have been discovered in spite of the fact that many investigators have looked for them.* This shortcoming limits the usefulness of the organism for classic genetic studies.

---

* *Editor's Note:* For a discussion of early claims of meiosis in *Euglena* see Vol. I, Chapter 5, Section V.

On the other hand, certain distinctive properties of *Euglena* make it an attractive subject for studies on the development and inheritance of plastids.

Of these properties, the most significant are:

(1) The ability of *Euglena* to grow heterotrophically in the dark without chloroplasts. Such "etiolated" cells contain small colorless "proplastids" which develop into full-grown chloroplasts when the cells are transferred to the light.

(2) The sensitivity of the plastids to damage by various mutagens. These agents cause the cells to lose permanently their ability to convert proplastids to chloroplasts. Such cells are referred to as "bleached."

In this chapter, we will consider primarily the hypothesis of the presence of cytoplasmic genes that control the development of the plastids.

B. Criteria for Cytoplasmic Inheritance

Cytoplasmic inheritance (Jinks, 1964) is often diagnosed on the basis of unusual behavior in crosses, for instance, lack of segregation of parental characters at meiosis or differences between reciprocal crosses in which the two gametes contribute unequal amounts of cytoplasm and organelles. In some cases unequal mitotic divisions produce daughter cells with presumably identical chromosomes but with different extrachromosomal complements. If the cells then differ persistently in certain characters, these characters may be due to cytoplasmic genes.

If genetic information is carried in an organelle outside of the chromosomes, the organelle in which it is located must be duplicated and distributed to the daughter cells at division. If lost, it will not arise *de novo* or be replaced by action of the nucleus.

Extrachromosomal mutations can sometimes be specifically induced, and at frequencies much higher than for any chromosomal mutation.

In view of present concepts of the molecular basis of heredity, the cytoplasmic gene is expected to consist of DNA which is self-replicating and which is active in making RNA.

In *Euglena* the absence of sexual stages rules out the possibility of analysis of crosses. Artificial transfer of plastids between different strains of *Euglena* by microsurgery has not yet been achieved, but such an approach was successful in the transfer of mitochondrial properties in *Neurospora* (Garnjobst *et al.*, 1965; Diacumakos *et al.*, 1965).

The cytoplasmic inheritance of the plastids of *Euglena* may be considered in terms of their physical continuity, their mutability, the presence of DNA within them, and the biochemical activities of this DNA.

II. Physical Continuity

Physical continuity of the plastids is manifested by their growth, division, and distribution into daughter cells. In *Euglena* three distinct phases must be considered: (1) the continuity of the mature chloroplast of light-grown cells, (2) the continuity of the proplastids of dark-grown cells, and (3) the relationship between the proplastids and the chloroplasts.

The large chloroplasts of *Euglena* can readily be seen to divide in actively dividing cells. Fluorescence microscopy is especially useful for these observations since chlorophyll and its porphyrin precursors have a characteristic red fluorescence. An example of a dividing chloroplast is presented in Fig. 1 (from Gibor and Granick, 1962a). A thinning connection between separating halves of the chloroplast is obvious in the bridge still joining the two daughter cells.

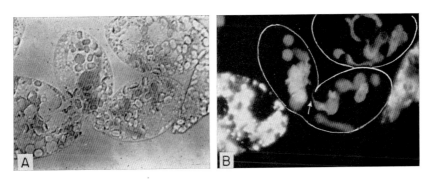

Fig. 1. Dividing cells seen in the bright field microscope (A) and in the fluorescence microscope (B). Note at the arrow the dividing plastid still bridging daughter cells. The outline of the cells has been drawn in B to facilitate comparison of the pictures. (Gibor and Granick, 1962a.)

Euglena cultures grown in the dark for many generations appear colorless. Epstein and Schiff (1961) described small fluorescing bodies which seemed to enlarge and to intensify their fluorescence when the cells were exposed to light. On continuous exposure to light these "proplastids" could be seen to develop into chloroplasts. Details of their development were studied by electron microscopy (Epstein and Schiff, 1961; Ben-Shaul *et al.*, 1964) and are described in Chapter 10.

Ben-Shaul *et al.* (1965) studied the fate of the chloroplasts when light-grown cells were put to grow in the dark. They concluded that proplastids arise from the chloroplasts by a gradual diminution in size of the organelles during consecutive cell generations and the disappearance of the photosynthetic lamellar system. The best morphological description of the entire-process was that it appears as the greening process run in reverse, resulting after several generations in small proplastids.

The multiplication of the proplastids in dark-grown cells can be seen by the following procedure. Dark-grown cells are exposed to light for 10 minutes and then are returned to grow in the dark. The short light exposure increases the amount of porphyrins in the proplastids; it is then easier to see them by their fluorescence. Dividing cells in such cultures can often be seen to possess pairs of fluorescing bodies, giving the impression that they divide in synchrony with the nucleus (Gibor, unpublished data).

It seems clear that chloroplasts arise by division of pre-existing chloroplasts or by maturation of proplastids. Proplastids in turn arise by division of pre-existing proplastids or from dark-adapting chloroplasts. The division of the plastids must then be synchronized to some extent with that of the cell in order to maintain the number of organelles per cell relatively constant.

That the number is not *exactly* constant was indicated by Gross and Villaire (1960), who found that plastid number varied with the age of the culture. In young, actively growing cultures it ranged from 0 to 8, while in older cultures it was between 5 and 11.

Observations on *E. gracilis* grown under continuous light revealed that in young cells all the plastids are connected to form a continuous branched tubular system rather than existing as discrete discontinuous entities (Fig. 2). Older cells or cultures maintained on a regime of 12 hours light and 12 hours dark did contain numerous seemingly discrete chloroplasts (Gibor and Granick, 1962a).

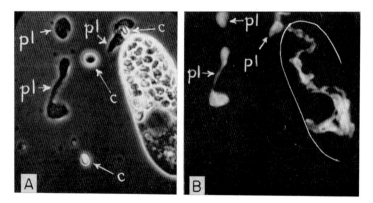

Fig. 2. The plastid system of young *Euglena* cells. A. The appearance of a cell and some freed plastids (pl) under phase. B. The same field as in A excited with ultraviolet light. Only the chloroplast fluorescence is seen. The outline of the cell has been drawn in to facilitate comparison of the pictures. A paramylum particle (c) lies within a concavity of the chloroplast at top right. (Gibor and Granick, 1962a.)

Bergeron and Smillie (1962) found fewer but larger chloroplasts with much more chlorophyll when their cells grew in the light, using carbon dioxide as the carbon source instead of organic compounds.

It is evident that the number, size, morphology, and pigment content of the chloroplasts vary, depending on environmental and metabolic conditions. Thus their physical continuity is not represented by unvarying, absolutely synchronized divisions but rather by what appears to be a balance of division and development fitted to the needs of the cell.

III. Mutability

The presence of genetic determinants in a self-reproducing organelle is revealed only if discernible mutations occur in the organelle. Many such mutations, both spontaneous and induced, have been described in *E. gracilis* strain Z and var. *bacillaris*. These mutations, resulting in bleached *Euglena*, are manifested as the loss of the ability of the cell to develop chloroplasts when they are exposed to light. [There are also other kinds of mutations that result in slower growth and thus in "petite" colonies (Gibor and Granick, 1962a). It is not known yet whether the "petites" result from mutations of the mitochondria as is the case with some "petite" yeast mutations (Gibor and Granick, 1964).]

A. Differences between Bleached Strains

It has become obvious that the bleached strains differ from one another. Some strains under the influence of light develop yellowish plastids which contain porphyrin precursors of chlorophyll. Occasional back mutations to normal green cells have been found within such bleached strains (Robbins et al., 1953; Gibor and Granick, 1962a).

Other strains contain plastids with abnormal lamellation and little or no chlorophyll. The development of the lamellae of these mutated plastids also depends on exposure to light (Liss *et al.*, 1965; Stern *et al.*, 1964).

Further damage to the plastids is manifested by other strains in which only small proplastids are present. Among these, some make enzymes for the synthesis of porphyrins from δ-aminolevulinic acid. These enzymic activities increase in cells that are exposed to light (Gibor and Granick, 1962a).

Table I summarizes the properties of some bleached strains that have been described in the literature.

Differences between bleached clones are not due to the different bleaching agents used to obtain them. A variety of clones can be isolated from an

23

ultraviolet-irradiated cell population (Gibor, unpublished data). Such clones are found to differ in the degree of damage to their plastids to the same extent as the clones obtained by different mutagens.

Table I

DESCRIPTION OF A VARIETY OF MUTANT STRAINS
PRODUCED BY DIFFERENT BLEACHING AGENTS[a]

Bleaching agent and strain produced	References
Ultraviolet	
White strain (*bacillaris*, W_3BUL) with no readily detectable plastids and no 1.686 satellite band DNA	2, 4, 7
Yellow strain (*bacillaris*, Y_3BUD) with small, abnormal plastids	4, 7
White strain (Z) containing ovoid bodies (2.5–4 μ long, 1–2 μ wide) with disorganized lamellae or crystallike projections from the bounding membrane	5
White strain (Z) showing small colorless bodies under phase contrast; no fluorescing porphyrins were formed, and carotenoid production could not be induced by light	3
Streptomycin	
White strain (*bacillaris*, $W_{10}BS_mL$) with no readily detectable plastids and no 1.686 satellite	2, 4
White strain (Z) with no apparent plastidlike structures	5
Strain (Z) containing bodies (0.1–1.0 μ long) with two to eight concentric lamellae when grown in the light, but containing no such bodies in the dark	6
Strain (Z) having plastids which appear to be of normal size under phase contrast	1
Strain (Z) with small, colorless, nonfluorescent bodies which develop red fluorescence in the presence of added δ-aminolevulinic acid; cells accumulate carotenoids in the light	3
Heat	
White strain (*bacillaris*, W_8BHL) with no readily detectable plastids and no 1.686 satellite	2, 4
White strain (Z) containing ovoid bodies (3–4 μ long, 2–4 μ wide) with lamellae arranged as straight or concentric rows or as large vesicles	5
Strain (Z) having structures like the concentric lamellar bodies in the streptomycin-bleached strain of Siegesmund et al (1962)	6
Strain (Z) having plastids which appear to be of normal size under light microscopy	1
Strain (Z) with small, colorless, nonfluorescent bodies which develop red fluorescence in the presence of added δ-ALA; cells accumulate carotenoids in the light but not in the dark	3

Table I (Continued)

Bleaching agent and strain produced	References
X-Rays	
Pale green strain (*bacillaris*, P₁BXL) which in the dark has proplastids and in the light has nearly normal plastids, lacking only some patches of lamellae; the 1.686 satellite band DNA is present	*2, 4, 7*
Olive green strain (*bacillaris*, O₂BX) which in the dark has proplastids and in the light has plastids with discontinuous lamellae, arranged in granalike blocks; satellite is present	*2, 4*
Yellow strain (*bacillaris*, Y₁BXD) which in the dark has proplastids and in the light has small, yellow plastids; satellite is present	*2, 4, 7*
Spontaneous	
Olive green strain (*bacillaris*, O₁BS) which in the dark has proplastids and in the light has abnormally large plastids with discontinuous lamellae and many unfused discs; satellite is present	*2, 4*
Dark brown strain (Z, B6In7W) with small (2 μ), yellowish, red-fluorescing bodies	*3*
Yellowish brown strain (Z) with small, yellowish bodies, only a few of which fluoresce faintly red	*3*
Faintly yellow strain (Z) with small, colorless, nonfluorescing bodies	*3*

[a] Key to references: *1*, Aaronson and Bensky (1962); *2*, Edelman *et al.* (1965); *3*, Gibor and Granick (1962a); *4*, Liss *et al.* (1965); *5*, Moriber *et al.* (1963); *6*, Siegesmund *et al.* (1962); *7*, Stern *et al.* (1964).

B. Delayed Appearance of the Mutagenic Effect

The mutagenic effect of the bleaching treatment is not always manifested in the cells being treated. For instance, cultures held at bleaching temperatures (35°C) can green in the light, even though each cell eventually gives rise to a bleached colony when plated (Brawerman and Chargaff, 1959). Similarly, ultraviolet-treated dark-grown cells are capable of greening if exposed to red light (blue light photoreactivates the ultraviolet damage), but colonies grown from such cells are all bleached (Schiff *et al.*, 1961b).

C. Theory of Plastid Loss

The phenomenon of bleaching in some strains has been interpreted as a result of the loss of self-reproducing plastids (Schiff *et al.*, 1961b; Schiff and Epstein, 1965). By the definition of self-reproduction, such a loss would be permanent. However, the differences between the bleached strains, the occasional regreening of some, and careful light and electron microscopy studies have established in our opinion that the organelles are *not* lost from the bleached cells.

Another argument supports this position, although it is based on the behavior of a *Euglena* which probably *does* lose its plastids under certain conditions. *Euglena mesnili*, a slow-growing species studied by Lwoff and Dusi (1935), reacts to growth in the dark differently than does *E. gracilis*. Instead of stopping chlorophyll synthesis and reducing the chloroplasts to proplastids, *E. mesnili* continues to make chlorophyll in the dark and to maintain full-sized chloroplasts. However, the number per cell decreases steadily until, after several months, most cells have one to two plastids and contain six to seven paramylum grains. Some cells then appear with no plastids; these cells make no paramylum. The loss of the chloroplasts may be a result of their multiplying in the dark more slowly than the cells. It was not possible to obtain a strain of these cells without plastids (Lwoff, 1944), perhaps because the plastids produce metabolites essential for the life of the cell even in the dark.

This experiment connects paramylum synthesis to the presence of plastids. Dark-grown *E. gracilis*, which contains only proplastids, can also make paramylum. Thus, Lwoff and Dusi (1935) suggest that the handling of glucose reserves is linked to the plastids even when they lack chlorophyll. If this is true, the presence of paramylum in bleached strains of *E. gracilis* is a strong indication that some plastid structure must remain.

Evidence that the plastid system continues to grow and replicate in cells treated with ultraviolet light was obtained by the following procedure (Gibor, unpublished data). Cells were irradiated with a sufficient dose to yield 100% bleached colonies. Individual cells from the irradiated population were grown as microcultures in agar on glass slides under red light. The bleached colonies that developed were observed by fluorescence microscopy. A well-developed vesicular system with red fluorescence was found in all the cells of these colonies (Fig. 3). The chlorophyll synthesized in the original irradiated mother cell under the red light was used here as a specific fluorescence marker for the growing plastid system. The general appearance of the plastid system in these cells is similar to that of normal cells at an early stage of greening.

Bleaching is thus due not to loss of the plastids but to genetic mutations which can block at various points the ability of the plastids to develop into chloroplasts.

D. Nature of the Mutable Factors

Are the mutable genetic factors located in the nucleus or in the cytoplasm? From a study of heat-bleaching and the effect of the rate of cell division on the bleaching, Brawerman and Chargaff (1960) concluded that *Euglena* contains a heat-sensitive self-reproducing system that controls the development of the plastid. The multiplication of this system is not always synchronized with the division of the chromosomes. This degree of autonomy did not, however, indicate whether this system is located in the nucleus or in the cytoplasm.

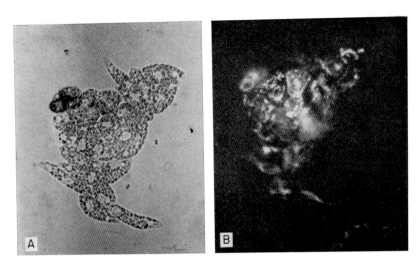

Fig. 3. A colony of *Euglena* grown from a single green *Euglena* cell which has received ultraviolet irradiation sufficient to cause all the progeny to become colorless. At the left is the colony seen in white light; the granules are paramylum, and the nuclei appear as colorless spheres in the center of the cells. At the right is the same colony seen in fluorescent light. The red fluorescence appears white and indicates that there is chlorophyll in a vesicular system throughout the cells. (Granick and Gibor, 1967.)

Ultraviolet bleaching experiments provide the best evidence for cytoplasmic genes that control the development of the chloroplasts. First, ultraviolet irradiation leads to bleaching only when it strikes the cytoplasm (Gibor and Granick, 1962b). Ultraviolet microbeam experiments have shown that irradiation of the nucleus alone may kill the cell but does not cause bleaching; on the other hand, irradiation of the cytoplasm, with the nucleus shielded, readily causes bleaching. Thus, whatever is sensitive to ultraviolet must lie in the cytoplasm. Second, the sensitive element is probably a nucleoprotein, because the action spectrum shows maxima at 260 and 280 mμ (Lyman *et al.*, 1961). Third, photoreactivation of the damage caused by ultraviolet light (Schiff *et al.*, 1961a; Hill *et al.*, 1966b) is similar to the photoreactivation studied for the ultraviolet effect on transforming DNA (Rupert, 1960; Setlow and Boling, 1963) and on bacteria (Jagger and Latarjet,

1956). The action spectra of both kinds of reactivation are in the blue region (300–450 mμ), and they are both enzymic reactions, sensitive to temperature changes. Fourth, the "shouldered" curves of survival of green colony-forming ability versus ultraviolet dose can be fitted by target theory (Lyman *et al.*, 1961; Hill *et al.*, 1966a), assuming that one hit inactivates one unit.* It was thus estimated that about 30 units must be inactivated to bleach the cell permanently. The value of 30 coincides with Epstein and Schiff's estimate (1961) of the number of proplastids in a dark-grown cell.

We can conclude from these facts that ultraviolet bleaching involves damage to about 30 cytoplasmic units of DNA. These *may* lie in the proplastids or chloroplasts, because the numbers fit and the chloroplasts are

* Rupert and Harm (1966) point out that shouldered survival curves can be expected in at least three cases: (a) multitarget, (b) multihit, and (c) recovery process. The multitarget theory makes the assumption of *n* equivalent targets, each of which must be hit at least once to be inactivated. The fractional survival S/S_0 is then given by

$$\frac{S}{S_0} = 1 - (1 - e^{-cD})^n \tag{1}$$

where D is the ultraviolet dose, c is a constant expressing the sensitivity of the target, and cD is the average number of hits per target. For large doses, higher powers of the exponential term can be ignored in the expansion, so that

$$\frac{S}{S_0} = 1 - \left[1 - ne^{-cD} + \frac{n(n-1)}{2!} e^{-2cD} - \cdots \right] \doteq ne^{-cD} \tag{2}$$

Then the curve that plots the logarithm of the survival will be

$$\ln\left(\frac{S}{S_0}\right) \doteq \ln(n) - cD \tag{3}$$

for large doses D. This represents a straight line of slope c; if it is extrapolated back to zero dose, it gives the value of n as the intercept. The Brandeis group uses this set of assumptions to interpret their data and estimates n as about 30. When they compare light- and dark-grown cells, the sensitivity c of the targets is different but the multiplicity n is the same (Lyman *et al.*, 1961; Hill *et al.*, 1966a).

The multihit case involves a single target which must be hit at least m times to be inactivated. Then

$$\frac{S}{S_0} = e^{-cD} \sum_{i=0}^{m-1} \frac{(cD)^i}{i!} \tag{4}$$

where we have summed the probabilities that the target will be hit 0, 1, 2,..., $(m-1)$ times for a given dose; none of these values are enough to inactivate, so their sum gives the probability of survival.

The presence of a dark-recovery process which operates efficiently at low doses but not at high doses can alter a one-hit curve to a shouldered curve (Haynes, 1964). In this case, the initial slope gives the sensitivity in the presence of the recovery mechanism, and the final slope gives the sensitivity when all recovery is inhibited.

There is no evidence at present to favor cases (b) or (c). The multitarget theory gives a good fit to the data and fairly consistent values.

known to contain DNA (see Section IV). The information in these units cannot be replaced from the nucleus since this organelle was shielded and hence undamaged during ultraviolet microbeam irradiation of the cytoplasm, and yet it could not make up whatever was damaged in the cytoplasm.

IV. DNA of the Plastids

A detailed discussion on the nucleic acids of *Euglena* is presented in Chapter 5. We will mention here briefly only those findings that bear directly on the genetics of the plastids.*

A. Presence and Activity of Plastid DNA

The ultraviolet action spectrum for the bleaching process (Lyman *et al.*, 1961) indicated that nucleoproteins were the targets being damaged by the irradiation. The microbeam irradiation experiments (Gibor and Granick, 1962b) showed that these nucleoprotein particles were outside the nucleus.

The finding that a unique species of DNA was associated with the chloroplasts of *Euglena* (Leff *et al.*, 1963; Ray and Hanawalt, 1964; Edelman *et al.*, 1964; Brawerman and Eisenstadt, 1964) suggested that it was this DNA that was damaged by ultraviolet light and that this damage resulted in bleaching. The base ratios and the increase in ultraviolet absorption and density by heat denaturation indicated that the satellite DNA was composed of double-stranded molecules (Edelman *et al.*, 1964).

Chloroplast DNA was found to contain a higher proportion of adenine and thymine than the DNA of the nucleus (Brawerman and Eisenstadt, 1964; Leff *et al.*, 1963). This fact might explain the higher sensitivity of the plastids to ultraviolet irradiation. It is thought that ultraviolet irradiation results in the dimerization of adjacent thymine bases of a single DNA strand (Beukers *et al.*, 1960; Wacker *et al.*, 1960; Beukers and Berends, 1960; Setlow and Setlow, 1962). Such neighboring thymines may be more frequent in the plastid DNA than in the nuclear DNA.

The composition of the chloroplast RNA was found by Brawerman (1962) to be higher in adenine and uracil, suggesting that the high adenine- and thymine-containing DNA of the plastids is the template for its synthesis.

Eisenstadt and Brawerman (1964) demonstrated amino acid incorporation by isolated chloroplasts. The incorporation was inhibited by treatment with actinomycin D. This indicates that the DNA of the organelle functions in RNA synthesis; the latter in turn promotes protein synthesis.

* *Editor's Note:* This topic is further covered in Chapter 10.

B. APPARENT LOSS OF DNA IN SOME BLEACHED STRAINS

A correlation between the chloroplast DNA and its functional role was provided by the findings of Edelman et al. (1965). They reported that some bleached strains of Euglena lacked the satellite-DNA band of density 1.686 normally associated with the chloroplasts. They interpreted its absence to mean that the plastids were completely lost from the cells (Schiff and Epstein, 1965). However, it could also mean either that each remaining mutated plastid contained only a portion of its original DNA or that fewer plastids were present per cell. A reduction by one order of magnitude in the amount of satellite DNA per cell would appear as a loss of the satellite by the techniques that were used. In any case, the experiments demonstrated that changes in the plastid DNA were correlated with the loss of the ability of the plastid to develop.

The fact that satellite DNA is not readily demonstrable should not be taken as evidence for the loss of the plastids themselves. This statement is based on the finding of Leff et al. (1963) that Polytoma, a naturally occurring bleached Chlamydomonas, lacks a satellite DNA present in normal Chlamydomonas. However, the presence of plastids in Polytoma was clearly shown in an electron microscopic study by Lang (1963).

C. SYNTHESIS OF RNA AND DNA

Actinomycin was found to inhibit the greening of dark-grown cells that were exposed to light (McCalla and Allan, 1964; Pogo and Pogo, 1964). This suggests the role of a DNA-dependent RNA synthesis in the process of chloroplast development. However, these findings do not exclude the possibility that the RNA is being synthesized on the DNA of the nucleus, rather than on that of the chloroplast.

Moreover, the presence of DNA in the plastids is not by itself proof that this DNA is replicating independently within the organelle. It is conceivable that the DNA is synthesized in the nucleus and migrates to the chloroplast. Sagan et al. (1965) studied the incorporation of DNA precursors into intact cells by radioautographic techniques. Incorporation of precursors into the chloroplasts and their removal after DNase digestion demonstrated new DNA synthesis but did not conclusively show that this DNA was synthesized in the chloroplasts. The ultraviolet microbeam experiments, on the other hand, showed that an unirradiated nucleus was not capable of curing the irradiated cytoplasm and an irradiated nucleus did not cause bleaching. It can be inferred from these experiments that the DNA of the plastids is not derived from the nucleus but replicates in the organelles themselves. Experiments with enucleated Acetabularia confirm that chloroplast DNA can be synthesized in the absence of the nucleus (Gibor, 1967).

The amount of DNA per plastid can be estimated as follows: the total amount of DNA per cell is 2.5–4.3 × 10⁻¹² gm (Neff, 1960; Buetow and Levedahl, 1962); Leff *et al.* (1963) estimated that in *Euglena* the satellite DNA comprises 4% of the total DNA. Lyman *et al.* (1961) estimated that each cell contains 30 ultraviolet-sensitive nucleoprotein units. From these figures we can estimate that each replicating ultraviolet-sensitive unit contains approximately 4 × 10⁻¹⁵ gm of DNA. This quantity of DNA is sufficient to code a large number of protein molecules and is of the same order of magnitude as that found in *E. coli* (Cairns, 1963). It is an order of magnitude higher than that estimated for *Acetabularia* chloroplasts (Gibor and Izawa, 1963).

V. Hypothetical Genetic System of the Plastids

From the facts concerning the induction of development of proplastids to chloroplasts, their multiplication, their mutability, and their DNA content, the following hypothesis is proposed for the genetic system of the plastids.

Each organelle contains a double-stranded DNA unit or multiples of this unit. A DNA unit represents numerous genes. Some of these genes function as constitutive genes while others are inducible. The constitutive genes control the multiplication of the plastids and perhaps other biochemical processes that are indispensable to the life of the cell. Light induces the activation of other genes responsible for the development of the entire photosynthetic apparatus of the chloroplasts. The inducible genes are unstable in some *Euglena* strains for unknown reasons. Mutations in any one of these genes result in a bleached cell line. These mutations might be due to point mutations or to deletions of segments of the DNA unit.

The differentiation of the proplastids into chloroplasts is probably regulated, not only by the light-inducible plastid genes, but also by nuclear genes. In higher plants many nuclear genes are known that affect the greening of the plastids. The nuclear control could conceivably work by limiting the supply of essential metabolites.

Nuclear genes might also be responsible for the instability of the plastids in certain strains of *E. gracilis* and not in others. Rhoades (1946) described for maize a recessive chromosomal allele (*iojap*) which when homozygous induced a change in the plastids. The change was irreversible so that the plastids could not develop normally even when they were brought by crosses into the presence of a homozygous wild-type nucleus. The change was induced by a nuclear gene but was inherited via the cytoplasm. Woods and DuBuy (1951a,b) found a similar gene in *Nepeta cataria*; plants homozygous for the gene *m* could undergo a variety of mutations in their plastids; the mutant form of the plastid then survived independently of the nuclear gene.

VI. Conclusion

Despite the absence of sexuality, considerable information has been obtained on the nature of the genetic system that controls the development of the plastids of *Euglena*. An independent, multigenic DNA-based genetic system is postulated to function in the plastids. Evidence for this genetic system has been obtained from studies on a few extremely mutable strains of *E. gracilis*. Further work on these strains, especially attempts to explain their extreme sensitivity, will undoubtedly shed much light on the controls over this genetic system.

ACKNOWLEDGMENTS

This work was supported in part by a grant from the National Science Foundation. We are indebted to Dr. S. Granick for his criticism of the manuscript.

References

Aaronson, S., and Bensky, B. (1962). *J. Gen. Microbil.* **27**, 75.
Ben-Shaul, Y., Schiff, J. A., and Epstein, H. T. (1964). *Plant Physiol.* **39**, 231.
Ben-Shaul, Y., Epstein, H. T., and Schiff, J. A. (1965). *Can. J. Botany* **43**, 129.
Bergeron, J. A., and Smillie, R. M. (1962). *Plant Physiol. Suppl.* **37**, xl.
Beukers, R., and Berends, W. (1960). *Biochim. Biophys. Acta* **41**, 550.
Beukers, R., IJlstra, J., and Berends, W. (1960). *Rec. Trav. Chim.* **79**, 101.
Brawerman, G. (1962). *Biochim. Biophys. Acta* **61**, 313.
Brawerman, G., and Chargaff, E. (1959). *Biochim. Biophys. Acta* **31**, 178.
Brawerman, G., and Chargaff, E. (1960). *Biochim. Biophys. Acta* **37**, 221.
Brawerman, G., and Eisenstadt, J. M. (1964). *Biochim. Biophys. Acta* **91**, 477.
Buetow, D. E., and Levedahl, B. H. (1962). *J. Gen. Microbiol.* **28**, 579.
Cairns, J. (1963). *J. Mol. Biol.* **6**, 208.
Diacumakos, E. G., Garnjobst, L., and Tatum, E. L. (1965). *J. Cell Biol.* **26**, 427.
Edelman, M., Cowan, C. A., Epstein, H. T., and Schiff, J. A. (1964). *Proc. Natl. Acad. Sci. U.S.* **52**, 1214.
Edelman, M., Schiff, J. A., and Epstein, H. T. (1965). *J. Mol. Biol.* **11**, 769.
Eisenstadt, J. M., and Brawerman, G. (1964). *J. Mol. Biol.* **10**, 392.
Epstein, H. T., and Schiff, J. A. (1961). *J. Protozool.* **8**, 427.
Garnjobst, L., Wilson, J. F., and Tatum, E. L. (1965). *J. Cell Biol.* **26**, 413.
Gibor, A. (1967). *In* "Biochemistry of the Chloroplasts" (T. W. Goodwin, ed.), Vol. II, p. 321. Academic Press, New York.
Gibor, A., and Granick, S. (1962a). *J. Protozool.* **9**, 327.
Gibor, A., and Granick, S. (1962b). *J. Cell Biol.* **15**, 599.
Gibor, A., and Granick, S. (1964). *Science* **145**, 890.
Gibor, A., and Izawa, M. (1963). *Proc. Natl. Acad. Sci. U.S.* **50**, 1164.
Granick, S., and Gibor, A. (1967). *Progr. Nucleic. Acid Res. Mol. Biol.* **6**, 143.
Gross, J. A., and Villaire, M. (1960. *Trans. Am. Microscop. Soc.* **79**, 144.

Haynes, R. H. (1964). *In* "Physical Processes in Radiation Biology" (L. G. Augenstein, R. Mason, and B. Rosenberg, eds.), pp. 51–72. Academic Press, New York.

Hill, H. Z., Schiff, J. A., and Epstein, H. T. (1966a). *Biophys. J.* **6**, 125.

Hill, H. Z., Epstein, H. T., and Schiff, J. A. (1966b). *Biophys. J.* **6**, 135.

Jagger, J., and Latarjet, R. (1956). *Ann. Inst. Pasteur* **91**, 858.

Jinks, J. L. (1964). "Extrachromosomal Inheritance" (Foundations of Modern Genetics Series). Prentice-Hall, Englewood Cliffs, New Jersey.

Lang, N. J. (1963). *J. Protozool.* **10**, 333.

Leff, J., Mandel, M., Epstein, H. T., and Schiff, J. A. (1963). *Biochem. Biophys. Res. Commun.* **13**, 126.

Liss, R., Schiff, J. A., and Epstein, H. T. (1965). Reference by Schiff and Epstein (1965) to manuscript in preparation.

Lwoff, A. (1944). "L'Évolution Physiologique—Etude des Pertes de Fonctions chez les Microorganismes." Hermann, Paris.

Lwoff, A., and Dusi, H. (1935). *Compt. Rend. Soc. Biol.* **119**, 1092.

Lyman, H., Epstein, H. T., and Schiff, J. A. (1961). *Biochim. Biophys. Acta* **50**, 301.

McCalla, D. R., and Allan, R. K. (1964). *Nature* **201**, 504.

Moriber, L. G., Hershenov, B., Aaronson, S., and Bensky, B. (1963). *J. Protozool.* **10**, 80.

Neff, R. H. (1960). *J. Protozool.* **7**, 69.

Pogo, B. G. T., and Pgoo, A. O. (1964). *J. Cell Biol.* **22**, 296.

Ray, D. S., and Hanawalt, P. C. (1964). *J. Mol. Biol.* **9**, 812.

Rhoades, M. M. (1946). *Cold Spring Harbor Symp. Quant. Biol.* **11**, 202.

Robbins, W. J., Hervey, A., and Stebbins, M. E. (1953). *Ann. N. Y. Acad. Sci.* **56**, 818.

Rupert, C. S. (1960). *J. Gen. Physiol.* **43**, 573.

Rupert, C. S., and Harm, W. (1966). *Advan. Radiation Biol.* **2**, 2.

Sagan, L., Ben-Shaul, Y., Epstein, H. T., and Schiff, J. A. (1965). *Plant Physiol.* **40**, 1257.

Schiff, J. A., and Epstein, H. T. (1965). *In* "Reproduction: Molecular, Subcellular, and Cellular" (M. Locke, ed.), pp. 131–189. Academic Press, New York.

Schiff, J. A., Lyman, H., and Epstein, H. T. (1961a). *Biochim. Biophys. Acta* **50**, 310.

Schiff, J. A., Lyman, H., and Epstein, H. T. (1961b). *Biochim. Biophys. Acta* **51**, 340.

Setlow, J. K., and Boling, M. E. (1963). *Photochem. Photobiol.* **2**, 471.

Setlow, R. B., and Setlow, J. K. (1962). *Proc. Natl. Acad. Sci. U.S.* **48**, 1250.

Siegesmund, K. A., Rosen, W. G., and Gawlik, S. R. (1962). *Am. J. Botany* **49**, 137.

Stern, A. I., Schiff, J A., and Epstein, H. T. (1964). *Plant Physiol.* **39**, 220.

Wacker, A., Dellweg, H., and Weinblum, D. (1960). *Naturwissenschaften* **47**, 477.

Woods, M. W., and DuBuy, H. G. (1951a). *Am. J. Botany* **38**, 419.

Woods, M. W., and DuBuy, H. G. (1951b). *J. Natl. Cancer Inst.* **11**, 1105.

CHAPTER 12

INHIBITORS OF THE CHLOROPLAST SYSTEM IN *EUGLENA*

John L. Mego

I. Introduction

Unlike most photosynthetic organisms, many strains of *Euglena* are unaffected by the loss of chloroplasts if they are supplied with a source of nutrition. This fact, and the ease with which the cells can be grown either in liquid or solid media, has resulted in extensive use of the organism in studies of chloroplast growth and development. A growing number of chemical and physical agents have been discovered that temporarily or permanently cause the loss of chloroplasts in *Euglena*. This sensitivity of the chloroplast to environmental factors, which may have little or no apparent effect on the cell, emphasizes the semiautonomous nature of these organelles. The presence of DNA (Leff *et al.*, 1963; Edelman *et al.*, 1964, 1965; Brawerman and Eisenstadt, 1964; Ray and Hanawalt, 1964, 1965; Sagan *et al.*, 1966) and a system for synthesizing proteins (Eisenstadt and Brawerman, 1963, 1964) suggests that chloroplasts may be semiindependent entities that provide the cell with a mechanism for converting light into chemical energy in return for a relatively protected environment. The chloroplasts of *Euglena*, however, appear to be somewhat more sensitive to outside influences than those in other organisms.

Euglena grown in the absence of light in a nutrient medium rapidly lose their chloroplasts and become colorless. When these dark-grown cells are exposed to light in a medium containing only phosphate and magnesium ions, chloroplast formation proceeds in the absence of cell division at the expense of cellular proteins (Brawerman and Chargaff, 1959a). There is apparently no plastid replication under these conditions; protochlorophyll is converted to chlorophyll, new ribosomes are formed, protein synthesis is induced, and chloroplast formation occurs. In higher plants and mosses, this process may be under the control of the phytochrome system (Marcus, 1960; Mego and Jagendorf, 1961; Keister *et al.*, 1962; Hahn and Miller, 1966); no such system has been detected in *Euglena*, and little is known about the mechanism that initiates chloroplast development in this organism. During cell division of *Euglena* in the presence or absence of light, plastid replication takes place. This process, clearly distinct from chloroplast formation, is also not well understood at present.

Agents that affect the *Euglena* chloroplast may be divided into two general categories: those that cause the permanent loss of plastid-forming ability by an apparent diluting-out process during cell division, and those that temporarily interfere with chloroplast formation in the light. Bleaching agents are usually effective during cell division, and they cause the permanent loss of chloroplasts from the cell. The inhibition of chloroplast formation is generally reversible; inhibitors temporarily interfere with the conversion of proplastids to green chloroplasts, or they may produce reversibly bleached cells in a growing culture. When the inhibiting substance is removed, the capacity to form chloroplasts is regained. These agents may be inhibitors of chlorophyll, protein, or nucleic acid synthesis.

II. Inhibitors of Chloroplast Formation

A. GROWTH IN THE ABSENCE OF LIGHT

Dark-grown *Euglena* contain small colorless proplastids in place of the large green chloroplasts of light-grown cells. When *E. gracilis* var. *bacillaris* is allowed to grow in the absence of light, chloroplast lamellae progressively disintegrate and are gradually lost, and chlorophyll disappears by dilution (Ben-Shaul *et al.*, 1965). About eight cell divisions are required for the complete conversion of chloroplasts to proplastids. In the dark, magnesium is lost from the chlorophyll molecule, and pheophytin appears in the cell (Wolken *et al.*, 1955; Wolken, 1956, 1961; Greenblatt and Schiff, 1959; Brown, 1963). In nondividing cells, no conversion into proplastids occurs in the dark. Baker (1933) observed no visible changes in chloroplasts of *E. gracilis* after 3 weeks in the dark in distilled water.

The transformation of green to irreversibly colorless *Euglena* probably involves a permanent alteration in some genelike structure in the chloroplast. Growth in the dark, therefore, even for prolonged periods, would not be expected to produce permanently bleached organisms.

Pringsheim (1948) grew *E. gracilis* in the dark for over a year, and Dubash and Rege (1967) maintained the organism in the absence of light for 6 years (over 300 transfers) without evidence of permanent chloroplast loss. Grenson (1964) was also unable to demonstrate loss of chloroplast-forming ability by growth in the dark. However, Lwoff and Dusi (1935) noted a diminution of chloroplast number in *E. mesnili* after 6-months in the dark, and after 15 months most organisms had two chloroplasts and some had none. Wolken (1961) also states that the loss of chloroplasts in the absence of light is not always completely reversible.

B. Effect of Growth Conditions on Chloroplast Development

The presence of a utilizable substrate has an effect on chlorophyll formation in dark-grown cells exposed to light. Chlorophyll formation in etiolated *Euglena* exposed to light in a medium lacking a carbon source is only about one-third that in cells under the same conditions in a complex nutrient medium (Mego and Buctow, 1966) App and Jagendorf (1963) found that the nature of the carbon source had an effect on protein and chlorophyll synthesis in greening cells. The presence of ethanol, which is a utilizable carbon source, repressed chlorophyll formation and the synthesis of the chloroplast enzyme fructose-1,6-diphosphatase. Repression was also found to occur if the cells were exposed to light in a medium containing the same carbon source as the one utilized during dark adaptation. Under these conditions, the repression was the same as in ethanol. The authors discuss the similarity of these results to a "glucose effect," i.e., the repression of inducible enzymes by substrates. Grenson (1964) also found that the carbon source greatly influenced the quantity of chlorophyll synthesized in *Euglena* cultures.

An excellent illustration of the great sensitivity of the *Euglena* chloroplast to external agents is the effect of acetate concentration on chlorophyll content. Buetow (1967) found that merely increasing the concentration of acetate resulted in a significant decrease in chlorophyll content of the cells accompanied by an increase in paramylon content. Total repression of chlorophyll synthesis by acetate was not observed, however. A maximum inhibition of about 75% occurred at 45.7 mM acetate and above, a result which indicates the existence of cellular control mechanisms that prevent total repression by acetate of chlorophyll synthesis in *Euglena*.

Variations in the pigment content of *Euglena* also occur during the normal growth cycle. At the late logarithmic and early stationary phases of growth, chlorophyll content of cells increases (Grenson, 1964). Brown (1959) found that light intensity during the growth of *Euglena* cultures produces alterations in the content of chlorophyll in the cells, particularily chlorophyll a.

Iron deficiency produces a decreased chlorophyll content in *Euglena* (Grenson, 1964; Price and Carell, 1964; Carell and Price, 1965). Iron levels that have no effect on growth rate may inhibit chlorophyll by two-thirds (Price and Carell, 1964). This element has been implicated in the biosynthesis of chlorophyll, particularily in the conversion of coproporphyrinogen to protoporphyrin (Lascelles, 1961). However, Carell and Price (1965) believe that the iron requirement for chlorophyll synthesis in *Euglena* is not due to the coproporphyrinogen-to-protoporphyrin reaction, and that only at iron concentrations that limit growth is there an accumulation of coproporphyrinogen. It has not been established whether iron-deficient *Euglena* chloroplasts are also deficient in chloroplast protein.

Since magnesium is a constituent of the chlorophyll molecule, media deficient in this element would be expected to produce achlorophyllous *Euglena*. Wolken (1956) observed the chloroplasts of *E. gracilis* var. *bacillaris* to collapse when grown in a Mg^{2+}-deficient medium. He concluded that any agent that disrupts the chlorophyll molecule will cause a collapse of chloroplasts and the production of spectral shifts due to the appearance of pheophytin in the cell.

C. 5-FLUOROURACIL AND OTHER ANTIMETABOLITES

One of the early events occurring during greening of dark-grown *Euglena* is the formation of new ribosomes (Brawerman *et al.*, 1961; Brawerman, 1963). These ribosomes are located in the plastids and function in the synthesis of chloroplast proteins. Any agent, therefore, that inhibits ribosome formation or nucleic acid synthesis may have an inhibitory effect on chloroplast formation in dark-grown *Euglena* when these organisms are exposed to light. Perhaps the first inhibitor of this type to be reported was 5-fluorouracil (Evans and Smillie, 1962). This analog is an effective inhibitor if added before the first 20 hours of illumination (Fig. 1). After this time no inhibition occurs, although only a small part of the chlorophyll content of the cell has been synthesized. The inhibitory effect of 5-fluorouracil may be reversed by the addition of an equimolar quantity of uracil but not by thymine. Smillie *et al.* (1963) also showed that the rate of incorporation of uracil-2-^{14}C into ribosomal RNA was inhibited by 5-fluorouracil, but its incorporation into soluble RNA was not inhibited. 5-Fluorouracil interferes with the formation of ribosomes (Aronson, 1961a,b); therefore, after these new ribosomes have been formed in plastids, the analog has no effect on protein synthesis and further chloroplast development (Smillie, 1963).

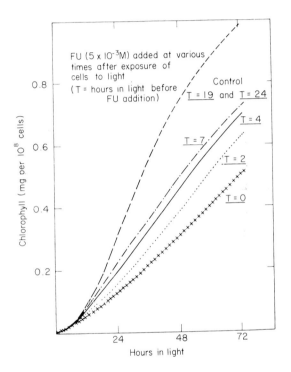

Fig. 1. Effective duration of 5-fluorouracil inhibition during chloroplast development (Smillie, 1963).

5-Fluorouracil has no effect on the synthesis of nonchloroplast proteins that are also induced during exposure of dark-grown *Euglena* to light (Smillie *et al.*, 1963). Therefore, these proteins are not subject to the same controls as plastid proteins. The chloroplast protein, cytochrome 552, is inhibited by fluorouracil to the same extent as chlorophyll, but glucose 6-phosphate dehydrogenase is not inhibited. On the contrary, this enzyme activity is higher than in untreated cells, and levels are maintained for longer periods than in untreated cells.

N-Formylhydroxyaminoacetic acid (hadacidin) inhibits greening of dark-grown *Euglena* when these organisms are exposed to light (Mego, 1964a). This substance, a structural analog of aspartic acid, prevents adenine synthesis by a competitive inhibition of the enzyme IMP : L-aspartate ligase (Shigeura and Gordon, 1962). The effect of hadacidin as an inhibitor of greening in nondividing *Euglena* cells can be reversed by aspartate or adenine in the medium, but not by uracil. Like 5-fluorouracil, hadacidin is not effective if added to greening cultures after 24 hours of illumination (Fig. 2).

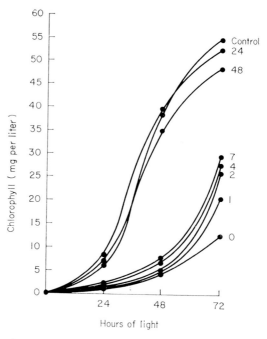

Fig. 2.   Effect of various lengths of time of illumination before the addition of hadacidin on greening of dark-grown *Euglena*. Numbers at the right of the curves refer to the light period in hours before addition of the inhibitor. Hadacidin concentration in all tubes was 0.01 *M* (Mego, 1964a).

By this time, however, most of the chloroplast matrix may be formed, and only chlorophyll remains to be synthesized.

The inhibitors of protein synthesis, chloramphenicol and actinomycin D, also interfere with greening in etiolated *Euglena* in light. Figure 3 shows the inhibition of chlorophyll synthesis in dark-grown cells exposed to light by various concentrations of chloramphenicol. In contrast to 5-fluorouracil, chloramphenicol is effective if added any time during greening (Smillie *et al.*, 1963), and it apparently does not interfere with ribosome formation (Pogo and Pogo, 1965). The antibiotic particularily inhibits incorporation of Mn^{2+} into lamellar components of the chloroplast as well as the synthesis of chlorophyll, cytochrome b_6, and cytochrome 552. Nonplastid proteins such as glucose 6-phosphate dehydrogenase are not inhibited (Smillie *et al.*, 1963). The effect of chloramphenicol on protein synthesis in chloroplasts

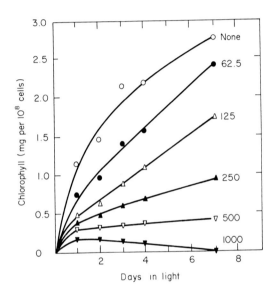

Fig. 3. Inhibition of chlorophyll synthesis by chloramphenicol in dark-grown *Euglena* exposed to light. The concentrations of chloramphenicol used are shown in micrograms per milliliter (Smillie *et al.*, 1963).

may occur at the ribosome level. Anderson and Smillie (1966) have demonstrated that chloroplast ribosomes in *Euglena* and higher plants have a greater capacity to bind the antibiotic than do cytoplasmic ribosomes. Chloroplast ribosomes, therefore, are similar to those of bacteria in this respect. Actinomycin D inhibits protein and RNA synthesis as well as greening (Pogo and Pogo, 1964; McCalla and Allan, 1964); however, the inhibition of protein synthesis and chlorophyll formation does not occur until after 12 hours of illumination. The antibiotic only partially inhibits the incorporation of uracil-2-^{14}C into total cell RNA. Since actinomycin acts by interfering with the formation of DNA-dependent RNA synthesis (Hurwitz *et al.*, 1962), these results suggest that chloroplast protein synthesis may be under the control of DNA. However, in view of the evidence that chloroplast RNA synthesis begins immediately upon exposure of etiolated *Euglena* to light (Smillie *et al.*, 1963; Mego, 1964a), one would expect actinomycin to inhibit greening and protein synthesis completely unless DNA-dependent RNA synthesis does not begin until after 12 hours of greening when most of the ribosomes have been formed.

Hydroxyurea is a known inhibitor of DNA synthesis in animal tissues and bacteria (Rosenkranz and Levy, 1965). The drug inhibits the incorporation of thymidine and phosphate into DNA of regenerating rat liver (Schwartz *et al.*, 1965) and phosphate into DNA of ascites tumor cells (Yarbro *et al.*, 1965), but it has no effect on RNA synthesis. A relatively high concentration (0.02–0.035 M) inhibits chlorphyll synthesis about 50% in dark-grown *Euglena* exposed to light (Buetow and Mego, 1967). However, concentrations as high as 0.2 M still allow some greening to take place in these cells (about 14% of the control). On a per milliliter basis, total cell DNA is most inhibited, RNA next, and protein is the least affected in dark-grown cultures allowed to green in a nutrient medium containing 0.05 M hydroxyurea. This suggests that the agent acts in *Euglena* cells in a manner similar to that in animal tissues, although its effect on chlorophyll synthesis or chloroplast formation requires further investigation in order to establish a relationship to chloroplast nucleic acids.

Actidione, an effective inhibitor of protein synthesis at the ribosome level (Bennett *et al.*, 1965), suppresses the incorporation of leucine-^{14}C into protein in *Euglena* equally in light or darkness (Kirk and Allen, 1966). Chlorophyll formation is inhibited whether the antibiotic is added immediately upon exposure of etiolated cells to light or after 4–8 hours of illumination: 1 μg per milliliter causes more then 90% inhibition in *E. gracilis* strain Z. Carotenoid synthesis is also inhibited but not as effectively as chlorophyll (Table I). Kirk and Allen (1966) conclude from these experiments that

Table I

EFFECT OF DIFFERENT CONCENTRATIONS OF ACTIDIONE ON SYNTHESIS OF CHLOROPHYLL a AND CAROTENOIDS[a]

Actidione (μg/ml)	0	0.13	0.32	1.0	3.2	10.0
Inhibition of chlorophyll synthesis (%)	—	50	80	93	100	100
Inhibition of carotenoid synthesis (%)	—	0	20	20	30	22

[a] Twice-washed, etiolated cells of *E. gracilis* strain G, were suspended in 5 ml 0.04 M phosphate buffer, pH 7.0, containing 0.001 M MgSO$_4$, and exposed to light for 4 hours (Kirk and Allen, 1966).

chlorophyll formation in *Euglena* is accompanied by protein synthesis, perhaps the protein associated with the chlorophyll holochrome. Carotenoids are less closely related to protein synthesis during the greening of etiolated cells since they are formed in the absence of light, and therefore the enzymes required would already be present. The fact that carotenoids are only slightly inhibited after 4 hours of greening provides further evidence for this hypothesis and suggests that protein is not produced during carotenoid formation.

Zannotti and Caldi (1963) noted that ethionine caused a reversible bleaching effect in *E. gracilis* var. *bacillaris*. They also observed that this amino acid analog of methionine produced nearly a doubling in nuclear DNA.

The herbicide 3-amino-1,2,4-triazole has been reported to cause a reversible bleaching effect in *Euglena* (Aaronson and Scher, 1960). Evidence has been presented that this agent inhibits the synthesis of histidine by interfering in the action of the enzyme imidazole glycerol phosphate dehydrogenase in algae (Siegel and Gentile, 1966).

III. Bleaching Agents

A. ULTRAVIOLET LIGHT

Ultraviolet irradiation of *Euglena* colonies produces a permanent loss of chloroplast-forming ability. The effect of ultraviolet is discussed in detail by Schiff and Epstein in Chapter 10.

B. STREPTOMYCIN AND OTHER ANTIBIOTICS

The bleaching effect of streptomycin in *Euglena* was first reported by Provasoli *et al.* (1948). There is still relatively little known about the mechanism of action of this antibiotic on chloroplasts. In *Euglena* it is most effective during cell division, particularily in the absence of light (De Deken-Grenson, 1959; Rosen and Gawlik, 1961; Mego and Buetow, 1966); but relatively high concentrations are required to produce the same effect under conditions of greening in the absence of cell division. Chlorophyll synthesis occurs in dark-grown *E. gracilis* strain Z exposed to light in a medium containing as much as 5 mg streptomycin sulfate/ml (Table II). As little as 0.01 mg/ml may inhibit chlorophyll formation completely in the light if cells are first grown in the dark in the presence of the antibiotic. However, the inhibition of chloroplast development by streptomycin in dark-grown cells exposed to light is influenced by the pH of the medium (Table III).

Table II

INHIBITION OF GREENING OF *E. gracilis* BY STREPTOMYCIN[a]

SM (μg/ml)	Dark-grown with SM (8 days); light in RM without SM (3 days)	Light-grown with SM (8 days)	Dark-grown without SM (8 days); light in RM with SM (3 days)
0.05	34 (0–67)		
0.1	64 (28–94)		
0.5	79 (49–96)	11 (6–22)	
1.0	93 (84–100)	40 (30–48)	
5.0	99 (97–100)	74 (55–83)	
10.0	100	92 (83–100)	6
100		100	16 (7–24)
500			37 (30–47)
1000			46 (29–54)
2000			59
5000			82

[a] All values represent percent inhibition as compared to a control to which no streptomycin was added. The figures are the means of two to four experiments with the range given in parentheses. Single values are the result of one measurement. SM, Streptomycin sulfate; RM, "resting" medium consisting of phosphate buffer, pH 5, and $MgCl_2$ (Mego and Buetow, 1966).

Table III

EFFECT OF pH ON THE INHIBITION OF CHLOROPHYLL FORMATION BY STREPTOMYCIN IN DARK-GROWN, NONDIVIDING *Euglena* EXPOSED TO LIGHT[a]

pH	Controls		Streptomycin-treated[b]	
	Chlorophyll (μg/10^7 cells)	pH 5 control (%)	Chlorophyll (μg/10^7 cells)	Inhibition (%)
5.0	70.5	100	61.8	12
6.0	64.2	91	50.4	22
7.0	69.9	99	32.0	54

[a] *Euglena gracilis* strain Z, was grown in the dark for 7 days in proteose–peptone–tryptone medium. The cells were washed and suspended in phosphate–$MgCl_2$, pH 5.0, 6.0, or 7.0, with or without streptomycin, and maintained in continuous light for 3 days (Mego and Buetow, 1966).

[b] 100 μg streptomycin sulfate/ml.

Vávra (1957) observed *E. gracilis* (Mainx) by fluorescence microscopy during growth in a medium containing streptomycin. The chloroplasts became diminished in size but not in number. The author concludes that the decrease in size is due to a loss of capacity for growth, and cell division further reduces the size of plastids until they disintegrate and disappear. Provasoli et al. (1951) also followed the changes in chloroplast morphology in E. gracilis by fluorescence microscopy during bleaching by streptomycin. The chloroplasts became smaller, pyrenoids were lost, and finally fragmentation occurred. These events were enhanced by rapid cell division.

Some workers have reported the presence of proplastidlike bodies in chemically bleached, streptomycin-, or heat-bleached cells (Siegesmund et al., 1962; Gibor and Granick, 1962; Moriber et al., 1963). Gibor and Granick (1962) measured the capacity of bleached cells to synthesize porphyrins. Some strains could produce porphyrin but others required the presence of the precursor δ-aminolevulinic acid. Some were unable to synthesize porphyrins in the presence of the precursor. Siegesmund et al. (1962), however, could find no proplastidlike structures in streptomycin-bleached Euglena that had been grown for several generations and sub-cultured several times in the absence of light. Perhaps the presence or absence of proplastids in bleached cells may be related to the time, or number of generations, during which the cells have been maintained in the chlorophyless state. Plastid remnants unable to form chloroplasts may persist for several generations in bleached Euglena.

De Deken-Grenson and Messin (1958) found that chloroplasts became diluted in Euglena cells during short periods of cell division in the presence of 0.2% streptomycin. Some cells had one chloroplast and some had none after the treatment period. Those with one chloroplast rapidly regained their normal complement of eight per cell when removed from the presence of the antibiotic; those with no chloroplasts remained bleached. In a later publication, De Deken-Grenson and Godts (1960) could find no relationship between the presence or absence of a chloroplast and the ability of a cell to become green after short treatment periods with streptomycin ($\frac{1}{2}$ to 2 hours). Cells that were bleached at the end of the treatment period could give rise to green organisms. These results, however, do not preclude the possibility that small plastids, devoid of chlorophyll but still retaining the mechanism for replication and chloroplast formation, may persist in organisms treated for short periods with streptomycin.

De Deken-Grenson and Godts (1960) found that clones of either white or green cells but no intermediate forms were produced when treated cells (streptomycin, $\frac{1}{2}$ to 2 hours) were plated on agar. One explanation for these results is that the antibiotic inhibits the replication of some genelike structure in the plastid which becomes diluted during subsequent cell divisions. If streptomycin becomes bound to these structures preventing replication, an interval of time accompanied by cell division may be required to remove it. Cell division may be required to facilitate removal of the antibiotic. However, if cell division is rapid during the interval before recovery takes place, more cells become bleached. Recovered cells containing at least one intact heredi-tary unit must replicate the unit in order to regain their full complement of chloroplasts. The rate of replication must be more rapid than the rate of cell division, or further bleaching will occur. Under most conditions, there-fore, in which *Euglena* is treated for short intervals with streptomycin and then washed free of the antibiotic and plated, the colonies should be either fully green or fully bleached. It may be possible to produce mixed colonies since, in some cases, the rate of cell division may be rapid enough to keep ahead of plastid replication within the cell. Robbins *et al.* (1953) obtained colonies varying from colorless, through yellow and pale green, to green after exposure of *Euglena* to various concentrations of streptomycin and plating on agar. Based on the observation that only fully green or bleached colonies were present after short treatment of cultures with streptomycin, Grenson (1964) eliminated the possibility that a particulate cellular con-stituent could be responsible for plastid replication in *Euglena*.

Streptomycin in low concentrations has little or no effect on growth rates (Provasoli *et al.*, 1948) and is relatively nontoxic for most protozoa (Jirovec, 1949). Kirk (1962a) found that streptomycin inhibits the incorpora-tion of acetate carbon into protein at the same concentration that inhibits chlorophyll synthesis, and the incorporation of leucine is inhibited slightly more than the synthesis of chlorophyll (Kirk, 1962b). The inhibition was also observed in the absence of light. In these experiments, however, Kirk used streptomycin in concentrations of 200–4000 μg/ml which is considerably higher than necessary to produce a permanent bleaching effect in strain Z.

Bleaching by streptomycin can be partially inhibited if any of several divalent cations are present (Rosen and Gawlik, 1961; Kirk, 1962a,b) including Mg^{2+}. Figure 4 shows that magnesium is not as effective as man-ganese or calcium. Kirk (1962a) also noted that manganese was more effective as a reversing agent than magnesium. This suggests that the bleaching action of streptomycin is not due to the chelation of Mg^{2+}, which is a con-stituent of chlorophyll. Manganese also reverses the inhibitory action of streptomycin on leucine-^{14}C incorporation into *Euglena* protein (Kirk, 1962b).

The effect of divalent cations on the bleaching action of streptomycin is difficult to explain without further experimental evidence. The antibiotic forms chelates with divalent cations (Foye *et al.*, 1954). If the action of streptomycin were due to chelation of metal ions, any chelating agent would cause bleaching in *Euglena*. More likely is an effect on transport of the antibiotic into the cell; this has been demonstrated in the alga *Nitella* (Pramer, 1956). Uptake of streptomycin in this alga appears to be mediated by an ion-binding carrier system which requires an expenditure of energy (Litwak and Pramer, 1957). Calcium and magnesium ions inhibit the uptake but monovalent cations have no effect.

Ebringer and Kupkova (1967) and Ebringer *et al.* (1967) reported that hydroxylamine reverses the bleaching action of streptomycin. Treatment of *Euglena* with 10^{-1} *M* hydroxylamine for only 1 hour after growth for 72 hours in the presence of 300 μg streptomycin/ml resulted in 100% green colonies after washing and plating the cells on agar. Growth for longer periods before treatment with hydroxylamine produced progressively more bleached colonies. Only 16 hours growth in the presence of streptomycin is required to produce all bleached colonies. The authors suggest that hydroxylamine inactivates or removes bound streptomycin perhaps from plastid DNA.

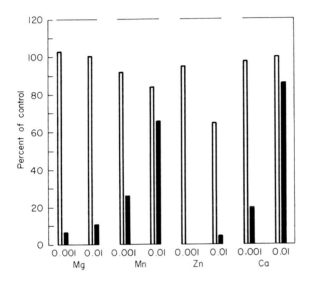

Fig. 4. Influence of cations on bleaching action of streptomycin. Light bars, no streptomycin; dark bars, 350 mg/liter dihydrostreptomycin. At 350 mg/liter, the antibiotic caused complete suppression of chlorophyll synthesis (Rosen and Gawlik, 1961).

Siegesmund *et al.* (1962) reported that *E. gracilis* strain Z, grown in the absence of light with 10 mg streptomycin/ml recovered their capacity to form chloroplasts if the cells were subcultured to antibiotic-free media several times before transfer to light. However, these workers used dihydrostreptomycin in their experiments. This antibiotic is not as effective as streptomycin as a bleaching agent in *Euglena* (Mego and Buetow, unpublished experiments). Although Siegesmund *et al.* (1962) used a relatively high concentration of dihydrostreptomycin (10 mg/ml), the action of this antibiotic may not be the same as streptomycin in *Euglena*. Using streptomycin sulfate in concentrations of 10 or 1000 μg/ml, we were unable to obtain green organisms after growth and subculture to antibiotic-free media several times in the dark (Mego and Buetow, 1966). Further studies on the bleaching effects of dihydrostreptomycin are clearly indicated.

Streptomycin is capable of precipitating polyanions such as polyphosphates and casein (Brock, 1964; Aronson et al., 1964), as well as nucleic acids (Cohen, 1947; Oxenburgh and Snoswell, 1965). Dihydrostreptomycin has no effect on the growth of mammalian cells in tissue culture, but streptomycin inhibits at high concentrations (Moskowitz and Kelker, 1963). The two antibiotics are equally effective as bacteriostatic agents. Dihydrostrepto-mycin is also much less effective as a precipitating agent for nucleic acids (Moskowitz, 1963). In addition, streptomycin is capable of preventing the attachment of certain streptococcal phages (Brock and Wooley, 1963), but dihydrostreptomycin is inactive in this process and is capable of reversing the effects of streptomycin (Brock, 1964). Aronson et al. (1964) proposed an interpretation of these observations based on the cationic moieties of the two antibiotics. Streptomycin is capable of forming a cyclic imminium salt in addition to the cationic guanido sites common to both antibiotics (Fig. 5). The additional cationic binding sites for streptomycin would result

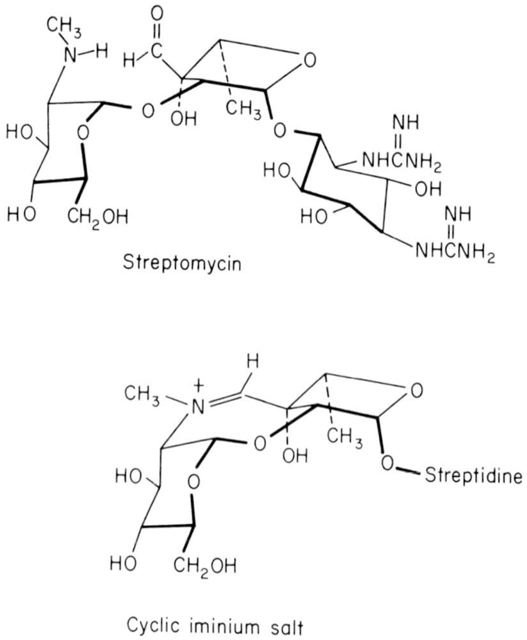

Fig. 5. Dihydrostreptomycin has a hydroxymethyl group in place of the aldehyde and therefore is incapable of forming the cyclic iminium salt (Aronson et al., 1964).

in the capacity for cross-linking polyanions, whereas dihydrostreptomycin binds to only one site. The latter would therefore competitively inhibit the cross-linking action of streptomycin. Removal of the cationic groups eliminates the antibiotic effect of dihydrostreptomycin (Polglase, 1965). This has led Polglase and others (Bragg and Polglase, 1963) to postulate that the cationic properties of the streptomycinoid antibiotics contribute to the biological activity of these agents. The fact that dihydrostreptomycin may also be a bleaching agent in *Euglena* suggests that a cross-linking action is not necessary, and that only a binding to the nucleoprotein may be required.

Portions of the streptomycin molecule such as *N*-acetylglucosamine, guanidine, streptamine, or streptobiosamine are inactive as bleaching agents (Hutner and Provasoli, 1951) which suggests that perhaps more than just cationic binding sites are required to inhibit replication of plastid DNA. Moreover, the bleaching capacity of streptomycin in *Euglena* is affected by pH (Kirk, 1962a; Mego and Buetow, 1966). Although the precipitating or cross-linking capacity of streptomycin is also pH-sensitive (Aronson *et al.*, 1964), the effect of pH on *Euglena* may be on transport across the cell membrane since the intracellular pH probably is not affected by the medium. The uptake of streptomycin in *Nitella* is also influenced by pH (Litwak and Pramer, 1957). In *E. gracilis* strain Z, higher concentrations of dihydrostreptomycin are required to produce the same bleaching effects as streptomycin (Mego and Buetow, unpublished experiments; see also Table VII). The additional cationic site which may be attributed to strepto-mycin perhaps accounts for the greater effectiveness of this antibiotic as a bleaching agent in *Euglena*.

It seems unlikely that streptomycin action on *Euglena* chloroplasts is the same as its effect as a bacteriostatic agent. In bacteria, streptomycin and dihydrostreptomycin are equally effective, and they cause a misreading of codons in ribosomes resulting in the production of nonfunctional protein (Davies *et al.*, 1964; Gorini and Kataja, 1964). At concentrations that cause bleaching in multiplying *Euglena*, the antibiotics do not inhibit chloroplast formation in nondividing, etiolated *Euglena*, a process involving a con-siderable amount of protein synthesis. Since high concentrations of strepto-mycin partially inhibit greening in nondividing cells (Table II), perhaps there is some effect on chloroplast ribosomes, but this cannot be the primary site of action of streptomycinoid antibiotics.

Kanamycin, paramomycin, neomycin (Zahalsky *et al.*, 1962; Ebringer, 1962b,c), erythromycin, carbomycin, picromycin, and methymycin (Ebringer, 1962a) are effective bleaching agents in *Euglena*. These antibiotics are related since they all contain amino sugars. According to Ebringer (1962b), the weakly basic properties of these substances may be responsible for their effects on chloroplasts. However, viomycin which does not contain an amino sugar has bleaching properties; but oleandomycin which contains this moiety has no effect on *Euglena* chloroplasts (Ebringer, 1962b). Like streptomycin, erythromycin is most effective during cell division. In a later attempt to relate the structure of antibiotics to bleaching activity, Ebringer (1966) reported that oleandomycin was also an effective bleaching agent when tested with a more sensitive strain in agar plates. In this study, all nonpolyene macrolide antibiotics caused irreversible bleaching with the exception of picromycin and methymycin which produced only a temporary inhibition of greening. The nonpolyene antibiotics are related by the presence of amino–hexose moieties, and the two most effective (carbomycin and tylosin) contain the same sugar groups: the aminohexose mycaminose and the neutral sugar mycarose. Picromycin and methymycin both contain d-desosamine but lack a neutral sugar. Antibiotics of this type that do not contain amino sugars (e.g., chalcomycin and lankamycin) were not effective bleaching agents.

Paramomycin and neomycin are toxic to *Euglena*, but kanamycin is a highly potent bleaching agent (Zahalsky et al., 1962; Ebringer, 1962c). According to Ebringer (1962c), kanamycin is not as toxic to *E. gracilis* var. *bacillaris* as streptomycin: 20 mg/ml does not inhibit cell division. The bleaching and toxic effects of the antibiotic are opposed by magnesium ions, histidine, urocanic acid, or a combination of pantothenate, nicotinic acid, and threonine. Histidine reverses the bleaching and killing effects of neomycin and paramomycin almost completely, but streptomycin and kanamycin are only partially reduced in effectiveness. Arginine and lysine also showed some weak protection. Zahalsky et al. (1962) postulate that magnesium and perhaps other agents such as histidine may reverse the bleaching effects of the streptomycinoid antibiotics by inhibiting transport across the *Euglena* cell wall. These agents may compete for the same binding site in the carrier system that transports antibiotics into the cell.

The antitumor agent, anthramycin, has recently been reported to cause bleaching in *Euglena* (Guttman and Tendler, 1966). The drug is more effective in light-grown organisms; and more bleached colonies were noted on the surface of the agar when cells were plated in the presence of the antibiotic. Anthramycin appears to inhibit DNA-dependent RNA synthesis in a manner similar to actinomycin (Pantelakis et al., 1966), although its effect as a bleaching agent in *Euglena* rather than as a temporary inhibitor of greening, and the effect of aerobiosis, suggest a different mode of action.

Aureomycin has some bleaching activity, although it is not nearly as effective as streptomycin. About 10% of the colonies were bleached when *Euglena* was grown in a concentration of 5 mg/ml (Robbins et al., 1953).

C. ANTIHISTAMINES AND OTHER CHEMICAL BLEACHING AGENTS

Antihistamines cause the permanent loss of chloroplasts in *Euglena* in a manner similar to the streptomycinoid antibiotics (Gross *et al.*, 1955). The most studied, and perhaps the most effective, is pyribenzamine, although the drug is not as effective as streptomycin on a molar basis (Fig. 6). Liang Tong *et al.* (1965) reported that subculture into pyribenzamine-free media after 20 days growth in the presence of the drug resulted in some regreening. Most of the antihistamines that cause bleaching in *Euglena* are toxic in relatively low concentrations (Gross *et al.*, 1955; Liang Tong *et al.*, 1965).

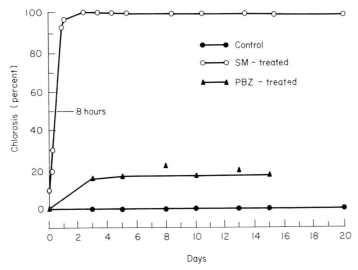

Fig. 6. Comparison of bleaching of *Euglena* by streptomycin (SM) and pyribenzamine (PBZ). Abscissa, percent bleaching; ordinate, days (Liang Tong *et al.*, 1965).

Zahalsky *et al.* (1962) tested a number of these drugs. All those tested inhibited cell division. Antazoline, pyrathiazine, and promethazine had no bleaching action; diphenylhydramine and phenindamine bleached reversibly at concentrations of 30 mg %; and tripelennamine, methapyrilene, and pyrilamine bleached irreversibly. Tripelennamine was most effective at 30 mg %, pyrilamine at 60 mg %, and methapyrilene bleached at 100 mg %.

N-Methyl-N'-nitro-N-nitrosoguanidine (MNG) has been shown to be an effective bleaching agent (McCalla, 1965b). A concentration of 8 μg/ml produced 98% bleached colonies after only 8 hours exposure to the drug before plating. MNG caused a temporary inhibition of cell growth for several hours; and the growth rate then returned to normal, but the cells were unable to produce chloroplasts.

McCalla (1962, 1965a) tested 12 derivatives of 5-nitrofuran on *E. gracilis*.
All the compounds caused some bleaching, but many were relatively toxic
(Table IV). Table IV shows that a nitro group in the 5-position is required

Table IV

EFFECTS OF VARIOUS NITROFURANS AND RELATED COMPOUNDS ON THE
CHLOROPLAST SYSTEM AND ON THE GROWTH OF *E. gracilis*[a]

Trivial name	Chemical name	Bleaching conc. (μg/ml)	Killing conc. (μg/ml)
Furfural	2-Furfuraldehyde	>512	>512
Furaldoxime	2-Furaldehyde oxime	>128	128
	2-Furaldehyde semicarbazone	>1000	>1000
Nitrofurfural	5-Nitro-2-furaldehyde	8–16	32
Nifuroxime	5-Nitro-2-furaldehyde oxime	16	64
Nitrofurazone	5-Nitro-2-furaldehyde semicarbazone	64–128	256
Nihydrazone	5-Nitro-2-furaldehyde acetylhydrazone	32	64
Furamazone	5-Nitro-2-furaldehyde semioxamazone	8	32
Nitrofurantoin	N-(5-Nitro-2-furfurylidine)-1-aminohydantoin	16	32–64
Furazolidone	N-(5-Nitro-2-furfurylidine)-3-amino-2-oxazolidone	8–16	64–128
Furmethonol	5-Morpholinomethyl-3-(5-nitro-2-furfurylidine-amino)-2-oxazolidinone	16	64
Thiofuradene	1-(5-Nitro-2-furfurylidine-amino)-2-imidazolidine-thione	32–64	128
	1,5-bis-(5-Nitro-2-furyl) pentadien-3-one	b	—
	1,5-bis-(5-Nitrofuryl)-3-pentadienone-guanylhydrazone	b	—
NFT	3-Amino-6-[2-(5-nitro-2-furyl) vinyl]-1, 2, 4-triazine	2.5	5.0

[a] *Euglena gracilis* strain Z, was grown for 1 week in 5 ml cultures in a complex medium (peptone, yeast extract, acetate) containing various concentrations of the drugs (McCalla, 1965a).

[b] Low solubility limited the testing of these agents, but both compounds caused bleaching.

to confer bleaching properties on these compounds. Since a high proportion
of bleached colonies results from exposure to the agents for only two generations, McCalla concluded that nitrofurans damage the chloroplast system
directly rather than by inhibiting replication. In addition to their action as
bleaching agents, nitrofurantoin and nitrofuraldehyde inhibit the greening
of dark-grown cells exposed to light. They differ in this respect from the

streptomycinoid antibiotics which do not inhibit greening under these conditions. *Escherichia coli* mutants selected on the basis of resistance to ultraviolet light were also resistant to derivatives of nitrofuran, and McCalla (1965c) concluded that DNA was damaged by these radiomimetic drugs. The bleaching effects of the nitrofurans in *Euglena*, therefore, may involve an interaction with plastid nucleic acids perhaps by inhibiting the function as well as the replication of chloroplast DNA.

In a later publication McCalla (1966) tested several analogs of N-methyl-N'-nitro-N-nitrosoguanidine as bleaching agents in *Euglena*. He observed that all active compounds contain an N-alkyl-N-nitrosamine group, and those analogs in which the nitroso group is replaced by a hydrogen or nitro group were not effective. Another interesting observation made by McCalla in this work was that there appeared to be little relationship between the effectiveness of these compounds as antileukemic agents and their capacity to cause bleaching in *Euglena*. The most effective bleaching agents also yield diazomethane in solution, and McCalla suggests that they may act as *in situ* precursors of this substance. Attempts to test diazomethane as a bleaching agent were not successful owing to the extreme instability of this material in aqueous solution.

o-Methylthreonine (β-methoxythreonine), an amino acid analog of L-isoleucine, inhibits multiplication and chlorophyll synthesis in *E. gracilis* strain Z (Aaronson and Bensky, 1962). Low concentrations (1–10 mg %) do not inhibit cell division but cause the cultures to become irreversibly bleached. The permanent loss of the capacity to produce chloroplasts is competitively inhibited by L-isoleucine, L-threonine, L-homoserine, aminobutyric acid, or ketobutyric acid. Tiglic acid, an intermediate in isoleucine biosynthesis, and L-methionine also reverse the action of o-methylthreonine. d-Isomers, such as d-threonine, are not effective as reversing agents, but they partially prevent the inhibition of cell division by o-methylthreonine. These observations suggest that o-methylthreonine interferes with the utilization of L-isoleucine. The analog may be incorporated in the place of isoleucine into some protein involved in plastid replication.

The supernatants of o-methylthreonine or streptomycin-bleached cultures contain large quantities of amino acids (Aaronson and Bensky, 1962). These amino acids, or the concentrated supernatants of green cultures, do not prevent bleaching by o-methylthreonine. The drug caused a 12% decrease in the incorporation of L-isoleucine-^{14}C into *Euglena* protein, and streptomycin inhibited 15%. Usually about 45% of isoleucine-^{14}C radioactivity was incorporated into the methanol extract, and in this fraction 22% was found to be in chlorophyll and carotenoids. Incorporation of isoleucine-^{14}C was inhibited 62% by o-methylthreonine and 50% by streptomycin. These observations suggest that isoleucine may be involved in the synthesis of photosynthetic pigments. However, since o-methylthreonine and streptomycin cause the irreversible loss of chloroplasts, inhibition of incorporation of isoleucine-^{14}C would be expected into protein as well as chlorophyll.

D. Magnesium Deficiency

Growth in the absence of light in a magnesium-deficient medium causes *E. gracilis* var. (*bacillaris*) to become permanently bleached (Dubash and Rege, 1967). Magnesium, therefore, appears to be required for maintenance of plastid continuity, perhaps in the synthesis of the small amount of "vestigial" chlorophyll associated with dark-grown cells. Inability to produce this chlorophyll apparently results in the loss of the entire plastid structure including the replicating mechanism. The authors suggest that this may be the first reported instance of a mutation caused by lack of a nutritional requirement.

E. Pressure

Some permanent damage to the chloroplast system of *Euglena* may be caused by high pressure (Gross, 1965). One-half to 1 hour at a pressure of 1000 atm results in only 1% viable organisms, and 20 minutes or 2 hours at this pressure produces 20% bleached colonies on agar. Only 1% color mutations resulted after 500-atm pressure for 2 hours. Pressure, therefore, is not an effective bleaching agent when compared with some chemical agents or elevated temperatures.

F. Temperature

Most strains of *Euglena* lose their chloroplasts and become permanently bleached by growth at 34–35°C; some strains have a maximum near 27°C (Pringsheim and Pringsheim, 1952). Since greening of dark-grown organisms, under nondividing conditions, is unaffected by bleaching temperatures (Brawerman and Chargaff, 1959b) the phenomenon is strictly related to cell division, and therefore replication of the plastids is probably affected. Growth of *E. gracilis* strain Z, is exponential at 34°–35°C, but the formation of chloroplasts is linear with time (Brawerman and Chargaff, 1959b). The rate of cell division is not greatly affected, but the final density attained is considerably less when *Euglena* is grown at 34.5°C (Mego and Buetow, 1965). The number of cell replications at the elevated temperature determines the degree of bleaching. If cells are inoculated at a high density, only a few divisions will occur at 34.5°C, and the organisms will not become bleached. However, if the cells are inoculated at an initial density of less than about 10^3 organisms per milliliter, a sufficient number of divisions will occur in a relatively short time (4–6 days) to produce an irreversibly bleached culture. We have estimated that at least seven divisions are required to produce a culture incapable of recovering from the bleaching temperature (Fig. 7). Loss of chloroplasts by growth in the absence of light (Ben-Shaul *et al.*, 1965) or in the presence of streptomycin (Ebringer *et al.*, 1968) also requires about this number of divisions.

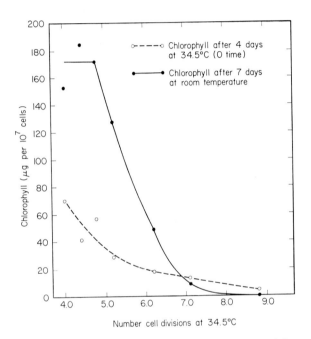

Fig. 7. Recovery of *E. gracilis* at room temperature as a function of the number of cell divisions at 34.5°C. Cells were inoculated at densities ranging from 230 to 29,000 cells/ml in order to obtain the varying numbers of divisions shown on the abscissa (Mego and Buetow, 1965).

Cells removed from the bleaching temperature before the loss of chloro-plasts is complete will rapidly regain the ability to produce chlorophyll to normal levels providing the rate of cell division is slow (Brawerman and Chargaff, 1959b, 1960). Figure 7 shows that cells that have lost about 70–80% of their chlorophyll are able to recover completely when removed from the bleaching temperature. The synthesis of chlorophyll begins after a lag period of about 24 hours during which a further reduction occurs. After 48 hours the chlorophyll level begins to rise in the cells. Figure 8 shows that partially bleached cultures which have been allowed to recover for 24 or 48 hours are capable of synthesizing chlorophyll at 34.5°C. This capacity to produce chlorophyll at the elevated temperature constitutes a measure of the recovery process and may be used to determine the degree of recovery after various experimental conditions. Another measure of recovery from the effects of temperature is the ability to produce chlorophyll at lower temperatures after additional cell divisions at 34.5°C. Cells are inoculated at a density of about 3000–6000 per milliliter into proteose–peptone–tryptone medium (Mego, 1964a) and allowed to grow at 34.5°C for 3 days. Chlorophyll is reduced from about 180–200 μg per 10^7 cells to 20–60 μg during approximately five to six cell divisions under these

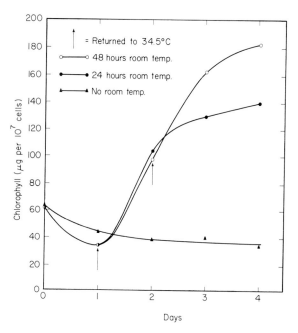

Fig. 8. Ability of partially heat-bleached *Euglena* to produce chlorophyll at 34.5°C after a recovery period of 24 or 48 hours at room temperature. One culture was not allowed a recovery period (Mego and Buetow, 1965).

conditions. The organisms may be removed to room temperature or other experimental conditions at this time and then reinoculated into fresh medium and returned to the elevated temperature. The partially bleached cells then undergo several additional divisions at 34.5°C. If recovery has occurred during the intervening experimental conditions applied before reinoculation, the cells will synthesize chlorophyll when removed from the elevated temperature. If the experimental conditions do not result in recovery from the initial growth period at 34.5°C, an additional one or two cell divisions will result in loss of capacity to green. For example, if partially bleached cells are removed from 34.5°C and maintained at 5°C for 48 hours and then reinoculated into fresh medium and returned to the bleaching temperature, the cells rapidly become incapable of producing chlorophyll. Controls maintained at room temperature for a similar period produce nearly their full complement of chlorophyll during 8 days after removal from the elevated temperature (Table V).

Table V

INABILITY OF PARTIALLY HEAT-BLEACHED *Euglena* TO RECOVER AT LOW TEMPERATURE[a]

Days at 34.5°C	Chlorophyll ($\mu g/10^7$ cells) 8 days after removal from 34.5°C			
	5°C, 24 hours	5°C, 48 hours	Room temp., 24 hours	Room temp., 48 hours
0	53	91	66	62
1	0	0	43	100
2	0	0	71	122

[a] Cells were grown at 34.5°C for 3 days after which time the chlorophyll had been reduced to 21 μg per 10^7 cells. Aliquots of the culture were removed and placed at 5°C for 24 or 48 hours and then reinoculated into fresh media and returned to the 34.5°C water bath or placed at room temperature (entries following days). Control samples were treated in the same manner except that they were placed at room temperature instead of 5°C. Samples were removed from the water bath after 1 or 2 days and placed at room temperature for 8 days (Mego and Buetow, 1965).

The ability of partially temperature-bleached *Euglena* to synthesize chlorophyll at room temperature is inhibited by 5-fluorouracil. Figure 9 shows that the same degree of inhibition occurs if the fluorouracil is added any time up to 48 hours after removal from the bleaching temperature. Furthermore, the presence of 5-fluorouracil does not prevent the recovery of partially heat-bleached organisms. Table VI shows that partially bleached cells that are allowed a 24-hour period at room temperature in the presence of 5-fluorouracil do not become irreversibly bleached after several additional divisions in fresh medium at the elevated temperature. This suggests that fluorouracil does not prevent recovery, but that the analog inhibits the synthesis of some component subsequent to the recovery period, probably ribosomes. These observations also suggest that chloroplast ribosome formation is prevented or reduced in rate during growth of *Euglena* at 34.5°C owing to the inhibition of some component required for their formation. This component becomes functional or is replenished during a period at room temperature, and ribosome formation may proceed at 34.5°C, providing the component has not been completely depleted. Partially bleached cells

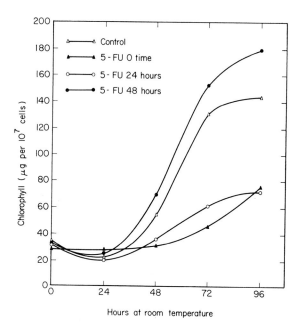

Fig. 9.   Effect of 5-fluorouracil (100 µg/ml) on chlorophyll synthesis at room temperature in partially heat-bleached *Euglena* (Mego and Buetow, 1965).

Table VI

EFFECT OF 5-FLUOROURACIL ON THE RECOVERY OF PARTIALLY HEAT-BLEACHED *Euglena*[a]

Days at 34.5°C	Chlorophyll (µg/10⁷ cells) 8 days after removal from 34.5°C		
	Control, no recovery	Control, 24-hour recovery	5-FU, 24-hour recovery
0	100	152	119
1	0 (2.0)	140 (2.8)	104 (0.9)
2	0 (1.8)	23 (1.2)	85 (1.1)
3	0 (0.9)	7 (0.9)	44 (1.8)

[a] Partially heat-bleached *Euglena* containing 40 µg chlorophyll per 10⁷ cells (3-days growth at 34.5°C) were placed in the dark at room temperature for 24 hours with and without 5-fluorouracil (5-FU), 100 µg/ml. The cells were then washed and reinoculated into fresh media and placed at 34.5°C. Samples were removed after 0, 1, 2, and 3 days and placed at room temperature for 8 days. The numbers in parentheses indicate the number of cell divisions occurring during the time at the bleaching temperature (Mego and Buetow (1965).

that have been allowed a period of recovery at room temperature in the presence of 5-fluorouracil are able to produce a net synthesis of chlorophyll when returned to 34.5°C. This suggests that replication of the component, rather than its function, is inhibited by growth of *Euglena* at elevated temperatures.

Low concentrations of streptomycin sulfate (10 μg/ml) completely inhibit chlorophyll synthesis in partially heat-bleached *Euglena* at room temperature if the antibiotic is added immediately upon removal of the organisms from 34.5°C. Figure 10 shows that addition of streptomycin after 24 hours at

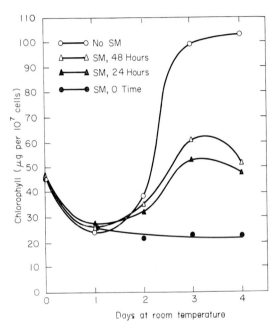

Fig. 10. Effect of streptomycin (10 μg/ml) on chlorophyll synthesis at room temperature in partially heat-bleached *Euglena* (Mego and Buetow, 1965).

room temperature does not prevent the synthesis of some chlorophyll (about 50% of the control). This effect of streptomycin is also partially overcome in the same manner if the cells are allowed to recover at room temperature in the absence of light (Mego, 1964b). Streptomycin appears to act prior to the fluorouracil-inhibited process in these organisms. A short period at room temperature, therefore, causes the cells to become partially resistant to the inhibitory effect of the antibiotic. The fluorouracil-sensitive process does not occur until at least 24 hours at room temperature. At this point, the cells behave similarly to dark-grown *Euglena* exposed to light.

Chloroplast development in light in dark-grown cells is not greatly affected by 10 μg streptomycin/ml or elevated temperature. Partially heat-bleached *Euglena*, therefore, appear to lack some component which is present in normal dark-grown cells. This component is rapidly recovered by a short period at room temperature but this recovery is prevented by streptomycin. The component may be required for plastid replication, and the streptomycin-sensitive process in the recovery of partially heat-bleached *Euglena* at room temperature may be a replication of plastids in the cells.

Dihydrostreptomycin also prevents chlorophyll synthesis in partially heat-bleached *Euglena* at room temperature. However, considerably higher concentrations of dihydrostreptomycin are required to produce the same degree of inhibition (Table VII).

Table VII

INHIBITION OF RECOVERY OF PARTIALLY HEAT-BLEACHED *Euglena*
AT ROOM TEMPERATURE BY STREPTOMYCIN AND DIHYDROSTREPTOMYCIN[a]

Streptomycin (μg/ml)	Inhibition (%)	Dihydrostreptomycin (μg/ml)	Inhibition (%)
0.1	19	0.25	0
0.25	34	0.5	0.5
0.5	61	1.0	4
1.0	68	2.5	21
10.0	100	5.0	53
		10.0	56

[a] Cultures of partially heat-bleached *Euglena* containing 58 μg chlorophyll per 10^7 cells (3 days growth at 34.5°C) were placed at room temperature in the presence of streptomycin or dihydrostreptomycin (sulfate) for 5 days. The cells were assayed for chlorophyll daily, and the percent inhibition of greening was calculated for each culture. The results shown in the table were those obtained on the fourth day when the cell densities had become relatively constant. (Mego and Buetow, 1965.)

Inhibition of chlorophyll synthesis in heat-bleached cells by streptomycin at room temperature can be removed if the organisms are washed, subcultured to fresh media, and allowed to grow for several generations. The full quantity of chlorophyll is regained after these treatments. This suggests that streptomycin is bound to some component that prevents recovery; but if the antibiotic is removed, the component may resume its function in chloroplast development. It is tempting to speculate that this component is chloroplast DNA which is responsible for plastid replication and chloroplast ribosome formation, but more direct experimental evidence must be obtained before this can be established.

IV. Some Speculations and Conclusions

Little direct evidence has been obtained on the mechanism of action of bleaching agents in *Euglena*. Evidence for an interaction with chloroplast DNA is circumstantial, although some of the most effective chemical bleaching agents are known to interact with DNA in other systems. Streptomycin and the nitrofurans are notable in this respect. However, the sensitivity of the *Euglena* chloroplast to a variety of bleaching agents suggests that more than DNA may be associated with the loss of chloroplasts. The antihistamines, *o*-methylthreonine, and elevated temperatures (29°–35°C) are some of the agents not known to affect DNA directly. *o*-Methylthreonine may be involved in the synthesis of plastid nucleoprotein, perhaps at the active site of an enzyme responsible for some aspect of DNA replication. It does not seem likely that inhibition of chlorophyll or carotenoid synthesis alone could result in the permanent loss of chloroplasts since chlorophyll is absent and carotenoids are greatly reduced in dark-grown cells. An intact nucleoprotein–chlorophyll (protochlorophyll)–carotenoid holochrome may be required to maintain hereditary continuity of the plastid. Any agent, therefore, that suppresses one component of this unit may prevent replication of the DNA. Some further evidence for this hypothesis is the observation by Dubash and Rege (1967) that magnesium deficiency in the absence of light causes bleaching of *E. gracilis*. Magnesium deficiency may prevent synthesis of the small amount of chlorophyll present in dark-grown organisms thus preventing replication of the entire holochrome. This hypothesis could account for the great variety of agents that cause the permanent loss of chloroplasts from *Euglena*.

DNA is present in the chloroplasts of normal green or dark-grown *Euglena*, but it is absent in permanently bleached cells. The bleaching action of ultraviolet light, which is most effective in the region in which nucleoproteins absorb, and the cytoplasmic localization of this effect, is perhaps the best evidence that DNA is involved in the hereditary continuity of chloroplasts. The similarity of action of ultraviolet light, elevated temperature, and chemicals (reversibility and a requirement for cell division) may indicate that all bleaching agents affect chloroplast DNA and plastid replication directly.

The ability of partially heat-bleached *Euglena* to synthesize chlorophyll at 34.5°C after a recovery period at room temperature eliminated the possibility that an enzymic function is inhibited. Equally unlikely, for the same reason, is an effect on some low melting-point lipid. Some chloroplast component appears to be lost during growth at elevated temperatures. The component may be restored at lower temperatures if it has not been completely eliminated. Restoration is not affected by 5-fluorouracil, but it appears to be sensitive to streptomycin, an agent known to precipitate nucleic acids. One possibility is that the component is responsible for some aspect of RNA or ribosome formation not sensitive to 5-fluorouracil. Recovery at room temperature allows the step to proceed, but chloroplast-specific ribosome formation is prevented by 5-fluorouracil. These events* are summarized in the accompanying diagram.

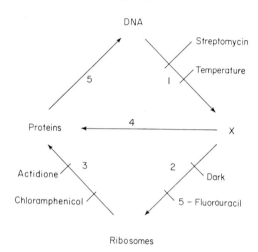

Bleaching agents such as elevated temperature or streptomycin may interfere with the replication of plastid DNA. If this is true, then "X" in the diagram would also be DNA. The steps 1,4, and 5 may proceed in light or darkness, and in the dark these steps are responsible for the continuity of the proplastid from generation to generation. Steps 2 and 3 are light-dependent and result in the production of chloroplasts. Other bleaching agents or inhibitors of chloroplast development may be included in the diagram. For example, ultraviolet light probably acts directly on DNA and may be placed at step 1. The nitrofurans also probably affect this step. Hadacidin may act at step 2. Other bleaching agents, such as o-methyl-threonine and the antihistamines, are more difficult to place in the diagram, although o-methylthreonine may block step 5.

* *Editor's note:* See also Chapter 10.

References

Aaronson, S., and Bensky, B. (1962). *J. Gen. Microbiol.* **27**, 75.

Aaronson, S., and Scher, S. (1960). *J. Protozool.* **7**, 156.

Anderson, L. A., and Smillie, R. M. (1966). *Biochem. Biophys. Res. Commun.* **23**, 535.

App. A. A., and Jagendorf, A. T. (1963). *J. Protozool.* **10**, 340.

Aronson, A. I. (1961a). *Biochim. Biophys. Acta* **49**, 89.

Aronson, A. I. (1961b). *Biochim. Biophys. Acta* **49**, 98.

Aronson, J., Meyer, W. L., and Brock, T. D. (1964). *Nature* **202**, 555.

Baker, C. L. (1933). *Arch. Protistenk.* **80**, 434.

Bennett, L. L., Ward, V. L., and Brockman, R. W. (1965). *Biochim. Biophys. Acta* **103**, 478.

Ben-Shaul, Y., Epstein, H. T., and Schiff, J. A. (1965). *Can. J. Botany* **43**, 129.

Bragg, P. D., and Polglase, W. J. (1963). *J. Bacteriol.* **85**, 590.

Brawerman, G. (1963). *Biochim. Biophys. Acta* **72**, 317.

Brawerman, G., and Chargaff, E. (1959a). *Biochim. Biophys. Acta* **31**, 164.

Brawerman, G., and Chargaff, E. (1959b). *Biochim. Biophys. Acta* **31**, 178.

Brawerman, G., and Chargaff, E. (1960). *Biochim. Biophys. Acta* **37**, 221.

Brawerman, G., and Eisenstadt, J. M. (1964). *Biochim. Biophys. Acta* **91**, 477.

Brawerman, G., Pogo, A. O., and Chargaff, E. (1961). *Biochim. Biophys. Acta* **48**, 418.

Brock, T. D. (1964). *Federation Proc.* **23**, 965.

Brock, T. D., and Wooley, S. O. (1963). *Science* **141**, 1065.

Brown, J. S. (1959). *Carnegie Inst. Wash. Yr-book* **59**, 330.

Brown, J. S. (1963). *Biochim. Biophys. Acta* **75**, 299.

Buetow, D. E. (1967). *Nature* **213**, 1127.

Buetow, D. E., and Mego, J. L. (1967). *Biochim. Biophys. Acta* **134**, 395.

Carell, E. F., and Price, C. A. (1965). *Plant Physiol.* **40**, 1.

Cohen, S. S. (1947). *J. Biol. Chem.* **168**, 511.

Davies, J., Gilbert, W., and Gorini, L. (1964). *Proc. Natl. Acad. Sci. U.S.* **51**, 883.

De Deken-Grenson, M. (1959). *Exptl. Cell Res.* **18**, 185.

De Deken-Grenson, M., and Godts, A. (1960). *Exptl. Cell Res.* **19**, 376.

De Deken-Grenson, M., and Messin, S. (1958). *Biochim. Biophys. Acta* **27**, 145.

Dubash, P. J., and Rege, D. V. (1967). *Biochim. Biophys. Acta* **136**, 185.

Ebringer, L. (1962a). *J. Protozool.* **9**, 373.

Ebringer, L. (1962b). *Naturwissenschaften* **49**, 334.

Ebringer, L. (1962c). *J. Antibiotics (Tokyo) Ser. A* **15**, 113.

Ebringer, L. (1966). *Folia Microbiol. (Prague)*, **11**, 379.

Ebringer, L., and Kupkova, H. (1967). *Folia Microbiol.* **12**, 36.

Ebringer, L., Mego, J. L., and Podová, G. (1967). *Biochem. Biophys. Res. Commun.* **29**, 571.

Edelman, M., Cowan, C. A., Epstein, H. T., and Schiff, J. A. (1964). *Proc. Natl. Acad. Sci. U.S.* **52**, 1214.

Edelman, M., Schiff, J. A., and Epstein, H. T. (1965). *J. Mol. Biol.* **11**, 769.

Eisenstadt, J., and Brawerman, G. (1963). *Biochim. Biophys. Acta* **76**, 319.

Eisenstadt, J., and Brawerman, G. (1964). *Biochim. Biophys. Acta* **80**, 463.

Evans, W. R., and Smillie, R. M. (1962). *Plant Physiol.* **37** (Suppl.), xxxviii.

Foye, W. O., Lang, W. E., Swintosky, J. V., Chamberlain, R. E., and Guinari, J. R. (1954). *J. Am. Pharm. Assoc. Sci. Ed.* **44**, 261.

Gibor, A., and Granick, S. (1962). *J. Protozool.* **9**, 327.

Gorini, L., and Kataja, E. (1964). *Proc. Natl. Acad. Sci. U.S.* **51**, 995.

Greenblatt, C. L., and Schiff, J. A. (1959). *J. Protozool.* **6**, 23.

Grenson, M. (1964). *Intern. Rev. Cytol.* **16**, 37.

Gross, J. A. (1965). *Science* **147**, 741.

Gross, J. A., Jahn, T. L., and Bernstein, E. (1955). *J. Protozool.* **2**, 71.

Guttman, H. N., and Tendler, M. D. (1966). *Federation Proc.* **25**, 562.

Hahn, L. W., and Miller, J. H. (1966). *Physiol. Plantarum* **19**, 134.

Hurwitz, J., Furth, J. J., Malamy, M., and Alexander, M. (1962). *Proc. Natl. Acad. Sci. U.S.* **48**, 1222.

Hutner, S. H., and Provasoli, L. (1951). *In* "Biochemistry and Physiology of Protozoa" (A. Lwoff, ed.), Vol. I, pp. 79–128. Academic Press, New York.

Jirovec, O. (1949). *Experimentia* **5**, 74.

Keister, D. L., Jagendorf, A. T., and San Pietro, A. (1962). *Biochim. Biophys. Acta* **62**, 332.

Kirk, J. T. O. (1962a). *Biochim. Biophys. Acta* **56**, 139.

Kirk, J. T. O. (1962b). *Biochim. Biophys. Acta* **59**, 476.

Kirk, J. T. O., and Allen, R. L. (1966). *Biochem. Biophys. Res. Commun.* **21**, 523.

Lascelles, J. (1961). *Physiol. Rev.* **41**, 417.

Leff, J., Mandel, M., Epstein, H. T., and Schiff, J. A. (1963). *Biochem. Biophys. Res. Commun.* **13**, 126.

Liang Tong, N. C. H., Gross, J. A., and Jahn, T. L. (1965). *J. Protozool.* **12**, 153.

Litwak, G., and Pramer, D. (1957). *Arch. Biochem. Biophys.* **68**, 396.

Lwoff, A., and Dusi, H. (1935). *Compt. Rend. Soc. Biol.* **119**, 1092.

McCalla, D. R. (1962). *Science* **137**, 225.

McCalla, D. R. (1965a). *J. Protozool.* **12**, 34.

McCalla, D. R. (1965b). *Science* **148**, 497.

McCalla, D. R. (1965c). *Can. J. Microbiol.* **11**, 185.

McCalla, D. R. (1966). *J. Protozool.* **13**, 472.

McCalla, D. R., and Allan, R. K. (1964). *Nature* **201**, 504.

Marcus, A. (1960). *Plant Physiol.* **35**, 126.

Mego, J. L. (1964a). *Biochim. Biophys. Acta* **79**, 221.

Mego, J. L. (1964b). *Biochim. Biophys. Acta* **88**, 663.

Mego, J. L., and Buetow, D. E. (1965). *In* "Le Chloroplaste; Croissance et Vieillissement" (C. Sironval, ed.). pp. 274-290 Masson, Paris.

Mego, J. L., and Buetow, D. E. (1966). *J. Protozool.* **13**, 20.

Mego, J. L., and Jagendorf, A. T. (1961). *Biochim. Biophys. Acta* **53**, 237.

Moriber, L. G., Herschenov, B., Aaronson, S., and Bensky, B. (1963). *J. Protozool.* **10**, 80.

Moskowitz, M. (1963). *Nature* **200**, 335.

Moskowitz, M., and Kelker, N. E. (1963). *Science* **141**, 647.

Oxenburgh, M. S., and Snoswell, A. M. (1965). *Nature* **207**, 1416.

Pantelakis, P. N., Tendler, M. D., Cole, D. R., Rousselot, L. M., and Korman, S. (1966). *Federation Proc.* **25**, 297.

Pogo, B. G. T., and Pogo, A. O. (1964). *J. Cell Biol.* **22**, 296.

Pogo, B. G. T., and Pogo, A. O. (1965). *J. Protozool.* **12**, 96.

Polglase, W. J. (1965). *Nature* **206**, 298.

Pramer, D. (1956). *Arch. Biochem. Biophys.* **62**, 265.

Price, C. A., and Carell, E. F. (1964). *Plant Physiol.* **39**, 862.

Pringsheim, E. G. (1948). *New Phytologist* **47**, 52.

Pringsheim, E. G., and Pringsheim, O. (1952). *New Phytologist* **51**, 65.

Provasoli, L., Hutner, S. H., and Schatz, A. (1948). *Proc. Soc. Exptl. Biol. Med.* **69**, 279.

Provasoli, L., Hutner, S. H., and Pinter, I. J. (1951). *Cold Spring Harbor Symp. Quant. Biol.* **16**, 113.

Ray, D. S., and Hanawalt, P. C. (1964). *J. Mol. Biol.* **9**, 812.

Ray, D. S., and Hanawalt, P. C. (1965). *J. Mol. Biol.* **11**, 760.

Robbins, W. J., Hervey, A., and Stebbins, M. E. (1953). *Ann. N.Y. Acad. Sci.* **56**, 818.

Rosen, W. G., and Gawlik, S. R. (1961). *J. Protozool.* **8**, 90.

Rosenkranz, H. S., and Levy, J. A. (1965). *Biochim. Biophys. Acta* **95**, 181.

Sagan, L., Ben-Shaul, Y., Epstein, H. T., and Schiff, J. A. (1966). *Plant Physiol.* **40**, 1257.

Schwartz, H. S., Garofalo, M., Sternberg, S. S., and Philips, F. S. (1965). *Cancer Res.* **25**, 1867.

Shigeura, H. T., and Gordon, C. N. (1962). *J. Biol. Chem.* **237**, 1937.

Siegel, J. N., and Gentile, A. C. (1966). *Plant Physiol.* **41**, 670.

Siegesmund, K. A., Rosen, W. G., and Gawlik, S. R. (1962). *Am. J. Botany* **49**, 137.

Smillie, R. M. (1963). *Can. J. Botany* **41**, 123.

Smillie, R. M., Evans, W. R., and Lyman, H. (1963). *Brookhaven Symp. Biol.* **16**, 89.

Vávra, J. (1957). *Folia Biol.* **3**, 108.

Wolken, J. J. (1956). *J. Protozool.* **3**, 211.

Wolken, J. J. (1956). *J. Protozool.* **3**, 211.

Wolken, J. J. (1961). "*Euglena.* An Experimental Organism for Biochemical and Biophysical Studies." Rutgers Univ. Press, New Brunswick, New Jersey.

Wolken, J. J., Mellon, A. D. and Greenblatt, C. L. (1955). *J. Protozool.* **2**, 89.

Yarbro, J. W., Kennedy, B. J., and Barnum, C. P. (1965). *Proc. Natl. Acad. Sci. U.S.* **53**, 1033.

Zahalsky, A. C., Hutner, S. H., Keane, M., and Burger, R. M. (1962). *Arch. Mikrobiol.* **42**, 46.

Zannotti, M., and Caldi, M. (1963). *Boll. Soc. Ital. Biol. Sper.* **39**, 489.

CHAPTER 13

EUGLENA—CELLS FOR BIOLOGICAL INVESTIGATION

Dennis E. Buetow

I. Introduction

Each topic in this two-volume treatise has been reviewed in its historical context and development, but emphasis has been placed on the current literature. The genus *Euglena* has been the subject of certain reviews and books in the past, but no publication of a *comprehensive* nature has appeared for a number of years. The large gain in knowledge concerning the bio-chemistry and physiology of these organisms in the last 10 years has not been fully reviewed. For those interested in the development of research on various species of *Euglena*, however, the following are particularly useful: Klebs (1883), Ternetz (1912), Walton (1915), Mainx (1927), Fritsch (1935), Chadefaud (1937), Hollande (1942), Jahn (1946, 1951), Hutner and Provasoli (1951), Gojdics (1953), Pringsheim (1956), and Wolken (1961). During the preparation of this treatise, a new edition (1967) of Wolken's book appeared. Like its predecessor, however, it emphasizes certain aspects of photosynthesis and phototaxis.

The genus *Euglena* shows a widespread ecological diversity. Variou species appear to have explored and adapted to waters of every descriptic (Jahn, 1946; Gojdics, 1953; Pringsheim, 1956; Lackey, Vol. I, Chapter 2 Species of *Euglena* are found in small freshwater pools rich in organ materials, in polluted streams and brackish waters, in damp mud along th banks of rivers, estuaries, and salt marshes, in water-filled coal mine pi (pH 1.8–3.9), in alkaline waters (up to pH 8.0; in fact some live, but d not divide, in laboratory culture at higher pH), on tree bark and in mois and dried soil in the form of cysts, in salt waters (some species are able t live in both fresh and salt waters), in tree holes and on snow. *Euglena dese* survives anaerobic conditions at 0–5°C for 30 days (Jahn, 1946).

A consideration of these many habitats should leave one without surpris that estimates of the number of species in the genus *Euglena* are high an range from about 56 to 250 (Gojdics, 1953; see also Vol. I, Chapter 1) Thus, Cook's conclusion (Vol. I, Chapter 6) that nearly the whole gamut o biological energy transformation (except possibly the anaerobic) has bee explored and adapted by *Euglena* species readily follows. Perhaps thes observations will end the still repeated reference to *Euglena* as a "singl organism." Instead, it should be clear that the genus *Euglena* offers a variet of cell types for biological investigation.

II. Areas for Investigatio

Problems for which *Euglena* species seem readily suited are many anc include areas varying from water pollution (Vol I, Chapter 2) to cytoplasmic inheritance (Chapters 10, 11, and 12). It is safe to assume that as more is revealed of the chemistry of more species of *Euglena*, the number of suitable problems will multiply. Each chapter in "The Biology of *Euglena*" suggests many problems for investigation. Several problems that seem particularly ready for extensive investigation are discussed in the following paragraphs.

A. CYTOPLASMIC INHERITANCE

1. *The Chloroplast*

The lability of the chloroplast in *Euglena* presents difficulties for the evolutionist on the one hand, but delights the biochemist on the other. The former must wrestle with problems concerned with the origin of colorless euglenoids (Johnson, Vol. I, Chapter 1) as well as whether or not the plastids themselves may at one time during phylogenesis have been independent microorganisms (Mereschkowsky, 1905; Famintzin, 1907; Schiff and Epstein, Chapter 10). The biochemist, however, is presented a unique

rganelle with which he can study the developmental biology of the chloroplast (Chapter 10) and has available a system for the study of cytoplasmic
inheritance (Chapters 11 and 12).

Euglena chloroplasts contain a unique species of DNA and evidence has
een presented for distinct chloroplast-associated RNA (Chapters 5 and 10).
It has been postulated that *Euglena* cells may provide a tool for mapping
genetic determinants of the chloroplast (Chapter 8). A question to be
answered is to what extent does the nucleus exert control over this organelle.
Gibor and Herron (Chapter 11) postulate that constitutive genes in the
plastid control its multiplication and that the differentiation of the proplastid
into a chloroplast is regulated by light-inducible plastid genes *and* by nuclear
genes. Gibor and Herron also postulate that the nucleus could be influential
by controlling supplies of essential metabolites. Brawerman (Chapter 5)
points out that various soluble enzymes associated with the photosynthetic
apparatus are under nuclear control. Kirk (1966) has tentatively concluded
that the genes determining the structure of enzymes for synthesis of chlorophyll and carotenoids and of enzymes concerned with photosynthesis are
in the nucleus. The demonstration by Leedale (Vol. I, Chapter 5, Section II,C
and Fig. 10) of connections between the perinuclear space and the endoplasmic reticulum "sheath" associated with each chloroplast in *E. gracilis*
certainly indicates a close relationship between the nucleus and the chloroplast.

The *Euglena* chloroplast is sensitive to a variety of chemical and physical
agents (Chapter 12), many of which do not otherwise appear to affect the cell.
"Bleaching" ("albinization") of *Euglena* cells could occur through loss of
the plastids themselves or through genetic mutations which block, at various
points, the development of plastids into chloroplasts. There is disagreement
in the literature concerning the nature of the "bleaching effect" of a given
agent (Chapters 10 and 11). However, the fact that the chloroplast is affected
by agents that apparently do not affect the cell otherwise leads to suggestions
of compartmentalization of cellular functions, e.g., protein synthesis
(Chapter 5). The chloroplast does have a system for protein synthesis, but
again the question arises as to what degree the chloroplast is an independent
entity. Another way of saying this is, if the supply of essential nutrients were
kept adequate, could chloroplasts replicate *in vitro* ? The degree of interplay
between the protein synthetic system of the chloroplast and that of the
cytoplasm must be determined. Furthermore, if the process of differentiation
of proplastid to chloroplast is under nuclear control (Chapters 5 and 11),
could plastids, in some stage short of being mature chloroplasts, be cultured
in vitro ? In other words, is the proplastid essentially genetically independent,
and does the proplastid then "lose" this independence when it "matures,"
i.e., becomes a chloroplast ?

2. *Mitochondria*

Another candidate for studies of cytoplasmic inheritance is the mitochon drion. Isolation from *Euglena* of mitochondria capable of oxidative phos phorylation has been accomplished (Buetow and Buchanan, 1963, 1964, 1965 The presence of a distinct species of DNA in isolated *Euglena* mitochondri has recently been demonstrated (Edelman *et al.*, 1966). Therefore, question posed about the degree of autonomy of the chloroplast can also be asked in regard to the mitochondrion. Successful artificial transfer of mitochondri between different strains of *Neurospora* (Garnjobst *et al.*, 1965; Diacumako *et al.*, 1965) perhaps opens the way to related studies with *Euglena*.

B. METABOLISM

1. *Carbon*

Euglena readily utilizes acetate for growth accompanied by relatively high respiratory rates (Chapter 2). Thus, *Euglena* has been classed among the "acetate flagellates." However, similar growth rates are observed with succinate (Wilson *et al.*, 1959) or glucose (Cook and Heinrich, 1965), bu neither of these carbon sources stimulates respiration above endogenous levels. It seems that a reassessment is due concerning ideas about what constitutes a "good" carbon source in this case, as well as how much energy is needed for growth and division. Furthermore, if endogenous respiratory levels are enough to support growth and division, why should such high respiratory rates be observed with acetate? Cook (Vol. I, Chapter 6) postulates the existence of oxygen-mediated reactions directly associated with the glyoxylate bypass in acetate-grown *Euglena*. Biosynthetic pathways for monounsaturated fatty acids used by *Euglena* under various nutritional conditions require molecular oxygen (Chapter 6). However, a complete study of nonrespiratory pathways that may require oxygen remains to be done in *Euglena*.

Strains of *Euglena* range from heterotrophic to obligately phototrophic (Vol. I, Chapter 6; Chapter 4). With the possible exception of anaerobic growth, nearly the whole range of biological energy transformation has been demonstrated in the genus *Euglena*. In addition, double carbon sources, e.g., CO_2 and acetate, appear to influence the utilization and distribution into cellular fractions of one another (Vol. I, Chapter 6; Chapter 4). Also, since CO_2 modifies the metabolism of different carbon sources in different ways in *Euglena*, Levedahl's conclusion (Chapter 4) that *Euglena* cells provide a valuable tool for investigation of control mechanisms involving CO_2 suggests many experiments. As Cook (Vol. I, Chapter 6) further points out, *Euglena*, which occupies a key transitory position between plants and animals, will probably play an important role in the elucidation of the origin and evolution of metabolic types. This suggestion becomes even more significant if one considers the fact that nearly the whole range of energy transformation is found within various strains of a *single* species, i.e., *E. gracilis*.

2. Nitrogen

A particularly potentially fruitful area of investigation in *Euglena*, though little touched, is that of nitrogen metabolism. It has been recognized for some time (Jahn, 1946; Vol. I, Chapter 6) that various strains and species of *Euglena* differ in respect to nitrogen requirements and that these requirements can further vary depending on whether the cells are grown in the light or in the dark. Some are able to use ammonium and nitrate compounds, others use peptones or proteins as nitrogen sources, while others are restricted and require certain amino acids. *Euglena gracilis*, however, is quite adaptable and will use as nitrogen sources for growth either ammonium and nitrate compounds (Schoenborn, 1942), or certain amino acids (Buetow, 1966).

The possible absence of certain enzymes involved in nitrogen metabolism or the possible presence of intracellular permeability barriers to certain amino acids in some *Euglena* are unsolved problems. It is also possible that certain amino acids are used primarily for specific biosynthetic processes. For example, arginine and phenylalanine are used by resting *E. gracilis* var. *bacillaris* (dark-bleached) for chloroplast development and greening (Huzisige *et al.*, 1957), but neither amino acid is used as sole nitrogen source for the growth and division of a permanently bleached *bacillaris* strain (Buetow, 1966).

More studies on nitrogen metabolism are needed in order to classify various species of *Euglena* into metabolic groups. Correlations between types of nitrogen metabolism and types of carbon metabolism may become apparent. Attempts along these lines have been made before (e.g., Jahn, 1946), but the great increase in available *defined* media and in the understanding of metabolic pathways over the last 20 years suggests that new attempts should be made. Such information will help clarify the origin and evolution of metabolic types as discussed above under carbon metabolism.

3. Lipids

Lipid composition of *Euglena* is labile and reflects the ability of these cells to adapt to either a plant or an animal mode of existence (Chapter 6). Furthermore, since these cells can be grown on a simple defined medium that does not contain any lipids, lipid composition reliably reflects the biosynthesis capacities of the cells. The evidence shows that *Euglena* cells are well endowed with lipid biosynthetic pathways.

Photoautotrophically grown *Euglena* contain large amounts of glycolipids which contain α-linolenic acid, whereas heterotrophically grown *Euglena* contain large amounts of phospholipids which contain γ-linolenic acid. The glycolipids containing the α-linolenic acid localize in the chloroplasts of *Euglena* and other eucaryotic photosynthetic organisms. Animal cells generally synthesize polyenoic fatty acids of the γ-linolenic series. Thus, *Euglena* cells in retaining the ability to synthesize either series show themselves useful for a study of the origin and evolution of metabolic types. Furthermore, those lipids pathways reserved specifically or primarily for the chloroplast are open to inspection in *Euglena*.

C. Nuclear Genetics

Other than the recent work on cytoplasmic inheritance, the genetics of *Euglena* has been little investigated. It has been postulated that fairly high degrees of polyploidy exist in most modern euglenoid species (Pringsheim, 1948, 1956; Leedale, 1958; Vol. I, Chapter 5). Meiosis has occasionally been reported for various Euglenineae, but its occurrence is possibly substantiated only in *Phacus pyrum* and *Hyalophacus ocellatus* (Leedale, 1962; Vol. I, Chapter 5). *Euglena* are generally considered asexual. If meiosis does occur in the genus, it apparently does so only in a rare instance (Vol. I, Chapter 5, Section V).

Pringsheim (1948) early stated that there were "size varieties" in some *Euglena* species. For example, he felt that *E. fusca* was only a name given to the larger cells of the species *E. spirogyra*. Therefore, *E. fusca* should not be a separate species, but should be classified merely as a variety of *E. spirogyra* (Leedale *et al.*, 1965). Now, provided that such a "size variety" as *E. fusca* remains constant, i.e., genetically stable, as it appears to be, then Pringsheim postulates that since *Euglena* cells are probably polyploid, any difference among "size varieties" could be due to differences in chromosome number. If such were the case, "*Euglena* size varieties" would present a situation wherein inheritable differences, based on chromosome number differences, could be studied in asexual organisms. Little seems to have been done to investigate Pringsheim's hypothesis.

Perhaps some support at least for the existence of polyploidy can be inferred from recent measurements showing different DNA contents for various *E. gracilis* strains (e.g., see Tables I and II, Chapter 5). In addition, DNA content appears to vary with conditions of growth. Bleached strains obtained by growth at 34°C often have higher DNA contents than the cells from which they were derived (Table V, Chapter 5). In one case a bleached strain has twice as much DNA as the normal parent strain (Brawerman *et al.*, 1960). Bleached *E. gracilis* var. *bacillaris* (strain SM-L1) shows a "normal" DNA content ranging from 3.15 to 6.20 pg per cell (daughter to parent cell range) with a population average of 4.40 pg per cell. Such cells treated with actinomycin D continue to synthesize and accumulate DNA up to about 6.20 pg per cell (Blum and Buetow, 1963b). On the other hand, carbon-limited cells stay alive but show a DNA content of 3.15 pg per cell for about 13 days. Cells deprived of external carbon apparently complete any mitoses in progress, but do not synthesize any net DNA. DNA per cell then further declines after 13 days and reaches a level of 2.25 pg per cell by 18 days (Blum and Buetow, 1963a). Such cells, when returned to medium with carbon, regenerate a normal morphology.

Since chromosome counts can now be made in *Euglena* with reasonable accuracy (Vol. I, Chapter 5), studies correlating these rather large DNA changes (as seen during growth at 34°C or during prolonged carbon deprivation) with changes in chromosome number or morphology are probably feasible. A relatively untapped area of genetics may be opened to investigation.

III. *Euglena gracilis*

By far, the most-studied *Euglena* species is *E. gracilis*. When one hears that *Euglena* does this or that, the reference is generally to *E. gracilis*. However, there are many strains of this species. Table I gives the generation time and dry weight of the three most commonly studied forms of *E. gracilis*. The dry weights of the different *E. gracilis* strains are quite variable in response to different growth conditions. The strains in Table I were all grown under the same conditions and all dry weights were measured in the exponential phase of growth within one to two divisions short of the stationary phase. The results can thus be compared.

Table I

GROWTH CHARACTERISTICS OF THREE STRAINS OF *E. gracilis*[a]

Characteristic	*E. gracilis* strain Z	*E. gracilis* var. *bacillaris*	*E. gracilis* var. *bacillaris*, strain SM-L1[b]
Generation time (hours)	14	24	21
Dry weight (Pg per cell)	570	640	995

[a] Grown on a defined medium (Buetow, 1965) in the dark at 27°C with 0.061 *M* sodium acetate.
[b] Streptomycin-bleached.

It is clear that generation times and dry weights are different for the three strains. Furthermore, real differences concerning acetate metabolism also appear to exist. In bleached *bacillaris*, the majority of labeled acetate assimilated during a 6-hour period can be recovered in carbohydrate, particularly paramylon (Chapter 2). The paramylon is then broken down for the synthesis of protein, lipid, etc. In contrast, in the green strain Z grown on labeled acetate for only 3 hours, the majority of label is found in lipid and protein (Cook, 1965; Vol. I, Chapter 6). Thus, there is a "paramylon bottleneck," so to speak, in *bacillaris*. This "bottleneck" either is not present or is, at least, less of a "block" in strain Z, the net result being a much shorter generation time for strain Z than for *bacillaris* (Table I). Also, dry weight of strain Z is less than *bacillaris*, particularly strain SM-L1. The difference reflects mainly paramylon content.

The presence of the "paramylon bottleneck" in *bacillaris* may also explain why its rates of synthesis of protein and RNA, for example, are slower than its rate of cell division (Vol. I, Chapters 6 and 7). In contrast, biosynthetic rates equal to the cell division rate in strain Z grown in the light have been achieved (Kempner and Miller, 1965). Whether the "bottleneck" would be of significance in dark-grown strain Z which would be dependent on an exogenously supplied organic carbon source is not known (Vol. I, Chapter 7). The observation that biosynthetic rates do not match cell division rates in a variety of metazoan cells (Vol. I, Chapter 7) suggests that a search for metabolic "bottlenecks" in these other cells is in order. The *bacillaris* strain of *Euglena* may serve as a model here.

The above-mentioned differences in acetate metabolism between *bacillaris* and strain Z show that the results obtained on one strain of *E. gracilis* do not always readily apply to another strain. This conclusion is perhaps further emphasized by the observations that strain Z grows well on a defined medium containing large quantities of metals (Kempner and Miller, 1965), whereas strain SM-L1 lyses and dies in this medium (Buetow, unpublished results). Only one more point need be reemphasized here and that is that within the species *E. gracilis* are strains that range from obligately phototrophic to heterotrophic (Pringsheim and Wiessner, 1960; Cook, Vol. I, Chapter 6). Strain differences obviously are to be expected.

IV. Final Statement

All aspects of the biology of *Euglena* have been covered in this treatise in an as up-to-date fashion as possible. The idea has been to achieve a synthesis of the very scattered literature on these organisms. It is hoped that this treatise will serve those who are interested in the structure and function of members of the genus *Euglena* themselves, as well as those interested in the use of these organisms as model systems for certain studies in cell biology. The fact that *Euglena* cells are found in the laboratories of individuals called taxonomists, botanists, zoologists, physiologists, biochemists, or biophysicists suggests that interest in these cells is widespread indeed.

The presence of a mitotic cycle, a labile chloroplast, and a simple nutrition in *Euglena* cells leads to pleasant thoughts for an increasing number of biologists. Continued work toward an understanding of a particular *Euglena* species similar to that of certain bacteria would be most desirable. The species *E. gracilis* appears to be the candidate for such understanding. A brief study of the present book will quickly show that much of its content concerns this species. This is perhaps fortunate since *E. gracilis* appears so well adapted to many natural habitats. Furthermore, study of this species accompanied by some well-chosen experiments on more specialized species, and all performed under controlled laboratory conditions, with appropriate attention to strain differences (see above), cannot but help us understand cellular mechanisms of adaptation and survival.

Note Added in Proof: After this chapter was completed, H. T. Epstein and E. Allaway published a paper [*Biochim. Biophys. Acta* (1967), **142**, 195] which has bearing on the experiments correlating DNA content and changes in chromosome number as suggested in Section II,C. In this study, *E. gracilis* subjected to prolonged phosphorus limitation showed a reduction in DNA content which was directly correlated with a reduction in ploidy.

References

Blum, J. J., and Buetow, D. E. (1963a). *Exptl. Cell Res.* **29**, 407.
Blum, J. J., and Buetow, D. E. (1963b). *Biochim. Biophys. Acta* **68**, 625.
Brawerman, G., Rebman, C. A., and Chargaff, E. (1960). *Nature* **187**, 1037.
Buetow, D. E. (1965), *J. Cellular Comp. Physiol.* **66**, 235.
Buetow, D. E. (1966). *J. Protozool.* **13**, 585.
Buetow, D. E., and Buchanan, P. J. (1963). *J. Cell Biol.* **19**, 10A.
Buetow, D. E., and Buchanan, P. J. (1964). *Exptl. Cell Res.* **36**, 204.
Buetow, D. E., and Buchanan, P. J. (1965). *Biochim. Biophys. Acta* **96**, 9.
Chadefaud, M. (1937). *Botaniste* **28**, 85.
Cook, J. R. (1965). *Plant Cell Physiol.* (*Tokyo*) **6**, 301.
Cook, J. R., and Heinrich, B. (1965). *J. Protozool.* **12**, 581.
Diacumakos, E. G., Garnjobst, L., and Tatum, E. L. (1965). *J. Cell Biol.* **26**, 427.
Edelman, M., Epstein, H. T., and Schiff, J. A. (1966). *J. Mol. Biol.* **17**, 463.
Famintzin, A. (1907). *Biol. Zentr.* **27**, 353.
Fritsch, F. E. (1935). "The Structure and Reproduction of the Algae." Cambridge Univ. Press, London and New York.
Garnjobst, L., Wilson, J. F., and Tatum, E. L. (1965). *J. Cell Biol.* **26**, 413.
Gojdics, M. (1953). "The Genus *Euglena*." Univ. of Wisconsin Press, Madison, Wisconsin.

Hollande, A. (1942). *Arch. Zool. Exptl. Gen.* **83**, 1.

Hutner, S. H., and Provasoli, L. (1951). *In* "Biochemistry and Physiology of Protozoa" (A. Lwoff, ed.), Vol. I, pp. 27–128. Academic Press, New York.

Huzisige, H., Terada, T., Nishimura, M., and Uemura, T. (1957). *Biol. J. Okayama Univ.* **3**, 209.

Jahn, T. L. (1946). *Quart. Rev. Biol.* **21**, 246.

Jahn, T. L. (1951). *In* "Manual of Phycology" (G. M. Smith, ed.), pp. 69–81. Chronica Botanica, Waltham, Massachusetts.

Kempner, E. R., and Miller, J. H. (1965). *Biochim. Biophys. Acta* **104**, 11.

Kirk, J. T. O. (1966). *In* "Biochemistry of Chloroplasts" (T. W. Goodwin, ed.), Vol. 1, pp. 319–340. Academic Press, New York.

Klebs, G. (1883). *Untersuch. Botan. Inst. Tuebingen* **1**, 233.

Leedale, G. F. (1958). *Nature* **181**, 502.

Leedale, G. F. (1962). *Arch. Mikrobiol.* **42**, 237.

Leedale, G. F., Meeuse, B. J. D., and Pringsheim, E. G. (1965). *Arch. Mikrobiol.* **50**, 133.

Mainx, F. (1927). *Arch. Protistenk.* **60**, 305.

Mereschkowsky, C. (1905). *Biol. Zentr.* **25**, 593.

Pringsheim, E. G. (1948). *Biol. Rev.* **23**, 46.

Pringsheim, E. G. (1956). *Nova Acta Leopoldina* **18**, (125), 1.

Pringsheim, E. G., and Wiessner, W. (1960). *Nature* **188**, 919.

Schoenborn, H (1942). *Physiol. Zool.* **15**, 325.

Ternetz, C. (1912). *Jahrb. Wiss. Botan.* **51**, 435.

Walton, L. B. (1915). *Ohio State Univ. Studies Ohio Biol. Survey Bull.* **1**, 343.

Wilson, B. W., Buetow, D. E., Jahn, T. L., and Levedahl, B. H. (1959). *Exptl. Cell Res.* **18**, 454.

Wolken, J. J. (1961). "*Euglena.* An Experimental Organism for Biochemical and Biophysical Research." Rutgers Univ. Press, New Brunswick, New Jersey.

Wolken, J. J. (1967). "Euglena. An Experimental Organism for Biochemical and Biophysical Research," 2nd ed. Appleton, New York.

AUTHOR INDEX

393

SUBJECT INDEX

A

Acetabularia, chloroplast DNA, 346
Acetaldehyde dehydrogenase, 60, 173
Acetate
    assimilation, 9, 60, 64–67, 182
    ion transport systems, 64
Acetate-activating enzyme, *see* Acetate thio-
    kinase
Acetate kinase, 60
Acetate thiokinase, 9, 46, 60, 90, 200
    effect of environmental and physiological
        changes on, 36
    induction of, 172
    partial repression during autotrophy, 39
    properties, 10
Acetocoenzyme A kinase, *see* Acetate thio-
    kinase
Acetyl-CoA deacylase, 33, 50
Acid phosphatase, 50
    in *A. longa*, 28
    carbon starvation, increase during, 37
    inducible, 28, 160
    intracellular distribution, 41–43
    occurrence and function, 28–29
    phosphate deficiency, increase during, 28,
        36
    paramylon granules, on surface of, 177
    (+)-tartrate inhibition, 210
Aconitate hydratase, 39, 46, 172
Acridine dyes, 206
Acriflavine, 203–206
Actidione, *see* Cycloheximide
Actinomycin D, 205
    inhibition of chloroplast amino acid in-
        corporation, 345

inhibition of greening, 346, 356
inhibition of growth, 202
Adenosine-5′-diphosphate ribose: ortho-
    phosphate adenylyl transferase, 23, 49
Adenylate kinase, 20, 49
Adenylylsulfate kinase, 21
Aflatoxin, 203, 205
Agaricus, 210
Akinetoplasty, trypanosomatids, 205
Albinization, *see* Bleaching
Alcohol dehydrogenase, 60, 173
Aldolase, 34, 37, 41
Algae, 137, 197; *see also* individual algae
    DNA of, 324–325
    heterotrophic CO_2 fixation, 92–93
Amethopterin, 207
"Amino acid-activating" enzymes, 23, 49
Amino acid esters, 200, 211
Aminoacyl-sRNA synthetases, 23
Aminoadipic pathway, 196–197
p-Aminobenzoic acid, 198–199, 210
γ-Aminobutyric acid, fluoride-poisoned
    Euglena, 209
Aminofluorene, 205
5-Aminolevulinate dehydrase, 27, 50
δ-Aminolevulinic acid, 305
    synthesis of porphyrins, bleached *Euglena*,
        339, 361
δ-Aminolevulinic synthetase, 221, 327
Aminotriazole, inhibition of chlorophyll
    synthesis, 196, 296, 359
Anabena variablis, 76
Anacystis nidulans, 76
Anaerobiosis, protection against strepto-
    mycin antibiotics, 198
Angiosperms, 199, 287

K

Kalanchoë crenata, 89
Kanamycin, 365
Khawkinea, 155, 161, 178
Kinetoplast, 196
Krebs cycle, *see* Tricarboxylic acid cycle

L

Lactate dehydrogenase, 7, 34, 36, 45
Laminaribiose phosphorylase, *see* β-1,3-
  Oligoglucan: orthophosphate glucosyl-
  transferase
Laminarin, 4, 157, 179
  phosphorylase, 5
Laminarinase, *see* β-1,3-Glucan hydrolase
Lankamycin, 366
Lecithin, *see* Phosphatidyl choline
Leishmania tarentolae, 205
Leishmanias, 196
Lepidium sativum, 203
Lepocinclis steinii, 156
Linoleic acid, 142
α-Linolenate pathway, 143
α-Linolenic acid, 75, 135, 142, 144, 146, 296,
  388
γ-Linolenate pathway, 144
γ-Linolenic acid, 135, 143, 144, 388
Lipid, *see also* individual lipids
  biosynthesis, 139–143, 387–388
  composition of euglenoids, 134–139, 387–
  388
  enzymes of metabolism, 24–27, 49–50
  inhibitors of metabolism, 202–203
  physiological and environmental influences on metabolism, 143–146
Lutein, 139
Lysosomes, 37, 195

M

Macrolide antibiotics, 200, 207, 366
Magnesium deficiency, bleaching effect of,
  370
Malate dehydrogenase, 41, 42, 46, 172
  in chloroplasts, NAD-dependent, 79
  isozyme of, 41

Malate synthase, 9, 46, 172, 173
Malic enzyme, 33, 89
Malonate, 201
Malonate condensation pathway, 139
Meiosis, 336, 388
Menadione, 204
Menoidium, 153, 156
6-Mercaptopurine, 208
Messenger (template) RNA, 114–118, 130
  chloroplast, 124, 126, 326, 328, 377–378
  development of chloroplast, 296
  nonspecificity of chloroplast ribosomes,
  125
Methapyrilene, 367
N-Methyl-*N*′-nitro-*N*-nitrosoguanidine,203,
  367, 369
o-Methylthreonine, 328, 369
Methymycin, 365
Mitochondria
  acid phosphatase, 43
  dehydrogenases, 41
  differentiation, 196
  DNA, 109, 320, 323, 386
  electron-transfer pathway, 11–12, 36, 47,
  56–58
  enzymes, 11–12, 47
Mougeotia, 261
Muciferous bodies, 152, 159
Mucin, 159
Mucor, 210
Mycobacterium tuberculosis, 207
Myristic acid, 135

N

NADP-reductase, *see* Pyridine nucleotide
  transhydrogenase
NADPH-diaphorase, *see* Pyridine nucle-
  otide transhydrogenase
NADPH-oxidase, *see* Pyridine nucleotide
  transhydrogenase
Naphthoquinones, 204, 205
Naphthylamine, 205
Neomycin, 365
Neoxanthin, 74, 138, 224, 294
Nepeta cataria, 347
Neurospora, 199, 323, 336, 386
Nicotinic acid, 203, 204, 207
Nitella, 362, 365

Printed in Belgium